In keeping with her groundbreaking role in in~~~~~~~~~ and addictions and providing gender-specific and gender-responsive programs, Dr. Stephanie Covington has done it again. Her revised *Beyond Trauma: A Healing Journey for Women* is a highly organized and structured program that is state of the art in terms of the information that is included. The facilitator guide is very descriptive and specific in a way that supports the group leaders and members every step of the way. Since group treatment provides a unique forum for healing both trauma and addictions, this is a most welcome contribution.

Christine A. Courtois, PhD, ABPP
Psychologist, Independent Practice, Washington, DC
Author, *It's Not You, It's What Happened to You; Healing the Incest Wound;* and *Treating Complex Trauma: A Sequenced, Relationship-Based Approach* (with Julian Ford, PhD)

In Dr. Covington's newest edition of *Beyond Trauma,* she masterfully combines the depth and nuance of her original evidence-based curriculum with new and important material, including up-to-date neuroscience research and a deeper integration of mind-body approaches to healing. Her gift for drawing on the experience and strength of survivors dealing with a range of complex issues and creating a healing process that touches the multiple dimensions of what makes us human—and in a culturally attuned and gender-responsive way—is a true contribution to the field.

Carole Warshaw, MD
Director, National Center on Domestic Violence, Trauma & Mental Health,
Chicago, Illinois

The Covington curriculum has become the definitive approach to helping women in a variety of settings address the trauma so many have experienced. Dr. Covington's work is thoughtful, insightful, and impactful. *Beyond Trauma* in its second edition continues the important work begun over a decade ago. Dr. Covington was among the first to draw our attention to the importance of addressing trauma in helping women reclaim their lives, and she has done it in a manner that professionals and laypeople as well can comprehend and use. This approach is sensible, is accessible, and offers the means of providing to women in custody the help they need and that we need to provide to fulfill our missions.

Martin F. Horn
Distinguished Lecturer at John Jay College of Criminal Justice in New York City,
Former Commissioner of Correction and Probation for the City of New York,
and Former Secretary of Corrections for the State of Pennsylvania

Comprehensive, beautifully written, and practical support for leading trauma recovery groups. This reflects Stephanie Covington's unique ability to take multiple threads and weave together a wholistic, gender-specific, and hopeful guide to support the healing of trauma survivors.

Janet Surrey, PhD
Founding Scholar, Jean Baker Miller Training Institute,
Stone Center, Wellesley College
Author of *The Buddha's Wife: The Path of Awakening Together*

Stephanie Covington here demonstrates a wonderful touch. In *Beyond Trauma*, she proves herself to be an astute clinician who has produced a magnificent work on helping women recover from toxic stress and trauma, to which so many have been exposed. While chapter 1 of this volume makes obvious Covington's extensive knowledge of the science behind her approach, her breadth and depth of experience are nowhere more evident than in chapter 2 and part 3, where she elaborates on the ways that facilitators can get it right. Her recommendations range from the minute to the grand but truly reflect the compassionate stance Covington embodies in her writing. She has quite literally thought of everything a prospective group leader might want to know about assisting women "beyond trauma." Covington expresses these guidelines clearly and with the illuminating voice of one who knows well what she so brilliantly speaks.

Roger D. Fallot, PhD
Independent Consultant in Trauma and Trauma-Informed Care and Adjunct Faculty,
Yale University School of Medicine, Department of Psychiatry

Beyond Trauma is vital to our work with the chemically dependent female—and there is no one who understands gender-specific work better than Stephanie Covington!

Claudia Black
Author, *It Will Never Happen to Me*

Stephanie Covington understands women: who they are and what they've experienced. She combines a thorough, practical approach to treatment with comprehensive and sophisticated theories about women who have experienced all kinds of trauma. This integrated, accessible treatment guide will be invaluable to therapists and the women they treat. It is a wonderful curriculum; Stephanie is a master teacher.

Stephanie Brown, PhD
Director, The Addictions Institute, Menlo Park, California
Author, *A Place Called Self: Women, Sobriety and Radical Transformation*

The revised version of *Beyond Trauma* incorporates the latest understanding of trauma and PTSD since the original publication of *Beyond Trauma* in 2003. The facilitator guide has expanded background information that is helpful to both new and seasoned group leaders. The program content is deeper and more expansive, skillfully weaving basic neuroscience and psychoeducation on the impact of trauma in with personal application through a variety of methods. As with the earlier edition, the new *Beyond Trauma* uses sociocultural theory, CBT, and expressive arts as fundamental components of the curriculum. However, there is a greater emphasis on practicing mindfulness, using soothing exercises, guided imagery, and yoga poses. The expansion of content lends itself to use in a variety of settings, including intensive outpatient programs. Much of the curriculum is also applicable in individual counseling sessions, making *Beyond Trauma* a flexible addition to the clinical toolbox.

Eileen M. Russo, MA, LADC
Associate Professor, Drug and Alcohol Recovery Counseling Program,
Gateway Community College,
New Haven, Connecticut

Thank you, Stephanie, for giving facilitators the tools needed to present and teach the *Beyond Trauma* curriculum. The new edition of the *Beyond Trauma* facilitator guide is exactly what our staff needed to continue providing these important groups to our clients.

Kimberly Bond
CEO and President, Mental Health Systems,
San Diego, California

This second edition of *Beyond Trauma* builds on the great work of the first edition, having been utilized all over the United States and abroad. Stephanie Covington has elaborated and expanded the content based on the feedback and insight of many clinicians who have shared their experiences with her. You will find this guide user friendly and a must-have for those doing trauma treatment with women. The CT Women's Consortium is excited to be offering training on this newly revised curriculum.

Colette M. Anderson, LCSW
Executive Director,
Connecticut Women's Consortium

BEYOND TRAUMA

A Healing Journey for Women

FACILITATOR GUIDE

Second Edition

Stephanie S. Covington, PhD

Hazelden Publishing
Center City, Minnesota 55012
hazelden.org/bookstore

Editor's note:
We have used the terms *program* and *curriculum* interchangeably when referring to *Beyond Trauma* to meet the needs of both criminal justice and behavioral health settings.

The yoga photos/instructions were provided by Machelle Lee and are reproduced from *Beyond Violence.* Copyright 2013 by S. Covington. This material is reproduced with permission of John Wiley & Sons, Inc., and Machelle Lee.

The SEEDS text (pages 17 and 202) is adapted from *The Brain Bible: How to Stay Vital, Productive, and Happy for a Lifetime* by John B. Arden, 2014. Reprinted with permission.

ISBN-13: 978-1-61649-682-1

Cover design: Linda Koutsky
Interior design and typesetting: Terri Kinne

CONTENTS

Part 2: Session Outlines, 81

Module A: Violence, Abuse, and Trauma, 83

CONTENTS *continued*

ACKNOWLEDGMENTS

Any project I've ever done has had important people behind the scenes, and this curriculum is no exception. I'm very fortunate to be surrounded by caring and competent people who have supported this new edition of *Beyond Trauma: A Healing Journey for Women* from beginning to end.

My first publication was a book on relationships, *Leaving the Enchanted Forest* (Covington and Beckett 1988). Now, many years later, there are many more publications, including ten trauma-informed, manualized interventions. All this work has been informed by the revolutionary and inspiring work of the four founding scholars at the Stone Center in Wellesley, Massachusetts: Jean Baker Miller, Janet Surrey, Irene Stiver, and Judith Jordan. The Stone Center (now referred to as the Jean Baker Miller Training Institute) changed my clinical work and influenced all my writing. It was an experience of reading material that was deeply resonant and both professionally and personally validating. The word *connection* has become my mantra. I am immensely indebted to these four women—especially to my dear friend, Janet Surrey.

I am also grateful to many of my other colleagues. Sandra Bloom's brilliant work on the concept of *sanctuary,* which emphasizes the importance of the environment, has deeply influenced my work, as has the work of Roger Fallot, who—with Maxine Harris—developed the concept of *trauma-informed cultures of care.* Carol Ackley, Eileen Russo, and Twyla Wilson have been willing to incorporate reviewing the manuscript into their busy schedules and have made suggestions that have improved my work. In addition, Candice Norcott, Kim Selvaggi, and Tammy Rothschild carefully read the adaptations for girls. Sue Thomas, my editor at Hazelden, has supported this project from start to finish. Laura Waligorski manages the office so I can go home and write. Arlette Ballew, editor extraordinaire, has worked with me for years, helping me to rewrite, reword, and create each new writing project. Last but not least, I am indebted to Penny Philpot for sharing her clinical knowledge, technical determination, and sense of humor, and for being an inspiration for this curriculum.

To all of you, I say "thank you" for your expertise, your support, and your dedication to helping women and girls move *Beyond Trauma*.

. . .

INTRODUCTION

It seems that our world is in crisis. We see pain and devastation everywhere. At home, we read about the growing incidence of child abuse, shootings in our schools and neighborhoods, and other violent crimes. Around the world, there is suffering and alienation: in the wars in the Middle East, Africa, and elsewhere; in acts of terrorism and widespread violence; in the raping of women on every continent; and in the international sex trade. This painful destruction is mirrored by the holes in the ozone layer, the clear-cutting of timber in the rainforests, the annihilation of plant and animal species, and our polluted air and water. Violence happens in multiple ways and on many levels.

Where do we look for answers? What is the key to our survival and healing? Just as the Chinese symbol for *crisis* is made up of two characters, one representing danger and the other opportunity, each time there is a crisis, there is also a chance for change and renewal. Today, many women and men from all walks of life are finding a key to their survival and growth by freeing themselves from the suffering created by trauma.

Although we see violence everywhere we look, we need to make a distinction between the suffering that we create and the suffering that we encounter as a natural part of life. Certainly, we cannot avoid the suffering that comes from natural disasters, such as earthquakes, floods, and tornadoes. We also often experience pain during the normal course of life, as we are born, grow up, get an education, move into the workplace and relationships, age, and experience death. Although these passages can be difficult, they are the foundation stones of our identities. They challenge us and help us define who we are and what we want from our lives. We can see these kinds of experiences as part of life's journey and use them to help us grow and create meaning in our lives.

However, there is also the suffering that we, as human beings, have created—the abuse and destruction generated by violence. Every day in America, women are sexually harassed in the workplace, raped, and beaten by their husbands, boyfriends, and strangers. Significant numbers of our children are neglected, abused, and killed by their parents and caretakers. No institution, person, or country is free from the effects of created suffering.

However, there is hope. Throughout the world, individuals and groups are coming together to create new ways of ending suffering. One of the first steps on this path is freeing ourselves from denial and acknowledging the impact of violence in our own lives. One can only heal from a problem that has been acknowledged.

This curriculum, *Beyond Trauma: A Healing Journey for Women,* is designed to be part of the solution by helping women and girls recover from the effects of trauma in their lives. The curriculum focuses on the kinds of created suffering that women are most at risk of experiencing: childhood abuse, rape, battering, and other forms of interpersonal violence. However, the coping skills that are presented in this curriculum can also be useful for other types of traumatic events.

Beyond Trauma presents an integrated approach to women's trauma treatment, based on theory, research, and clinical experience. It can be used in any setting (outpatient, residential, therapeutic community, criminal justice, and private practice). In developing effective treatment for women and girls, we must include the experience and impact of living as a female in a male-based society as part of the clinical perspective. The term *gender-responsive* describes this type of treatment approach; it is defined as follows: creating an environment—through site selection, staff selection, program development, and program content and materials—that reflects an understanding of the realities of women's and girls' lives and that addresses and responds to their challenges and strengths (Covington 2002). *Beyond Trauma* is a gender-responsive curriculum.

This revised edition of the program includes:

- new and updated foundational information for the facilitator in part 1

- new statistics about abuse and other forms of trauma in part 1 and in the sessions

- new discoveries, publications, and insights in the field

- longer sessions (two hours rather than one and a half hours) and an additional session, which enables us to include more new lectures and activities for the participants that reflect current thinking and practice

- a variety of yoga poses, grounding activities, and self-soothing activities

- information at the end of each session about adapting the curriculum for use with adolescent girls

- new national resources (organizations and groups) for the facilitator and participants

- two new videos: one for facilitators and one for use with participants

This curriculum promotes a strength-based approach that seeks to empower women and girls and increase their sense of self. In using this kind of model, you, the facilitator, will help the women in the group to see the strengths they have and to increase the skills they need for healing. The curriculum also focuses on emotional development. Dealing with the expression and containment of feelings is a critical part of trauma work. You will be using psychoeducational and cognitive-behavioral therapy (CBT) techniques, expressive arts, body-focused exercises, mindfulness, and relational therapy.

The *Beyond Trauma* program materials consist of a facilitator guide, a participant workbook, a facilitator training video, and a participant video. This facilitator guide has two parts. The first part gives you background information about trauma. Having a basic understanding of the depth and complexity of the issues will help you facilitate the group process. The second part of the guide includes session outlines or lesson plans. There are twelve sessions divided into three modules: (A) Violence, Abuse, and Trauma; (B) The Impact of Trauma on Women's Lives; and (C) Healing from Trauma.

The women in the group will go through a process of:

1. Understanding what has happened to them. They will learn more about what trauma is and how widespread trauma is in women's lives.

2. Exploring how trauma has affected them.

3. Learning coping mechanisms, doing activities to help them feel grounded, and focusing on safety.

Some of you also may be facilitating the *Helping Women Recover: A Program for Treating Addiction* curriculum (the community or criminal justice version). The *Beyond Trauma* curriculum can be used alone or in addition to *Helping Women Recover (HWR)*. These programs are complementary to each other, and *Beyond Trauma* expands and deepens the trauma work in *HWR*.

Thank you for making the decision to help facilitate the process of the healing journey for women (or girls). Although you may find this work particularly challenging, it will also reward you. Many of you are recovering from trauma yourself and know that there is no more powerful transformation than that of a woman reclaiming her life.

Stephanie S. Covington

Stephanie S. Covington, PhD
June 2016
La Jolla, California

PART 1

Overview of Trauma and the *Beyond Trauma* Program

CHAPTER 1

Background Information

What Is Trauma?

Violence-related trauma occurs on multiple levels, from the general and ongoing oppression of an entire group of people to discrimination based on gender or gender identity, race, poverty, sexual orientation, disability, or age to the repeated sexual abuse of a child. Violence and trauma take many forms, including emotional, physical, and sexual abuse, as well as assault, war, natural disasters, and political terrorism.

A definition of *trauma* based on the *Diagnostic and Statistical Manual of Mental Disorders,* or *DSM-5,* is exposure to actual or threatened death, serious injury, or sexual violence in one or more of four ways: (a) directly experiencing the event; (b) witnessing, in person, the event occurring to others; (c) learning that such an event happened to a close family member or friend; (d) experiencing repeated or extreme exposure to aversive details of such events, such as with first responders (American Psychiatric Association 2013, 271–280). This experience causes significant distress or impairment in social relationships, capacity to work, or other important areas of functioning.

In the introduction, two categories of suffering were discussed: natural suffering and created suffering. Natural suffering comes from the normal course of life and from natural disasters. Created suffering is created by human beings. Sometimes researchers distinguish between three types of traumatic events: disaster, assault, and combat (Forbes et al. 2013; Forneris et al. 2013; Kessler et al. 2012). Others discuss accidental and intentional disasters and the resulting trauma (Avdimiretz, Phillips, and Bratu 2012; Nickerson et al. 2011). One noted researcher, Bessel van der Kolk, differentiates between public and private trauma (2014). The public traumas we read about in the news—events such as school shootings or the Boston Marathon bombing—differ from the far more private traumas that psychotherapists typically treat.

In the case of public trauma, people gather around the victim(s), there is acknowledgment of the reality of what happened, and sympathy and comfort are offered. That is very different from private traumas that involve assault, incest, rape, or domestic violence. These are hidden traumas, and the victims rarely get to publicly acknowledge what took place and rarely get the support they need to move on in their lives. When they have communities that rally around them, the victims of public traumas tend to cope or recover better. Too often, the victim of a private trauma ends up with a deep sense of shame and invisibility, along with silent rage about not being acknowledged or protected.

Still others define *trauma* not as an event but as a reaction to an event that overwhelms people physically and psychologically (Scaer 2014). So the word *trauma* is used to describe both an event and a reaction or response to an event. In fact, *trauma* has become a buzzword and is somewhat overused. Someone may say she has had a traumatic day when she actually has had a stressful day. Stress becomes toxic and traumatic when the body's alarm system goes off too often and for too long. *Beyond Trauma* is designed for women who have experienced threatening events that have overwhelmed their psychological and/or physiological coping mechanisms—especially private, created suffering.

There also are differences between women and men in terms of trauma. Compared to men, women are more likely to be exposed to physical abuse, rape, sexual molestation, childhood parental neglect, and childhood physical abuse (Bedi et al. 2011; Iverson et al. 2013; Miller et al. 2011). In fact, violence against women is so pervasive that the United Nations has addressed and defined violence against women as "any act of gender-based violence that results in, or is likely to result in, physical, sexual or psychological harm or suffering to women, including threats of such acts, coercion or arbitrary deprivations of liberty, whether occurring in public or in private life" (United Nations General Assembly 1993). The World Health Organization abides by this definition in its current work in examining the many forms of violence against women (World Health Organization 2013).

Women and Trauma

The World Women Live In

The following statistics illustrate how pervasive interpersonal violence is in the lives of women and girls. (All statistics refer to rates of violence in the United States, unless otherwise stated.)

- More than one in nine children are exposed to family violence annually in the United States, and one in four children are exposed to family violence in their lifetimes. More than 90 percent of children who are exposed to intimate-partner violence actually see the violence. A vast majority of the violence witnessed is perpetrated by males. However, girls are more likely to be exposed to psychological and physical intimate-partner violence throughout their lifetimes (Hamby et al. 2011).

- Based on an analysis of studies from across the world, one in six girls and one in fourteen boys experience childhood sexual abuse (Stoltenborgh et al. 2011). Within the United States specifically, approximately 16 percent of men and 25 percent of women report having experienced childhood sexual abuse, and those who experienced sexual abuse also have higher rates of childhood physical abuse, maltreatment, and neglect (Pérez-Fuentes et al. 2013).

- Approximately 65 percent of adolescent girls are victims of physical, emotional, verbal, and/or sexual abuse from a dating partner. More than a third of girls experience such abuse from two or more dating partners during their teen years, and most are age thirteen to fifteen at the start of the abuse (Bonomi et al. 2013).

- The number of sexual offenses on college campuses reported to the U.S. Department of Education was 3,357 in 2009 (Krebs et al. 2009) and almost doubled, to 6,073, in 2013 (Lhamon and Runcie 2015). Officials say sex offenses are underreported crimes, and the true number of such cases is likely much higher.

- In 2010, there were 84,767 forcible rapes in the United States. That averages out to 233 women being raped each day and nine women being raped every hour (Federal Bureau of Investigation 2011).

- Nearly one in five women (18.3 percent) and one in seventy-one men (1.4 percent) in the United States have been raped at some time in their lives (Black et al. 2011). This corresponds to estimates of more than twenty-three million women and more than two million men experiencing rape (Breiding et al. 2014).

- More than 70 percent of all rapes occur before age twenty-five, and more than 40 percent of rapes of women occur before age eighteen (Breiding et al. 2014).

- Approximately 80 percent of victims of rape and sexual violence know their attackers. This includes perpetrators who are intimate partners, friends or acquaintances, and relatives. Only 20 percent of perpetrators of sexual assault against women are strangers (Berzofsky et al. 2013).

- A majority of victims of intimate-partner violence (four out of five victims) are women (Catalano 2012).

- Approximately two-thirds of women's experiences of intimate-partner violence include physical attack. The most common forms of intimate-partner violence against women are aggravated assault and sexual assault. Women are almost three times more likely to have injuries from intimate-partner violence than men are. Of women who are homicide victims, 40 percent are murdered by their intimate partners, contrasted with only 3 percent of male homicide victims (Catalano 2012).

- Nationally, more than 6.9 million women annually are victims of rape, physical violence, and/or stalking by an intimate partner (Black et al. 2011). Correspondingly, more than 93 percent of emergency room visits for intimate-partner violence are women in need of health care (Davidov, Larrabee, and Davis 2015).

- Based on studies across the world, women who experience intimate-partner violence are more likely to experience depression and attempt suicide (Devries et al. 2013).

- Among women who have experienced three or four forms of violence (e.g., intimate-partner violence, rape, other forms of sexual assault, and stalking), 90 percent experienced a resulting mental health disorder, and 47 percent experienced a substance use disorder (Rees et al. 2011).

- There are differences in risk of abuse between females and males. Girls and boys both are at risk in childhood for physical and sexual abuse, especially from people they know. However, risk changes over the course of life. Adolescent boys are at particular risk for abuse if they are young men of color, gay, or gang members. Their risk is from peers, from people who dislike them, and from the police. In contrast, the risk for teenage girls comes from those with whom they are in relationships—people they are saying "I love you" to. For adult men who serve in a branch of the military, the greatest risk is from the enemy. If a man lives in a non-custodial setting, the risk is being a victim of a crime committed by a stranger. For a woman in the military, the greatest risk is from the men she is serving with. If she is living in a noncustodial setting, her greatest risk is from the person to whom she is saying "I love you" (Covington 2013, 2014; Kendall-Tackett 2005).

- Women involved with the criminal justice system have experienced high rates of trauma; for example, 98 percent have experienced a general disaster, 87 percent have experienced interpersonal violence, and 75 percent have histories of childhood sexual and/or physical abuse (Wolff et al. 2011).

- An incarcerated woman has experienced an average of six traumatic events in her lifetime, whereas a typical woman in the community has experienced an average of two traumatic events in her lifetime. Incarcerated women also have higher rates of posttraumatic stress disorder (PTSD) than women in the community (40 percent versus 12 percent) and are ten times more likely to use substances in response to trauma (64 percent versus 6 percent) (Grella, Lovinger, and Warda 2013).

- Although relationship violence happens to women of every race and ethnic background, African American women are harmed at a higher rate than Caucasian women and women of other races. In 2011, 94 percent of female homicide victims were killed by men they knew, a majority of whom were their husbands, boyfriends, or intimate acquaintances. Most of these homicides occurred during arguments. The average age of female victims was thirty-nine; for African American women it was thirty-four. African American women were murdered at a rate more than two-and-a-half times higher than the rate for Caucasian women and at a rate even higher than women of other races (Violence Policy Center 2013).

Duplicating this page is illegal. Do not copy this material without written permission from the publisher.

11

As has been mentioned, trauma occurs on multiple levels. "Trauma is not limited to suffering violence; it includes witnessing violence, as well as stigmatization because of gender, race, poverty, incarceration, or sexual orientation" (Covington 2002, 60). Root also expands the conventional notion of trauma to include not only direct trauma but also indirect trauma and insidious trauma. Insidious trauma "includes but is not limited to emotional abuse, racism, anti-Semitism, poverty, heterosexism, dislocation, [and] ageism" (1992, 23). The effects of insidious trauma are cumulative and are often experienced over the course of a lifetime. For example, women of color are subject to varying degrees of insidious trauma throughout their lives. According to Root (1997), the exposure to insidious trauma activates survival behaviors that might easily be mistaken for pathological responses if their source is not understood. Misdiagnosis of pathology can be a consequence of a lack of understanding of the effects of insidious trauma on women who have lived with racism, heterosexism, and/or class discrimination all their lives. Care providers are urged to understand insidious trauma in order to provide more effective and relevant services to women (Quiros and Berger 2015).

Gender-Responsive Services

Because of the high rates of interpersonal violence against women and the differences between males and females in their risk for interpersonal violence, it is important to consider gender differences when developing interventions and treatment models for women.

As was defined in the introduction, gender-responsive, woman-centered treatment is the creation of an environment—through site selection, staff selection, program development, and program content and materials—that reflects an understanding of the realities of women's and girls' lives and that addresses and responds to their challenges and strengths.

Gender-Responsive Principles

In a research-based report for the National Institute of Corrections, which states the guiding principles for working with women, gender is the first principle. A multidisciplinary review of the literature and research on women's lives in the areas of substance abuse, trauma, health, education and training, mental health, and employment was conducted as part of this project. The following principles from this report are applicable to any setting that serves women (Bloom, Owen, and Covington 2003):

- *Gender:* Acknowledge that gender makes a difference.

- *Environment:* Create an environment based on safety, respect, and dignity.

- *Relationships:* Develop policies, practices, and programs that are relational and promote healthy connections to children, family members, significant others, and the community.

- *Services:* Address substance abuse, trauma, and mental health issues through comprehensive, integrated, and culturally relevant services.

- *Socioeconomic status:* Provide women with opportunities to improve their socioeconomic conditions.

- *Community:* Establish a system of comprehensive and collaborative community services.

Understanding Trauma

The women in your group may be at various stages in facing and dealing with the trauma they've experienced. Some will remember their traumatic experiences clearly, some will remember certain aspects, and some will not remember anything. Some will talk openly about their trauma right away, and some will not. Because women are at different stages and because all need to feel safe, you will begin this program by normalizing the existence of interpersonal violence and other forms of trauma. Therefore, the session outlines in module A are focused on the prevalence of trauma, particularly violence, in women's lives. For facilitators who have little or no experience working with trauma, figure 1 on page 14 will help you understand the process of trauma. You will also be teaching this process to the women later in the curriculum.

The Process of Trauma

Trauma begins with an event or experience that overwhelms a woman's normal coping mechanisms. The first response that a person has when threatened is fight, flight, or freeze. Then there are physiological and psychological reactions in response to the event: hyperarousal, altered consciousness, numbing, collapsing, and so on. These are normal reactions to an abnormal situation. Trauma causes changes in the brain, and a woman's nervous system also becomes sensitized and is vulnerable to any future stressors in her life. The

Duplicating this page is illegal. Do not copy this material without written permission from the publisher.

13

FIGURE 1

THE PROCESS OF TRAUMA

Traumatic Event

Overwhelms the physical and psychological coping skills

Response to Trauma

Fight, flight, or freeze

Altered state of consciousness, Body sensations, Numbing

Hypervigilance, Hyperarousal, Collapse

Sensitized Nervous System

Changes in the Brain

Brain-Body Connection

Psychological and Physical Distress

Current stressors, Reminders of trauma (triggers)

Sensations, Images, Behavior, Affect (emotions), Memory

Emotional and/or Physical Responses

Retreat	**Harmful Behavior to Self**	**Harmful Behavior to Others**	**Physical Health Issues**
Isolation			
Dissociation	Substance use disorders	Aggression	Lung disease
Depressive disorders	Feeding and eating disorders	Violence	Heart disease
Anxiety disorders	Deliberate self-harm	Rages	Autoimmune disorders
	Suicidal actions	Threats	Obesity

Trigger list adapted from *In an Unspoken Voice: How the Body Releases Trauma and Restores Goodness* by Peter Levine (Berkeley, CA: North Atlantic Books, 2010).

changes in the brain can also affect the functioning of her body; this is called the brain-body connection. She may also experience triggers in her current life that remind her of the traumatic event(s) that happened in the past. These triggers may come from sensations in her body, images, behavior that she does or someone else does, feelings, and/or memories. There may be nightmares and flashbacks to the earlier experience. This creates a painful emotional state and subsequent emotional and/or physical responses. The responses we often see can be placed into four categories: retreat, harm to self, harm to others, and physical health problems. Women are more likely to retreat or be self-destructive, while men are more likely to engage in destructive behavior toward self or others. Women often internalize their feelings, and men often externalize theirs. Both women and men can experience physical health problems.

The Effects of Trauma

One of the most important developments in health care since the 1980s is the recognition that serious traumatic experiences often play an unrecognized role in a woman's subsequent physical and mental health problems (referred to as co-occurring disorders).

The Adverse Childhood Experiences (ACE) Study (Felitti and Anda 2010; Felitti et al. 1998; Felitti 2000) revealed a strong link between childhood trauma and adult physical and mental health problems. Ten types of childhood traumatic events were assessed (emotional abuse, emotional neglect, physical neglect, physical abuse, sexual abuse, family violence, family alcoholism, parental separation/divorce, an incarcerated family member, and out-of-home placement). A score of four or more events increased the risk of both mental and physical health problems in adult lives. The women in the ACE study were 50 percent more likely than the men to have a score of five or more. Having a score of five or more increases a woman's risk of having a variety of chronic health problems, including heart disease, autoimmune diseases, lung cancer, pulmonary disease, skeletal fractures, and sexually transmitted infections.

This study was a model for research done on women in the criminal justice system, and similar results were found. The women with the higher scores had more physical and mental health problems. For women who scored seven or more, the risk of a mental health problem increased by 980 percent (Messina and Grella 2006).

Duplicating this page is illegal. Do not copy this material without written permission from the publisher.

15

A number of studies indicate that a history of trauma (especially sexual and/or physical abuse) puts a woman at a higher risk for anxiety disorders, depressive disorders, eating disorders, sleep-wake disorders, suicide attempts, self-inflicted injury, and psychiatric hospitalization (Bedi et al. 2011; Chen et al. 2010; Gladstone et al. 2004; Mitchell et al. 2012; Noll et al. 2003).

Women who have been exposed to trauma and have a moderate to severe substance use disorder are at higher risk for mental disorders. In a review of studies that examined the combined effects of PTSD and substance abuse, Najavits, Weiss, and Shaw (1997) found more comorbid mental disorders, medical problems, psychological symptoms, inpatient admissions, and inter-personal problems; lower levels of functioning, compliance with aftercare, and motivation for treatment; and other significant life problems (such as homelessness, HIV, domestic violence, and loss of custody of children) among those with both PTSD and substance abuse, compared to those with one of those problems alone.

Mental and Emotional Effects of Trauma

A traumatic event can affect a person in multiple ways. It can affect both the inner self (thoughts, feelings, beliefs, and values) and the outer self (relation-ships and behaviors).

Many traumatized people have difficulty identifying and expressing their feelings. The term often used to describe this is *emotional dysregulation*. Emotions are most often experienced in the body, as in "I feel it in my gut," or are identified by facial expressions. Many survivors express that they are "out of touch" with their feelings; they may sense that they are feeling something (sensations in their bodies) but they cannot identify, let alone express, the feelings (Courtois 2014). Many also have difficulty regulating their emotions. They often feel out of control. Trauma also affects beliefs about the world. For example, some women believe that "You can't trust anyone," "The world is a very unsafe place," or "I am crazy and worthless," and "I deserved it."

Trauma can also affect the outer self, which consists of one's relationships and behaviors. Many women who have experienced trauma struggle with their relationships—with family members, friends, and sexual partners. For example, parenting is a relationship that can become even more com-plicated by the experience of trauma. Some women who have experienced childhood abuse may find that their own children "trigger" them back to their abuse. It is particularly risky when a woman's child becomes the age she was when the abuse began.

Neuroscience research shows that the only way we can help women who have experienced trauma change how they feel is by helping them become aware of their inner experiences and learn what is going on inside them. Most of our conscious brains are dedicated to focusing on the outside world. Some of the activities in *Beyond Trauma* are designed to help women focus on the inside to identify and accept the emotions embedded in their bodies. One neuroscientist who studies the impact of trauma on the brain has developed the concept of SEEDS (Arden 2014). These are the five factors that can help people heal the brain and live vital, productive, and happy lives:

S—social connectivity—being in connection and relationship with others.

E—exercise—thirty minutes a day can make a big difference.

E—education—learning something new each day.

D—diet—eating foods that nourish versus starve the brain.

S—sleep—resting the brain and the body so they can regenerate each day.

These things can help women who are trauma survivors reduce their risk of having physical and mental health problems. Our task is to help women begin to plant these SEEDS in their lives.

Clinically diagnosed disorders that are related to trauma include posttraumatic stress disorder (PTSD), borderline personality disorder, brief psychosis, dissociative identity disorder, dissociative amnesia, conversion disorder, depersonalization disorder, somatic symptom disorder, and antisocial personality disorder. In women, there is a high level of correlation between posttraumatic stress disorder and depressive disorders, anxiety disorders, substance use disorders, and physical disorders (McLean et al. 2011; Pacella, Hruska, and Delahanty 2013). Clinical interventions for the mental health disorders listed above are more effective when the case and the client's life are viewed with an understanding of trauma (Courtois and Ford 2013; van der Kolk 2014).

Posttraumatic Stress Disorder (PTSD)

PTSD is a trauma- and stressor-related disorder that acknowledges the multiple and complex ways that trauma affects one's physical and psychological health (American Psychiatric Association 2013). The symptoms of PTSD are common among many victims of abuse. It is helpful for anyone working with women who have experienced trauma to be familiar with the symptoms of PTSD and with the criteria for resolving it. The *Diagnostic and Statistical Manual of Mental Disorders (DSM-5)* of the American Psychiatric Association (2013) lists the following symptoms of PTSD:

- recurrent, involuntary, and intrusive distressing memories
- re-experiencing the event through nightmares and flashbacks
- prolonged distress when reminded of the trauma in any manner
- avoidance of stimuli associated with the event (for example, if a woman was raped in a park, she may avoid parks, or if she was assaulted by a blond man, she may avoid men with blond hair)
- inability to remember key aspects of the trauma
- negative self-perception (for example, "I am a bad person" or "I am dirty and flawed") or negative beliefs about the world (for example, "No place in the world is safe")
- persistent inappropriate self-blame for the trauma
- persistent distressing feelings, such as sadness, guilt, shame, terror, self-disgust, and anger
- inability to feel interested in important activities (activities that were significant before the trauma)
- persistent inability to feel positive emotions
- estrangement (the inability to be emotionally close to anyone)
- numbing of general responsiveness (feeling nothing most of the time)
- self-destructive and/or aggressive behavior toward others
- hypervigilance (constantly scanning one's environment for danger, whether physical or emotional)
- an exaggerated startle response (a tendency to jump at loud noises or unexpected touch)
- problems sleeping and/or concentrating

Some women may experience high levels of dissociative symptoms with PTSD. According to *DSM-5* (American Psychiatric Association 2013), these symptoms include feelings of depersonalization (e.g., feeling detached or disconnected from oneself—as though observing someone else experiencing events rather than oneself) and derealization (e.g., experiencing life events as not really happening).

It is important to be aware that women may experience a few, some, or all of these symptoms. However, when you discuss the effects of trauma with women, you will probably want to speak less technically. For example, here are the four basic reactions:

1. Re-experiencing (includes disturbed sleep, intrusive memories, distressing dreams, nightmares, flashbacks, and reliving the event)

2. Attempts to have emotional numbness and avoidance (avoiding any thoughts, feelings, people, places, and other reminders of the trauma)

3. Distressing negative changes in mood and thoughts (low self-esteem, neglect of health, dissociation, ability to remember events or feelings but not both, memory loss for certain events, loss of faith and hope, mistrust of others, isolation and disconnection)

4. Hyperarousal (intense emotions, difficulty sleeping, panic and anxiousness, self-harm, risky behaviors, irritability, anger, difficulty concentrating)

There are two types of PTSD: simple and complex. Simple PTSD stems from a single incident (such as an earthquake or automobile accident), usually experienced as an adult.

Complex PTSD (or complex traumatic stress reactions) is the consequence of a history of repeated (or multiple) traumatic experiences, such as childhood sexual abuse and domestic violence. Generally, there are more symptoms and a more complicated recovery process with complex PTSD (Herman 1997; Najavits 2002; Roth et al. 1997; Williams and Sommer 2013).

It also is important to acknowledge the long-term effects of trauma. Traumatic events may affect women for the rest of their lives. However, there are criteria you can use when assessing a woman's recovery. Healing from trauma means the following (Harvey 1996, 2007):

Duplicating this page is illegal. Do not copy this material without written permission from the publisher.

19

- The physical symptoms of PTSD are within manageable limits.

- The person is able to bear feelings associated with traumatic memories.

- The person has authority over her memories (that is, her memories don't limit what she does; she chooses what to do, instead of being immobilized in some areas).

- The memory of trauma is linked with feelings.

- Damaged self-esteem is restored (for example, a rape victim realizes that the rape did not occur because she was a "bad" woman).

- Important relationships have been reestablished.

- The person has reconstructed a system of meaning and belief that encompasses the story of the trauma (for instance, she understands that the rape was not caused by her and that some men use power and control to get what they want).

Several trauma specialists suggest that PTSD should not be labeled a "disorder." They assert that it is "posttraumatic stress" and should not be considered or treated as a disorder or a disease (Herman 2014; van der Kolk 2014). Their concern is the labeling or overpathologizing of people as "sick" when the reality is they have been harmed or wounded.

Developmental Trauma Disorder

Although the *DSM-5* does not mention developmental trauma disorder (DTD), prominent trauma researchers and clinicians identify it as the result of exposure to a developmentally adverse interpersonal trauma such as abuse, abandonment, or betrayal (Courtois and Ford 2014; Herman 2014; van der Kolk 2014). When these extreme and prolonged stressors are experienced by a child, they have a great potential to severely compromise the child's development, including the way the brain develops (Gatt et al. 2010; Herman 1997). This is also referred to as toxic stress (National Scientific Council on the Developing Child 2007). Learning how to cope with adversity is an important part of healthy development. Moderate, short-lived stress responses in the body can promote growth. Toxic stress is a strong, unrelieved experience that can adversely affect healthy development, particularly in a child. Without caring adults to buffer children, the unrelenting stress caused by extreme neglect, poverty, or abuse can weaken the developing brain and have long-term consequences on both physical and mental health (National Scientific Council on the Developing Child 2007).

Physical Effects of Trauma

Just as trauma can affect a woman's ability to understand her emotions, it can affect her ability to be "in touch" with her body. For example, if a woman is not aware of what her body needs, she can't take care of it. If you don't feel hungry, you don't nourish yourself. If you mistake anxiety for hunger, you eat. And if you don't feel full, you keep eating. This is why sensory awareness is an important part of trauma recovery and healing (Ogden and Fisher 2013).

Stress is the body's alarm system. When the alarm system goes off too often or for too long, it creates a lot of wear and tear on the body. This increases the risk of the body "breaking down" and developing chronic health problems. This is a major difference between what we might consider routine stress and traumatic stress.

As previously mentioned, on the ACE study, having a score of five or more traumatic events increases a woman's risk of having a variety of chronic health problems, including heart disease, autoimmune diseases, lung cancer, pulmonary disease, skeletal fractures, and sexually transmitted infections.

Trauma and the Brain

It is important for clinicians to understand that the brain chemistry's responses to trauma can predispose a woman to substance use disorders, eating disorders, self-harming behavior, and other mental health problems.

Some of the most important advances in the understanding of trauma come from studies of the biological aspects of PTSD. It has become clear that exposure to trauma can have lasting effects on the endocrine, autonomic, and central nervous systems. New studies on trauma are finding complex changes in both the function and structure of specific areas of the brain. For example, across studies, abnormalities have been found in the brain's structures that link fear and memory (see review in Woon, Sood, and Hedges 2010).

Although all survivors want to move beyond their trauma, the part of the brain that is devoted to survival (deep below the rational brain) is not very good at denial. Long after a traumatic experience is over, it can be activated at the slightest hint of danger. Then brain circuits are mobilized, and massive amounts of stress hormones are released. This creates unpleasant emotions

Duplicating this page is illegal. Do not copy this material without written permission from the publisher.

21

and intense physical sensations. It can trigger impulsive and aggressive actions. These posttraumatic reactions can be confusing, incomprehensible, and overwhelming. The fear of being out of control can create a sense of over-powering fear, helplessness, and hopelessness (van der Kolk 2014). The fund-amental issue in resolving traumatic stress is to restore the balance between the rational and the emotional brain. This allows a woman to feel in charge of how she responds and conducts her life.

Dissociation

Women who have experienced trauma, particularly in childhood, often learn how to separate themselves from the distress associated with the trauma through dissociation. Some women can tell you horrific details of their abuse and yet have no feelings. People who enter a dissociative state at the time of trauma are at greater risk for PTSD.

Dissociation is a mental process, a psychological response that discon-nects the mind and the body. Laboratory studies indicate that dissociation, a term initially developed through clinical observation, is also a neurobiological process. Like other disorders, dissociation exists on a continuum and reflects a wide range of experiences and symptoms. At one end are the mild dissocia-tive experiences, such as daydreaming. At the opposite end are the dissociative identity disorders, in which a woman may have various "voices" or identities (often referred to as "alters") (Alderman and Marshall 1998).

Depersonalization is one of the symptoms of the massive dissociation created by trauma. It is represented by blank stares and absent minds: the outward manifestations of the biological freeze reaction (see figure 1, The Process of Trauma, on page 14).

Trauma and Substance Use Disorders

A history of abuse drastically increases the likelihood that a woman will acquire a substance use disorder. Researchers have found that a history of family violence may be the single most influential risk factor for acquiring a substance use disorder by both women and men (Kilpatrick, Saunders, and Smith 2003; Margolin and Vickerman 2007). In one of the earliest compari-son studies of women who had a moderate to severe alcohol use disorder and women who did not, 74 percent of the women with an alcohol use disorder had experienced sexual abuse, 52 percent reported physical abuse, and 72 percent reported emotional abuse (Covington and Kohen 1984). In contrast, 50 percent of the women who did not have an alcohol use disorder reported sexual abuse, 34 percent reported physical abuse, and 44 percent reported emotional abuse.

Other clinical studies of women in substance abuse treatment programs have documented that 55 percent to 99 percent of this population have a history of physical and/or sexual abuse (Messina, Calhoun, and Braithwaite 2014; Najavits, Weiss, and Shaw 1997; Prendergast et al. 2011). PTSD often precedes substance use disorders (Kessler 2000). Females who have a substance use disorder are estimated to have a 30 percent to 59 percent rate of current posttraumatic stress disorder (Najavits et al. 1998), which is higher than the percentage of men who have a substance use disorder (Brown and Wolfe 1994).

Co-occurring disorders are complex, and the historic division in the fields of mental health and substance abuse often has resulted in contradictory treatment. Women in early recovery often show symptoms of mood disorders, but these can be temporary conditions associated with withdrawal from alcohol or other drugs. Also, it is difficult to know whether a psychiatric disorder existed before a woman began to abuse alcohol or other drugs, or whether the psychiatric problem emerged after the onset of the substance use disorder (Najt, Fusar-Poli, and Brambilla 2011).

The connection between interpersonal violence and substance use disorders is often complex, especially for women. Survivors of abuse can become dependent on alcohol and other drugs in part as a way of managing trauma symptoms and reducing tension and stress from living in violent situations. Men who have a substance use disorder are at risk of violence against women and children, and women who use substances are also more vulnerable to violence because of relationships with others who use substances, impaired judgment while using alcohol or other drugs, and presence in risky and violence-prone situations. Thus begins a cycle of "victimization, substance use, retardation of emotional development, limited stress resolution, more substance use, and heightened vulnerability to further victimization" (Steele 2000, 72).

Consequently, any substance use disorder treatment program for women must take into account that most women will have suffered trauma, particularly abuse (Covington 2002). Counselors and others need to understand that they are probably treating trauma survivors. For example, many women who have a substance use disorder have been considered treatment failures because they relapsed. Now they can be better understood as trauma survivors who returned to alcohol or other drugs in order to medicate the pain of trauma. The vast majority of women who are entering recovery for substance use disorders and other addictive behaviors have experienced some form of abuse: emotional, physical, and/or sexual. Our increased understanding of trauma offers new treatment possibilities for trauma survivors with substance use disorders or other forms of addiction (Covington 2008; Dass-Brailsford and Myrick 2010; Miller and Guidry 2001; Najavits 2002).

Self-Harm

One of the most challenging behavioral symptoms experienced by some women with trauma histories is self-harming (or "self-injurious") behaviors. Cutting and burning are among the most common forms of self-harm, which is a chronic, unsuccessful attempt to avoid experiencing intense psychological distress (Courtois and Ford 2013; Ford and Courtois 2013). One of the similarities between substance abuse and self-harm is that they are both used to alter psychological or physical states. These are short-term methods of coping (Alderman 1997).

Women who engage in self-harm say that it:

- distracts them from emotional pain

- marks or scars their bodies, which they hate

- lets something "bad" out

- expresses anger

- punishes them

- relieves tension and anxiety

- helps them feel more alive by feeling pain or seeing injury

- helps them feel calm or numb; provides a release

- provides a high

- communicates their pain and anger to others

- is a way of seeking nurturing for their wounds

A Model for Women's Recovery:
Women's Integrated Treatment (WIT)

The recurring theme of the interrelationship between substance use and trauma in women's lives indicates the need for a multifocused approach to services. One treatment model, developed by the author, is called Women's Integrated Treatment (WIT). The WIT model is based on (1) the definition of and principles for gender-responsive services, (2) a theoretical foundation (discussed below), and (3) multidimensional therapeutic interventions. Several studies (e.g., Covington et al. 2008; San Diego Association of Governments 2007), including two experimental, randomized control-group studies (Messina, Calhoun, and Warda 2012; Messina et al. 2010) show positive results for the WIT model. It is important to note that no one can "treat" rape, molestation, or any of the other horrific events that have happened to women and girls. These experiences cannot be undone. What we *can* do is deal with the imprint these experiences have left on the mind, body, and soul and help women and girls heal from the aftermath of their traumas.

Theoretical Foundations

In order to develop gender-responsive services and treatment for women, it is essential to begin with a theoretical framework. This is the knowledge base on which programs are developed. The three fundamental theories underlying the WIT model are relational-cultural theory, addiction theory, and trauma theory.

Relational-Cultural Theory

A link between understanding women's addiction and creating effective treatment programs for women is understanding the unique characteristics of women's psychological development and needs. Theories that focus on female development, such as relational-cultural theory (Jordan et al. 1991) posit that the primary motivation for women throughout life is the establishment of a strong sense of connection with others. Relational-cultural theory (RCT) was developed from an increased understanding of gender differences and, specifically, from an understanding of the different ways in which women and men develop psychologically. According to this theory, females develop a sense of self and self-worth when their actions arise out of, and lead back into, connections with others. Connection, not separation, is the guiding principle of growth for women and girls.

RCT describes the outcomes of growth-fostering relationships, as well as the effects of disconnections. Disconnections happen at the sociocultural level, as well as the personal level, through racism, sexism, heterosexism, and classism. The issues of dominance and privilege also are aspects of RCT (Jordan and Hartling 2002).

Addiction Theory

In recent years, health professionals in many disciplines have revised their concepts of all diseases and have created a holistic view of health that acknowledges the physical, emotional, psychological, and spiritual aspects of disease. In a truly holistic model, the environmental and sociopolitical aspects of disease are also included. The WIT model uses a holistic model of addiction (which is essentially a systems perspective) to understand every aspect—physical, emotional, and spiritual—of the woman's self as well as the environmental and sociopolitical aspects of her life, in order to understand her addiction. An addicted woman typically is not using alcohol or other drugs in isolation, so her relationships with her family members and other loved ones, her local community, and society are taken into account. For example, even though a woman may have a strong genetic predisposition to addiction, it is important to understand that she may have grown up in an environment in which addiction and drug dealing were commonplace (Covington 2007).

Although the addiction treatment field considers addiction a "chronic, progressive disease," its treatment methods are more closely aligned to those of the acute-care medical model than the chronic-disease model of care (White, Boyle, and Loveland 2002). An alternative to the acute-care model for treating disease is behavioral health recovery management (BHRM). This concept grew out of and shares much in common with "disease management" approaches to other chronic health problems; it focuses on quality-of-life outcomes as defined by the individual and family. It also offers a broader range of services earlier and extends treatment well beyond traditional (medical) services. The more holistic BHRM model extends the current continuum of care for addiction by including (1) pretreatment (recovery-priming) services; (2) recovery mentoring through primary treatment; and (3) sustained, post-treatment, recovery-support services (Kelly and White 2010).

An integration of BHRM and the holistic health model of addiction is the most effective theoretical framework for developing treatment services for women because it is based on a multidimensional framework. It allows clinicians to treat addiction as the primary problem while also addressing the complexity of issues that women bring to treatment: genetic predispositions, histories of abuse, health consequences, shame, isolation, or a combination of these. When addiction has been a core part of multiple aspects of a woman's life, the treatment process requires a holistic, multidimensional approach.

Trauma Theory

The third theory integrated into the WIT model is based on the principles of trauma-informed services (Harris and Fallot 2001) and the Three-Stage Model of Trauma Recovery developed by Dr. Judith Herman (1997). Trauma is discussed in detail in the following sections.

An Integrated Treatment Approach

The connection between addiction and trauma for women is intricate and not easily disentangled. A treatment provider cannot assume that one is a primary problem and the other secondary. Nor is it always beneficial to delay working on trauma symptoms until the client has been abstinent for a specific amount of time.

One of the counselor's major functions in treating a woman in recovery with a trauma history is to acknowledge to the woman the connection between violence and substance abuse. This explanation helps validate a woman's experience, confirming that she is not alone and clarifying that her experience is not shameful (Finkelstein 1996).

Gender differences exist in the behavioral manifestations of mental illness; men generally turn anger outward, and women turn it inward. Men tend to be more physically and sexually threatening and assaultive, while women tend to be more depressed, self-abusive, and suicidal. Women engage more often in self-harming behaviors, such as cutting, as well as in verbally abusive and disruptive behaviors.

Given the complexity of and interrelationship between substance abuse, trauma, and mental health in women's lives, it is critical that services become integrated. Researchers and clinicians consistently recommend an integrated model as "more likely to succeed, more effective, and more sensitive to clients' needs" (Najavits, Weiss, and Shaw 1997, 279). A more integrated approach also addresses women's multiple roles, their complex psychological identities, and the cultural and social realities in which they live and work as individuals, mothers, daughters, and partners (Minkoff 1989).

Research on the Curricula

One study of the Women's Integrated Treatment model, using *Helping Women Recover* (*HWR*) and *Beyond Trauma* (*BT*) with women in a residential program with their children, demonstrated a decrease in depression (using the Beck Depression Inventory) and trauma symptoms (using the Trauma Symptom Checklist–40 scale) (Covington et al. 2008; San Diego Association of Governments 2007). The first forty-five days in treatment were used as an orientation phase. The decrease in trauma symptoms from admission to day forty-five indicates the importance and potential impact of the treatment environment. The women then participated in the seventeen-session *Helping Women Recover* program, followed by the *Beyond Trauma* program. There was a significant decrease in both depression and trauma symptoms at the completion of *HWR* (p<.05). There was further improvement (p<.05) when the women participated in the *BT* groups that followed *HWR*.

Empirical validation for *HWR* and *BT* was rigorously tested in two experimental studies funded by the National Institute on Drug Abuse (NIDA). Evidence from the first NIDA study showed significant improvement during parole among previously incarcerated women who were randomized to a women's integrated prison treatment program using *HWR* and *BT* sequentially, as compared to women who were randomized to a standard prison therapeutic community. Women who participated in the WIT program were significantly more likely to be participating in voluntary aftercare treatment services (25 percent versus 4 percent) and significantly less likely to be incarcerated at the time of the six-month follow-up interview (29 percent versus 48 percent) compared to women who participated in the standard treatment (Messina et al. 2010). Another randomized study among women participating in drug court treatment settings found that the women in the gender-responsive treatment group (using *HWR* and *BT*) had better in-treatment performance, more positive perceptions related to their treatment experience, and trends indicating reductions in PTSD (Messina, Calhoun, and Warda 2012).

Focus group results also indicate strong support for and high satisfaction with the curricula mentioned above from drug court and prison participants and staff members (Bond, Messina, and Calhoun 2010; Calhoun et al. 2010; Messina and Grella 2008).

Working with Trauma

Trauma-Informed Services

Trauma has become so prevalent in our society that we now realize any system that works with people needs to become trauma informed.

Trauma-informed services are those that take into account the knowledge about violence against women and its impact on their lives. By doing so, a facilitator or therapist is much more effective in providing services. Trauma-informed services:

- take the trauma into account

- avoid triggering trauma reactions and/or traumatizing the individual

- adjust the behavior of counselors, other staff, and the organization to support the individual's coping capacity

- allow survivors to manage their trauma symptoms successfully so they are able to access, retain, and benefit from services (Harris and Fallot 2001)

It is important that the agency or system that you are working in becomes trauma informed. This process includes everyone in admissions, bookkeeping, housekeeping, transportation, the administrative staff, and the medical staff, as well as those in clinical services. Becoming trauma informed is a culture change that creates a safe, supportive, and empowering environment for both clients and staff members.

The Therapeutic Environment

In the therapeutic process, the environment becomes the foundation for a therapeutic experience and is a cornerstone of the healing process. The importance of environment is stressed in the field of child psychology (Winnecott 1965; Stern 1985), which demonstrates that the optimum context for childhood development consists of a safe, nurturing, consistent environment in which the child experiences warmth and a sense of being cared for and understood. These are the same environmental qualities needed in trauma work.

The therapeutic milieu model provides an example of the environmental context needed for trauma survivors. The therapeutic milieu is a carefully arranged environment that is designed to reverse the effects of exposure to interpersonal violence. In using the materials in *Beyond Trauma,* you will help the women in your group explore their pasts, deal with their feelings in healthy ways, see the strengths they have, and increase the skills they need. The women in the group will go through a process of understanding what has happened to them and exploring how violence and abuse have affected them.

A trauma-informed, therapeutic environment contains the following core elements or values (adapted from Fallot and Harris 2008):

- *safety* (ensuring physical and emotional safety)
- *trustworthiness* (maximizing trustworthiness, modeling openness, maintaining appropriate boundaries, and making tasks clear)
- *choice* (emphasizing individual choice and control)
- *collaboration* (ensuring equality in participation, sharing power, and creating a sense of belonging)
- *empowerment* (striving for empowerment and skill building)

In a therapeutic program, safety is most important. The women in the program need to feel safe in order to learn and grow. Facilitators can help them feel safe by trying to keep the treatment program free of physical, emotional, and sexual harassment. You can also help the women feel safe internally by teaching them self-soothing and grounding techniques.

Although you cannot ensure a woman's safety outside the group, you can maintain an atmosphere of safety within the group by adhering to the group agreements, in particular, the confidentiality agreement. This is essential for a sense of psychological safety. What is said in the group remains in the group unless it involves a threat to a woman's safety or that of someone else.

The environment in many criminal justice settings is particularly challenging for women with histories of trauma, and the therapeutic process will not be successful if the setting mimics the behaviors in the dysfunctional environments the women already have experienced (Covington 1998a; Covington and Bloom 2003). One psychiatrist argues, "We have come to believe that retraumatizing people by placing them in environments that reinforce helplessness, scapegoating, isolation, and alienation must be viewed as anti-therapeutic, dangerous, immoral, and a violation of basic human rights" (Bloom 2000, 85). Rather, the design of treatment strategies should be aimed at undoing some of the prior damage. A therapeutic environment's norms are consciously designed to be different: Safety with oneself and with others is paramount, and the entire environment is designed to create living and learning opportunities for everyone involved, staff and clients alike. *Sanctuary* is the word that best describes the ideal environment (Bloom 2000).

Trauma Treatment

Trauma treatment can be divided into present-focused approaches and past-focused approaches. Present-focused approaches are designed to help women function more effectively by developing coping skills, correcting distorted thinking, and instilling hope. Past-focused treatment approaches encourage women to examine in detail their traumatic experiences in order to eliminate their traumatic stress reactions.

The *Beyond Trauma* curriculum is a present-focused intervention that also allows women to look at the past. It uses a variety of therapeutic approaches, including psychoeducational, cognitive behavioral, expressive, mindfulness, body oriented, and relational.

The psychoeducational approach is one of the first steps in—and a core component of—trauma treatment. It helps women begin to link some of their current difficulties to their trauma histories. Also, many women do not know what abuse is or its impact. For example, learning about PTSD often elicits these responses from women: "Oh, someone knows about this? I've been hiding this for years" and "I just thought I was crazy." Many women express relief when they find out that their thoughts, feelings, and behaviors are normal responses to abnormal or extreme events.

A number of years ago, clinicians were trained to use cognitive-behavioral therapy and/or exposure therapy as the sole or primary interventions. In the past ten years, there has been a shift in thinking as a result of the insights of neuroscience and our increased understanding of the brain. These advances have given us a better understanding of how trauma changes brain development, self-regulation, and the capacity to stay focused and in tune with others.

One of the leading trauma researchers and clinicians, Dr. Bessel van der Kolk (2014), now recommends a wide range of what were previously considered unconventional treatment strategies. These include the mind-body approaches of yoga, mindfulness, EMDR (eye movement desensitization and reprocessing), EFT (Emotional Freedom Techniques), neurofeedback, sensorimotor therapy, martial arts, animal-assisted therapy, guided imagery, and theater. When facilitating *Beyond Trauma,* you will be utilizing some of these therapeutic strategies.

Stages of Recovery

Over the past hundred years, there have been many studies of trauma. It is now understood that there are commonalities between rape survivors and combat veterans, between battered women and political prisoners, and between survivors of concentration camps and survivors of abuse in the home. Because the traumatic syndromes have basic features in common, the recovery and healing process also follows a common path.

Some theorists have based their constructs on a stage model of recovery, describing the stages in different language but referring to the same process (see figure 2 below). The central task in the first stage of Dr. Judith Herman's model is establishing safety. Safety is so crucial for women in early recovery

FIGURE 2

Trauma: Stages of Recovery

SYNDROME	STAGE 1	STAGE 2	STAGE 3
Hysteria	Stabilization, symptom-oriented treatment	Exploration of traumatic memories	Personality reintegration, rehabilitation
Combat trauma	Trust, stress management, education	Reexperiencing trauma	Integration of trauma
Complicated posttraumatic stress disorder	Stabilization	Integration of memories	Development of self, drive integration
Multiple personality disorder	Diagnosis, stabilization, communication, cooperation	Metabolism of trauma	Resolution, integration, development of postresolution coping skills
Traumatic disorders	Safety	Remembrance and mourning	Reconnection

that we will refer to it repeatedly. It is important to recognize not only the need for safety but also the lack of it in women's lives. This is a social problem, not just an individual one. Women spend their lives negotiating their safety in various settings. In Herman's model, Stage 1 recovery focuses on self-care in the present. An example of a Stage 1 group is a Twelve Step group. Stage 1 groups should be homogeneous (consisting of women only).

The second stage, experiencing remembrance and mourning, is coming to terms with the trauma story. Stage 2 recovery groups focus on the trauma that occurred in the past. The participants tell their stories of trauma and mourn their old selves, which the traumas destroyed. An example of a Stage 2 group is a survivors group.

The third stage, reconnecting with ordinary life, is where social connections are repaired and enlarged (Herman 1997). Psychodynamically focused psychotherapy groups, which traditionally are unstructured and heterogeneous, reflect the third stage of recovery. In this stage, the survivors face the task of developing new selves and creating futures for themselves.

Figure 3 on page 34 indicates the type of group structure and therapeutic process that Dr. Herman recommends for each stage of trauma recovery work. These stages are not meant to be applied rigidly. They are actually rather fluid in application. In early trauma recovery, the priority is safety and self-care. This does not mean that the topic of trauma is avoided. Acknowledging the trauma and understanding and naming the consequences begin the process of making meaning. Survivors begin to understand that their feelings and behaviors make sense in the context of what they have experienced. The question changes from "What is wrong with you?" to "What has happened to you?" or, as Christine Courtois titled her self-help book for survivors (2014), *It's Not You, It's What Happened to You.*

Several treatment models are based on this three-stage process (Bloom 2000; Covington 2003, 2008; Harris 1998; Najavits 2002). The group models appropriate to each stage are outlined in figure 3.

FIGURE 3

Trauma: Three Group Models

GROUP	RECOVERY: STAGE 1	RECOVERY: STAGE 2	RECOVERY: STAGE 3
Therapeutic task	Safety	Remembrance and mourning	Reconnection
Time orientation	Present	Past	Present, future
Focus	Self-care	Trauma	Interpersonal relationships
Membership	Homogeneous	Homogeneous	Heterogeneous
Boundaries	Flexible, inclusive	Closed	Stable, slow turnover
Cohesion	Moderate	Very high	High
Conflict tolerance	Low	Low	High
Time limit	Open-ended or repeating	Fixed limit	Open-ended
Structure	Didactic	Goal-directed	Unstructured
Example	Twelve Step programs	Survivor group	Interpersonal psychotherapy group

Creating Safety

Stage 1, Safety, is a critical and primary element in trauma work. It is fundamental to all models and is the stage to which facilitators of *Beyond Trauma* need to be most attuned. This program addresses the participants' safety concerns in all the domains identified by Herman. It includes sessions that discuss abuse directly, but safety is the priority for the participants throughout the program.

As a facilitator, you can help the women (or girls) in your groups feel safe by trying to keep the treatment program free of physical, emotional, and sexual harassment and by assessing the risk of domestic violence when a woman returns to her home. Facilitators also can help women feel safe internally by teaching them grounding and self-soothing techniques. These techniques are healthy alternatives to using alcohol or other drugs to comfort themselves.

Herman emphasizes that a trauma survivor who is working on safety issues needs to be in a homogeneous group. This means that the group is composed solely of women and that the facilitator is female. Women may not want to talk in depth about physical or sexual abuse in groups that include men until they are ready for a Stage 3 trauma recovery group. Coed programs seldom prioritize women's needs or highlight women's talents. Women in coed groups often participate less and defocus from the self. Research supports the assertion that single-sex groups are important, particularly for women in substance use disorder treatment and for trauma survivors (Greenfield et al. 2007; Nelson-Zlupko et al. 1996). Likewise, a study of one thousand women in treatment found more positive long-term outcomes in terms of less substance abuse and fewer mental health symptoms (including fewer arrests) for women in single-sex treatment than for women in coed treatment (Evans et al. 2013). Although mixed (heterogeneous) groups may have their place later in a woman's recovery, all-female groups help women develop self-esteem, validate their experiences, and become empowered.

For those working in correctional settings, it is important to acknowledge that abuse can occur in correctional settings as well as in the free world (Covington 1998b). Safety is not guaranteed in the jail, prison, or probation/parole environment, just as it is not guaranteed in the outside world. Although a facilitator cannot ensure a woman's safety outside the group, she can maintain an atmosphere of safety within the group.

As mentioned earlier, confidentiality is essential for a sense of psychological safety. What is said in the group remains in the group unless it involves a threat to a woman's safety or that of someone else. In order to help ensure confidentiality in a criminal justice setting, the facilitator may provide time in the group setting for women to do their Between-Sessions Activities in their workbook. Think about how, in your particular environment, you can provide safety by creating options for storing the workbooks, so the women need not worry about having them read by others.

Although safety is a core element of *Beyond Trauma,* the women who participate in the program will also have an opportunity to begin Stage 2: remembrance and mourning. There are activities to help them reflect on their histories of trauma and their experiences of loss.

The Spiral of Trauma and Healing: A Transformational Model

The Spiral of Trauma and Healing model (which mirrors what happens in *Beyond Trauma*) provides another way of thinking about trauma and healing. Instead of the more linear model of stages of recovery, the spiral shows the circularity and complexity of trauma work (see figure 4 on the next page). The downward spiral represents the limitations and constrictions that trauma can create in a woman's life. The line through the middle represents the traumatic event. It becomes the organizing principle in her life. There is a turning point, a place of change, at the bottom of the downward spiral. Here a woman steps onto a new path, the upward spiral. The upward spiral represents the process of healing, in which a woman's life begins to expand. The trauma is still the line through the middle, but it has less of an influence; it has loosened its grip. There is space now for new activities and new relationships. The trauma becomes a thread in the tapestry of her life; it is no longer the core.

The upward spiral also represents resilience and the potential for posttraumatic growth. Resilience is the ability to adapt well in the face of difficult life events. It is the ability to recover from or adjust to misfortune or change. Although some people are more naturally resilient, a way to develop resilience is by working through the emotions and effects of toxic stress and painful events. Resilience develops as people develop better coping skills. It also comes from supportive, caring relationships with others. One of the goals of the *Beyond Trauma* program is to increase women's resilience.

FIGURE 4

Spiral of Trauma and Healing

(Transformation)

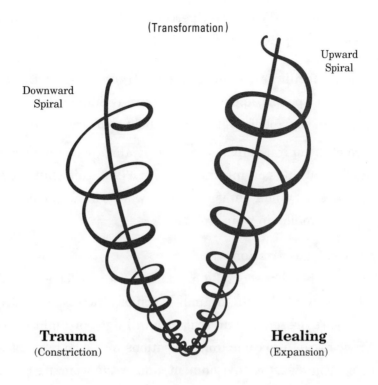

Downward
Spiral

Upward
Spiral

Trauma
(Constriction)

Healing
(Expansion)

Adapted from the Spiral of Addiction and Recovery in *Helping Women Recover.*
Copyright 1999, 2008 by Stephanie S. Covington.

Posttraumatic growth occurs when a person experiences positive changes resulting from a major life crisis. First identified in the mid-nineties by psychologists Lawrence Calhoun and Richard Tedeschi (1999, 2013), posttraumatic growth goes beyond resilience. By actively searching for good in something terrible, a person can use adversity as a catalyst for advancing to a higher level of psychological functioning. Five positive changes signify posttraumatic growth:

1. Personal strength—While vulnerability can creative a sense of powerlessness, paradoxically it can boost self-confidence.

2. Relationships—Bonding can occur on a deeper level after a tragic event.

3. Greater life appreciation—Tragedy can shift a person's perspective, creating a new focus on gratitude and joy.

4. Beliefs—These may change or be reinforced by grief. People often see their role in the world differently.

5. New possibilities—People may perceive new opportunities and pursue them.

Several factors facilitate the process of posttraumatic growth: receiving care from supportive people, approaching versus avoiding grief, and recognizing that they are in control of the timing of their recovery process.

The image of the spiral helps us see that healing is a transformative process. Transformation is an internal process. When this shift occurs, a woman is able to say, "Who I am is not who I was." This is a model you will be teaching to the women in your groups.

Triggers and Retraumatization

A trigger is a stimulus that sets off a memory of trauma. That is, a single environmental cue related to the trauma—such as a noise, a sound, a smell, or another person's presence—can trigger a full fight-or-flight-or-freeze response. Triggers can also come from sensations in the body, images in the mind, feelings, memories, the environment, and/or the woman's or another person's behavior. Profound dysregulation of psychological and physiological systems is a result of trauma and leaves women both overresponding to neutral cues and underresponding to danger cues. Traumatized women are, therefore, at increased risk of similar and repeated victimization.

Triggering is inevitable; retraumatization is not. Because participants may be naturally triggered in a therapeutic group setting, attention should be paid to increasing their attention, care, and coping skills for managing emotional distress (Najavits 2002). Trauma survivors are used to having their boundaries ignored and their opinions or objections dismissed. A crucial element of successful treatment involves attention to these components of women's experience in treatment (Harris and Fallot 2001):

- boundary violations

- lying and breaking integrity

- chaotic treatment environments

- lockstep-rigid agency policies that do not allow a woman to have what she needs

- agency dysfunction

- disruption in routines

- secrets in the group

- not listening to the woman

- not believing her account of the abuse

- labeling intense rage and other feelings as pathological

- minimizing, discrediting, and/or ignoring the woman's responses

- conducting urinalysis in a nonprivate and disrespectful manner

- stripping a participant (such as a woman offender) with male correctional officers present

Dissociation and Grounding

When women dissociate, they seem to watch from a distance to maintain a sense of what's happening without having to be part of the experience. For example, while you are facilitating the group, you may have women who are attending the group but periodically "aren't there." They have psychologically left the group. Women often experience dissociation as "losing time." Dissociation is a common response to a trigger (e.g., a sight, sound, smell, or touch).

This defense mechanism is a very functional one when a person is being abused. It allows the victim not to be present. However, depending on its severity, dissociation can be very challenging. Conventional talk therapy in these situations is virtually useless. The use of physical activity and having the women focus on their bodily sensations is more effective. Treatment for dissociation consists primarily of first grounding the woman, ensuring that she has the ability to self-soothe and manage stress. You will find specific grounding and self-soothing techniques throughout this curriculum. Several sessions in *Beyond Trauma* include mind-body techniques.

Depersonalization

As noted earlier, depersonalization is one of the symptoms of the massive dissociation created by trauma. It is represented by blank stares, absent minds, and the outward manifestation of the biological freeze reaction. The woman can tell you the horrific details of her abuse, yet she has no feelings. As with dissociation, conventional talk therapy is virtually useless with

Duplicating this page is illegal. Do not copy this material without written permission from the publisher.

39

depersonalization. The use of physical activity and having women focus on their bodily sensations is more effective. Several of the sessions in this program incorporate mind-body techniques to address depersonalization as well.

Self-Harm

Self-harm was discussed earlier, on page 24. Successful treatment of self-inflicted violence or self-injurious behavior includes teaching women new ways of coping with stressors so underlying painful feelings can be dealt with.

Self-Help/Mutual-Help Groups

Self-help or mutual-help groups exist in many communities. These groups are composed of people who voluntarily come together to discuss a common problem and to share solutions and coping techniques. The key feature of any mutual-help group is that there is no involvement by professionals or experts who wield authority or knowledge.

The use of mutual-help groups to recover from alcohol and other drug problems has become widespread. Moreover, the Twelve Step model, which originated in Alcoholics Anonymous (AA), is now used in more than 126 anonymous groups to deal with a host of other problems. People meeting in mutual self-help groups modeled after AA now address overeating, gambling, sexual abuse issues, and other relationship topics.

Twelve Step programs have been critiqued in various ways. Some feminists have been concerned that the language of the Twelve Steps seems simplistic, sexist, and reductionist (Bepko 1991; Berenson 1991; Kasl 1992; Rapping 1996). Certainly, Twelve Step programs have limitations. They stress individual change as the solution and ignore social and political factors that affect women's recovery and healing. Also, much of the Twelve Step literature is thirty to sixty years old and is overtly sexist. Atheistic and agnostic women may be uncomfortable with references to a "Higher Power," even though the Twelve Steps welcome a broad range of understandings of the Higher Power, including "Goddess," "Buddha," and a "Deeper Self."

Feminists are particularly concerned about the Twelve Steps' emphasis on powerlessness. However, feminist analysis often misses the fact that the masculine "power over" is being relinquished in order to experience the feminine "power with," "power to be able"—that is, a sense of empowerment (Miller 1982). "The process of recovery from addiction is a process of recovering a different, more feminine, sense of power and will" (Berenson 1991, 74). There is also confusion between surrender and submission. "When we submit, we give in to a force that's trying to control us. When we surrender, we let go of our need to control" (Covington 1994, 48). Recovery groups encourage surrender and giving up the illusion of control.

Other critics say that to ask women to admit their powerlessness over alcohol and other drugs and then over persons, places, and things encourages the women to think of themselves as victims who have no control over their lives. However, this critique misses the paradox of powerlessness: by admitting her powerlessness in those aspects of her life that she cannot control, a woman accesses areas of her life in which she does have power.

Because women grow and develop in relationships and connections, and because Twelve Step programs are free and available in most communities, it makes sense to help women access them. It's best to refer a woman to a meeting you have visited or know something about. There are also Twelve Step materials designed for women (Covington 1994, 2000b, 2009) that are trauma informed.

Mutual-help groups can be particularly important for women in the criminal justice system who are making the transition back into the community. Twelve Step programs can also be incorporated into community correctional settings, offering an already-existing "continuity of care."

We know that attending Twelve Step groups can be very difficult for trauma survivors. They are asked to go into unfamiliar or uncomfortable areas with a lot of people (often men), who want to greet them, touch them, and stay in contact with them. This is very challenging for many trauma survivors, who can be overwhelmed, or avoidant, in these situations. We recommend developing a buddy system, pairing women well established in recovery with women just starting out in this venue, sending women in groups, accompanying them, and using women-only meetings initially.

Sponsors who encourage the discontinuation of psychotropic medicines and undervalue the impact of trauma on recovery processes for women should be carefully evaluated, as obtaining a new sponsor might be in the best interest of the trauma survivor's recovery.

Duplicating this page is illegal. Do not copy this material without written permission from the publisher.

41

Mutual-help groups cannot be used as substitutes for professional counseling when a female has been raped or battered or is the victim of incest. In addition, some trauma survivors are not ready for this group experience. However, as part of a multifaceted support system, mutual-help groups can be very useful for women. They can provide the kind of safe environment that is needed for trauma recovery and a growth-fostering relational context that serves women's psychological development.

Considerations for Professionals

Professional Self-Care

Helping women recover and heal can be a very rewarding experience. It is an honor because it requires the trust of someone whose trust has been broken in other relationships. It also can be very demanding and challenging (Berry 2003). It is a challenge because it requires the clinician to maintain self-awareness while being attuned to the client's needs.

The type of connection needed in order for healing to happen can have a negative effect on the helping professional. This process is called vicarious traumatization (VT). "VT is the negative transformation in the helper that results from empathic engagement with trauma survivors and their trauma material, combined with a commitment or responsibility to help them" (Pearlman and Caringi 2014, 202). Burnout, compassion fatigue, and secondary traumatic stress are other terms used to describe this type of stress (Figley 2002; Figley et al. 1995).

It is important for the facilitator to be able to use some of the information processing, emotional regulation, and grounding skills in this program for herself. In addition, some of the effective coping strategies that have been used for handling difficult trauma material include routine self-care: a healthy diet, regular exercise, spiritually oriented activities, and emotional support from others.

Clinical Supervision

Clinical supervision is an important part of doing trauma work. Regular, process-oriented, and psychoeducational clinical supervision needs to address the multiple issues that can arise (such as transference, countertransference, vicarious traumatization, and the staff's own traumatic experiences). Regular clinical supervision through which counselors can share information they have been asked to "hold" can help them unburden themselves. When clinical knowledge, coping skills, and support are delivered in a safe, accepting environment, this process models the therapeutic relationship.

As the trauma field has become more sophisticated, many programs and agencies now understand the need for trauma-informed supervision. This type of supervision includes the following:

- reframing the client's behavior as an adaptation to trauma

- a focus on the supervisee's responses to clients and an awareness of vicarious trauma

- supervisory relationships built on the five core values of trauma-informed services: safety, trustworthiness, choice, collaboration, and empowerment (Fallot and Harris 2008)

In addition, a relational model of supervision is the most relevant for trauma therapy. "Relational models of supervision can provide relationships based on mutuality and offer horizontal as opposed to vertical forms of person-person contact" (Bloom, Yanosy, and Harrison 2013, 126–46). For more information on trauma-informed supervision, you may refer to the Institute for Health and Recovery publication *Developing Trauma-Informed Organizations: A Tool Kit* (2012).

Cultural Competence

The foundation of cultural competence is the belief that each of us represents a range of aspects of diversity and that being culturally competent means that the helping professional is aware of her own identities as well as those of the participants. The ADDRESSING model (Hays 2007) makes explicit the multiple identities that we all have:

A: Age-related factors

DD: Disability-ability

R: Religion and spirituality

E: Ethnic origins, race, and culture

S: Social class

S: Sexual orientation

I: Indigenous heritage/colonization

N: National origin, immigration

G: Gender/biological sex, gender identity

Duplicating this page is illegal. Do not copy this material without written permission from the publisher.

43

Being culturally competent as a therapist or helping professional means you are always growing and learning. It requires ongoing supervision and consultation (Brown 2014).

Ethical Issues

Clients who have had traumatic experiences have increased vulnerability to issues that are present in the therapeutic relationship and structure: the use and abuse of power, privacy, and boundary violations. Facilitators, therapists, and counselors should abide by the code of ethics that governs the policies of their agency and/or their credentials and professional affiliations.

. . .

CHAPTER 2

Introduction to the Program

The Curriculum

Beyond Trauma is designed as a group process. Facilitated groups help the women to see that their experiences are not unique and help reduce the shame and isolation that is common to trauma survivors. However, the activities found in each session can be adapted for individual work.

This curriculum is designed for working with women in community-based programs, private settings, or correctional settings. There are three primary focus areas: understanding the dynamics of violence, abuse, and trauma; understanding the impact of trauma on women's lives; and learning how to live with and heal from trauma.

This revised edition of the curriculum includes:

- new and updated foundational information for the facilitator in part 1
- new statistics about abuse and other forms of trauma in part 1 and in the sessions
- new discoveries, publications, and insights in the field
- longer sessions (two hours rather than one and a half hours) and an additional session, which enables us to include more new lectures and activities for the participants that reflect current thinking and practice
- a variety of yoga poses, grounding activities, and self-soothing activities
- information at the end of each session about adapting the curriculum for use with adolescent girls
- new national resources (organizations and groups) for the facilitator and participants
- two new videos: one for facilitator training and one for use with the participants

As mentioned earlier, the curriculum promotes a strength-based approach that seeks to empower women and increase their sense of self. In using this kind of model, the facilitator helps the women or girls in the group to see the strengths and skills they already have that will aid in their healing. She looks for seeds of health and strength and mirrors this back to the women in the group. The curriculum also focuses on emotional development; dealing with expression and containment of feelings are critical parts of trauma work.

The *Beyond Trauma* program materials consist of this facilitator guide, a participant workbook, one facilitator training video, and a participant video.

Group Composition

The suggested number of participants in a group is between six and ten women. The curriculum can be adapted for larger groups and open groups if this is essential for the treatment setting.

Ideally, each group would be a "closed group"; that is, the group would be closed to new members after the first session so the entire group would begin and end the program together. This helps establish connection among group members and reinforces the feelings of safety and group cohesion. The material in this curriculum builds from session to session, and the first session is an orientation session that lays the foundation for trust among the group members.

If it is impossible in your setting to run a closed group, consider how to introduce new women into an ongoing group. Some suggestions are:

- Admit the new women at the beginning of each module (A, B, or C) but not when a module has already begun.

- Assign a "big sister" or a "buddy" to each new woman and ask this person to review with the new woman the part(s) of the program that the group already has completed. This allows the new person to have some background about the previous work done in the group. The big sister can also be the one who introduces the new woman to the group.

- Offer modules A and B to all the women and then let the women decide if they want to continue on to module C. Modules A and B have open enrollment, and module C is closed.

There are specific sessions in which adding new members would be particularly difficult: session 4, in which the topic is abuse in childhood, adolescence, and adulthood; and session 6, with the family sculpture.

Once the program is completed, it may be decided (depending on the setting and if the group members so desire) to let the group continue as an ongoing support group.

Using the Facilitator Guide

The facilitator guide contains two parts. Chapter 1 of part 1 gives the facilitator some background information about trauma and its effects. Chapter 2 of part 1 gives advice about facilitating the group sessions. Having a basic understanding of the depth and complexity of these topics will help the group facilitation process.

Part 2 includes the session outlines or lesson plans. The session outlines are laid out in three columns: The left column indicates the topic and the approximate time it takes to cover the topic, the middle column contains notes to the facilitator, and the right column describes the discussion with the women in the group.

The curriculum has three modules (or themes), with a total of twelve sessions. The sessions may be arranged in a variety of ways; however, the curriculum is laid out in the suggested sequence. The three modules are:

1. Violence, Abuse, and Trauma

2. The Impact of Trauma on Women's Lives

3. Healing from Trauma

Your role as facilitator is to maintain the structure of the group, contain and move the group process through each session, lead by example by having appropriate boundaries and expressing and containing your feelings, and allow the women to have their own experiences of the group.

At the end of the facilitator guide are appendices, resources, and references. All these can be helpful.

Session Outlines

Each session is organized in the following way:

1. Goals and participant objectives, general topics to be covered, and materials needed (listed at the beginning of each session for the facilitator).

Duplicating this page is illegal. Do not copy this material without written permission from the publisher.

47

2. Structured quiet time and a brief check-in: The quiet time helps the women become present in the group. The check-in is a time to connect and share.

3. Teaching component: The key topic(s) for the session are presented to enhance the women's understanding (for example, what constitutes abuse, why the women may have felt out of control and confused, what they can do to soothe and ground themselves, and so on).

4. Interactive component: The women discuss the issues, ask clarifying questions, and process the new information.

5. Examples are given throughout the curriculum. These are examples of typical responses from women, so the facilitator has a sense of what to expect from the activity or the question she is posing. Additionally, the examples may be useful prompts for the facilitator to stimulate discussion among the participants.

6. Experiential component: The women do activities and exercises to try out new skills—based on the information just presented—in a safe, supportive environment.

7. Practice: Between-Sessions Activities in the participant workbook give the women opportunities to practice the new skills they have learned and to develop new insights.

8. Reflection: This provides an opportunity to explore the implications of the new learning/behavior.

9. A grounding or self-soothing activity frequently helps end the session.

10. Closing.

Each individual or small-group activity is identified as such. General discussion questions for the full group are not listed as activities.

Adult learning theory suggests that, for maximum attention and retention, "nonlecture" activities be interjected approximately every seven to ten minutes. Therefore, the curriculum is designed to be interactive, with facilitator-generated activities and questions for the participants. Different people learn best in different ways: by seeing, by hearing, and by doing or feeling. The curriculum allows the women to hear, see (via a role model), and try out (role-play) new ideas and concepts.

Materials Needed for the Sessions

MODULE	SESSION	MATERIALS NEEDED
Module A: **VIOLENCE, ABUSE, AND TRAUMA**	**Session 1:** **Introduction to the Program**	• Name tags for the facilitator and each woman in the group • Relaxing music and equipment to play music • A participant workbook for the facilitator and each woman • A pencil or pen for the facilitator and each woman • A piece of flip-chart paper (or poster) showing the Spiral of Trauma and Healing • *Optional: A DVD player and monitor and segment 1 and segment 2 of the* Beyond Trauma *Participant Video* • A sheet of blank paper for each woman • A newsprint flip-chart pad, an easel, and felt-tip pens • Masking tape • Facial tissues • *Optional: Five Senses cards (found in appendix 1), which can be printed on card stock or laminated*
	Session 2: **The Connections between Violence, Abuse, and Trauma**	• Name tags for the facilitator and each woman in the group • Relaxing music and equipment to play music • Each participant's and the facilitator's workbook • A pencil or pen for the facilitator and each woman • A variety of crayons or colored pencils for the women • A newsprint flip-chart pad, an easel, and felt-tip pens • *Optional: A DVD player and monitor and segment 3 of the* Beyond Trauma *Participant Video* • Masking tape • Facial tissues

Materials Needed for the Sessions *continued*

MODULE	SESSION	MATERIALS NEEDED
Module A: **VIOLENCE, ABUSE, AND TRAUMA** *continued*	**Session 3:** **Power and Abuse**	• Name tags for the facilitator and each woman in the group, if needed • Relaxing music and equipment to play music • Each participant's and the facilitator's workbook • A pencil or pen for the facilitator and each woman • A newsprint flip-chart pad, an easel, and felt-tip pens • *Optional:* Life Prayers from Around the World: 365 Prayers, Blessings, and Affirmations to Celebrate the Human Journey *or* Circle of Stones • *Optional: A DVD player and monitor and segment 4 of the* Beyond Trauma *Participant Video* • A blank sheet of paper for each woman • Masking tape • Facial tissues
	Session 4: **The Process of Trauma and Reactions to Trauma**	• Relaxing music and equipment to play music • Each participant's and the facilitator's workbook • A pencil or pen for the facilitator and each woman • A newsprint flip-chart pad, an easel, and felt-tip pens • Masking tape • Three sheets of blank paper for each woman • Small bottles of bubble soap (one bottle for every two women) • A bubble wand for each woman • A small brown paper lunch bag with various items in it for each woman • *Optional: A DVD player and monitor, segment 5 of the* Beyond Trauma *Participant Video, and segment 6 of the* Beyond Trauma *Participant Video* • Facial tissues

INTRODUCTION TO THE PROGRAM

Materials Needed for the Sessions *continued*

MODULE	SESSION	MATERIALS NEEDED
Module B: **THE IMPACT OF TRAUMA ON WOMEN'S LIVES**	**Session 5:** **How Trauma Affects Our Lives**	• Relaxing music and equipment to play music • Each participant's and the facilitator's workbook • A pencil or pen for the facilitator and each woman • A newsprint flip-chart pad, an easel, and felt-tip pens • Magazines for the collage activity • A piece of poster board for each woman • Colored felt-tip pens or crayons for each woman • Enough glue sticks and scissors for two or three (maximum) women to share each set • Masking tape • Facial tissues
	Session 6: **Abuse and the Family**	• Relaxing music and equipment to play music • Each participant's and the facilitator's workbook • A pencil or pen for the facilitator and each woman • *Optional: A piece of writing paper and a marker* • A newsprint flip-chart pad, an easel, and felt-tip pens • Masking tape • *Optional: A childhood photo of each participant* • *Optional: A DVD player and monitor and segment 7 of the* Beyond Trauma Participant Video • Facial tissues • A sturdy chair

Materials Needed for the Sessions *continued*

MODULE	SESSION	MATERIALS NEEDED
Module C: **HEALING FROM TRAUMA**	**Session 7:** **The Connection between Trauma and Addiction: Spirals of Recovery and Healing**	• Relaxing music and equipment to play music • Each participant's and the facilitator's workbook • A pencil or pen for the facilitator and each woman • A newsprint flip-chart pad, an easel, and felt-tip pens • Masking tape • *Optional: A DVD player and monitor and segment 8 of the* Beyond Trauma *Participant Video* • Crayons or colored pencils for the women • Facial tissues
	Session 8: **Grounding and Self-Soothing**	• Relaxing music and equipment to play music • Each participant's and the facilitator's workbook • A pencil or pen for the facilitator and each woman • A newsprint flip-chart pad, an easel, and felt-tip pens • Masking tape • *Optional: A DVD player and monitor and segment 9 of the* Beyond Trauma *Participant Video* • Facial tissues
	Session 9: **The Mind and Body Connection**	• Relaxing music and equipment to play music • Each participant's and the facilitator's workbook • A pencil or pen for the facilitator and each woman • A newsprint flip-chart pad, an easel, and felt-tip pens • Crayons or colored pencils for the women • Masking tape • Facial tissues • *Optional: Butcher paper for life-size body images* • *Optional: Small boxes for the Creating a Container activity*

Materials Needed for the Sessions *continued*

MODULE	SESSION	MATERIALS NEEDED
Module C: **HEALING FROM TRAUMA** *continued*	**Session 10: Our Feelings**	• Relaxing music and equipment to play music • Each participant's and the facilitator's workbook • A pencil or pen for the facilitator and each woman • A newsprint flip-chart pad, an easel, and felt-tip pens • Masking tape • Facial tissues
	Session 11: Healthy Relationships	• Relaxing music and equipment to play music • Each participant's and the facilitator's workbook • A pencil or pen for the facilitator and each woman • A newsprint flip-chart pad, an easel, and felt-tip pens • Magazines for the collage activity • A piece of poster board for each participant • Colored felt-tip pens or crayons, glue sticks, and scissors for the participants (a set for every woman or every two women is preferable) • Masking tape • *Optional: A DVD player and monitor and segment 10 of the* Beyond Trauma *Participant Video* • Facial tissues
	Session 12: Endings and Beginnings	• Relaxing music and equipment to play music • Each participant's and the facilitator's workbook • A pencil or pen for the facilitator and each woman • A newsprint flip-chart pad, an easel, and felt-tip pens • Masking tape

continued on next page

Materials Needed for the Sessions *continued*

MODULE	SESSION	MATERIALS NEEDED
Module C: **HEALING FROM TRAUMA** *continued*	**Session 12:** **Endings and** **Beginnings**	• A pretty piece of fabric, a scarf, or a tablecloth • *Optional: A meaningful object (as described in session 11)* • *Optional: A DVD player and monitor and segment 11 of the* Beyond Trauma *Participant Video* • Facial tissues

The facilitator is encouraged to enhance the learning experience by tailoring information and activities to the conditions and needs of the participants. This includes cultural issues, educational levels and literacy, and unique concerns of criminal justice settings.

The Role of the Facilitator

As was stated previously, it is important that the facilitator be a woman. Her role is that of a guide on a journey seen through the eyes of women in the group. Many of the issues addressed in this curriculum are common to all women.

The following qualities in a facilitator will help ensure a positive group experience:

1. Prepares ahead of time for each session

2. Is trustworthy

3. Is credible

4. Is available

5. Is reliable and consistent

6. Is hopeful

7. Is warm and compassionate

8. Is energetic

9. Is emotionally mature

10. Sets healthy boundaries and respects confidentiality

11. Is committed to and interested in women's issues

12. Is sensitive and responsive to multicultural issues

13. If a trauma survivor, is confident that she is at a place in her own recovery that will allow for healthy and positive outcomes for herself and the women in the group

14. Is a content expert (has read and understands this facilitator guide)

15. Is skilled as a facilitator (has had prior experience conducting a group)

To help empower the women in the group, you, as the facilitator, will point out and emphasize the women's strengths. As the facilitator, you can encourage women to make conscious decisions. You can help women take ownership of their feelings and act out their feelings in appropriate ways, rather than suppressing them or being consumed by them. You can encourage social action as part of the healing process. The facilitator is the provider of hope. Your belief that the women's lives can get better and become more satisfying and rewarding is important to the women in the group.

Reliability

Facilitators need to commit to attending each session to build trust, show that they are committed to the group, and maintain a sense of continuity that plays a part in creating safety within the group. Facilitators must model the behaviors listed in the group agreements, such as starting and ending the sessions on time, modeling appropriate feelings, and maintaining confidentiality (more on this is presented later). It is important that the facilitator be emotionally constant for the women in the group.

Style

A welcoming style sets the tone for the sessions. Acknowledging that there will be benefits to each woman in the group for attending and expressing that you are pleased the women are going to be part of the group set the tone for this. Other important parts of the facilitator's style are as follows:

- Be culturally sensitive and use culturally relevant examples (for your group) throughout the program. Differences in age, sexual orientation, religion, race, class, disability, culture, and ethnicity can influence women's levels of comfort with the issues discussed in this program.

- Be supportive and nonjudgmental with the participants. For example, if a member is hesitant to ask something, you may say, "That's a good question. I am glad you raised that."

- Keep your language simple and clear. Avoid jargon. If acronyms or abbreviations are used (such as *DSM-5* and PTSD), explain what they mean.

- Summarize individual or group feelings regularly. It is also helpful to summarize common themes that have arisen throughout the group session.

- Be conscious of group trust and confidentiality. Be mindful of interactions that have the potential to affect the cohesiveness of the group. This might include competition among members, absenteeism, silence, nonparticipation, subgrouping, or a breach of confidentiality. Verbally check in with the group regarding these issues (for example, ask, "What does this silence mean?").

- Set standards for an acceptable way of relating with others through the group agreements (for example, no physical or verbal abuse, no interrupting, or no name-calling).

Knowing the Women in the Group

It is very helpful to know something about the women in your group. This is not only respectful but will help your facilitation. If possible, find out:

- who they are (backgrounds and demographics)

- why they are there (reasons for attending) and whether they are required to be there or are attending voluntarily

- if they are required to be there, whether any of them are resistant

- what they want to know and learn

- what their levels of experience in the topics to be covered are

- what their issues and concerns regarding the topics are

- what their concerns regarding socioeconomic issues (such as race, economic level, age, reading ability, and education) are

- what their current emotional states are

- what their levels of functioning are

- what any particular group dynamics are

Women may be either self-referred or recommended by a counselor. It is important to clarify this when starting a group. Sometimes a woman who has been referred by a counselor or the court may feel resentful about attending. It is very helpful to assess the motivation of the group members.

You may wish to develop a questionnaire to help gather this information before the first session. Time is also allowed during the session itself to discuss this information with the participants. For example, you may want to ask during most of the lectures and activities if there are any cultural issues that the group members feel weren't addressed and need to be added.

If you find that some women are experiencing cognitive or psychiatric disabilities that may affect their ability to participate in the group discussions and activities, you will need to modify the group to accommodate them. This may be done by shortening the length of the group sessions, simplifying the language, or conducting a separate group for women with these challenges.

Cultural Awareness

Race, ethnicity, and gender are not mutually exclusive. Together they are part of the complex lens through which many women see and experience the world they live in. Simply discussing issues related to women, generically, does not recognize the importance of the racial and/or ethnic identities of the women in the group. The traumas and burdens each woman has faced may be the result of being female, poor, a woman of color, and so on. The facilitator can help the women see the social/cultural contexts for these issues. Awareness of this can help reduce the personal shame or blame a woman may feel.

Encouraging the women to value diversity not only works to dismantle various negative stereotypes about race, ethnicity, and culture; it may also work to counter the stereotypes that individual women in the group have internalized in their lives.

The facilitator can also encourage the women to get involved in some sort of social action, such as letter writing, lobbying, political action, and volunteering in the community to fight injustices and create change in their lives and the lives of others.

Co-facilitating

This curriculum is designed to be led by one facilitator. However, having two women co-facilitate is highly recommended for trauma-focused groups. (This is often difficult to arrange if an agency is understaffed.)

If you do have a co-facilitator, spend some time in advance talking with the other facilitator about how to divide up the modules, facilitating methods and styles of delivery, and "sharing the stage."

- Review goals and procedures for the sessions.

- Identify who will give each lecture, run each activity, and lead each discussion.

- Have a backup plan in case a facilitator is unable to attend a session.

- Discuss how you will interact. For example, are you both comfortable if the other facilitator interjects examples or ideas?

- Sit across from each other in group and make eye contact often.

At the end of each session, the facilitators should debrief the session and review any feedback:

- Discuss the group process.

- Review and discuss the participants' feedback, reactions, and responses.

- Discuss how each woman in the group is doing and plan for any special attention that might be needed to get group members to connect with one another. If you encourage the women to connect with one another between sessions, you will help build strong networks of caring women.

- Decide ahead of time how each of you will handle any one-on-one time with individual group members between sessions.

Prior to the Program

The following sections on basic group facilitation are designed for new facilitators and provide a review for those with experience.

- Before beginning the program, it is suggested that facilitators allow six to eight hours for reading and comprehending the curriculum materials. It is also useful to review the current session materials again right before the session. This is necessary in order for the facilitator to feel comfortable with and absorb the information. Facilitators will want to be able to present the materials by just referring to their notes and not "reading" them. After you have facilitated the program a few times, you will find that you may be able to do this quite easily.

- Putting goals, the group agenda, and topical points on a whiteboard or newsprint flip chart is helpful while conducting the sessions and delivering lecture materials. These listings can be saved and reused. This is also a good way to review and become familiar with each session before facilitating it.

- Help each woman find a support person (friend or mental health provider) to be available for her between sessions. This may be especially challenging in a criminal justice setting, where support may not be readily available.

- Be sure that all needed equipment (for example, newsprint flip charts and easels, CD/DVD players or iPods with speakers, and art supplies) is available in advance and in the session room at the beginning of the session.

- Check to be sure all logistics are accounted for (for example, special needs, transportation, room setup, chairs, name tags, doors unlocked). Use name tags for the first several sessions until the group members learn one another's names. Can chairs be moved to form a circle? Is music allowed? Is privacy allowed or are staff members allowed to walk in and out of the room during the group sessions? Will other issues affect the setting and environment the facilitator is trying to create? Will there be interruptions, such as women being called out for drug testing or medical appointments? You might need to find a secure place for the women's workbooks if the program is being used in a correctional setting.

- Room size is important. The room should be large enough to accommodate the group comfortably; participants should have easy access in and out of their chairs without disturbing others, and they should not feel too cramped. You will need adequate space to do the yoga poses. However, rooms that are too large can make the setting feel cold and impersonal.

- Good ventilation and room temperature are important for an effective and comfortable group environment. The room should have windows and/or natural light, if possible.

- The physical environment in your group meeting room is important. Ideally, you could create a soothing, healing atmosphere in the room by providing a flower or plant; calm, relaxing music; soft, warm lighting (nonglaring, nonfluorescent); comfortable chairs already arranged so there is no chaos when the women enter the room; drinking water nearby; a box of tissues; and the like. The room should be free from distractions created by others outside the room. Likewise, the participants should

Duplicating this page is illegal. Do not copy this material without written permission from the publisher.

59

not be visible to others outside the room. Establishing this kind of group atmosphere may be challenging in criminal justice settings.

- If the sessions are held at night, there should be adequate lighting outside the meeting room and in the parking lot. Depending on the location, you may want to escort participants to and from their cars to give a sense of safety. Make sure restrooms are located nearby and easily accessible to group members.

- Good acoustics facilitate good communication. If the room is too large or not soundproofed from outside noises, it may not be an effective session location. Noise distractions can be disruptive; participants may fear that others outside can hear them and breach confidentiality.

- Be sure the room meets the Americans with Disabilities Act (ADA) standards and accommodates any special needs of participants and facilitators.

- Facilitators should arrive at the group room at least fifteen to twenty minutes before the session begins. This allows time for them to be sure that all equipment is there and functioning and that the chairs are in a circle.

Your preparation will also include assembling whatever materials are needed to conduct the activities. (See pages 49–54 for a list of supplies needed for each session.) If an activity requires preparation (before the session) on your part, it will be indicated in the instructions for the session. You will note that many of the activities call for the women to have pens or pencils. It is preferable to have them do as much writing as possible in their workbooks, so they have as many of their reflections and responses as possible in one place.

The things you will need for every session are a newsprint flip chart, an easel for holding the flip chart, and colored felt-tip marking pens for writing. You will use the flip chart to write important points as you deliver the lectures, list important points or suggestions from the women during discussions, list instructions, and so on. You will also want to have masking tape available so that you can post some of the sheets on the wall so all participants can see them. If the room you are using contains a large chalkboard or a whiteboard, you may use that (with colored chalk or whiteboard pens) instead of the newsprint flip chart and easel.

You may need to modify some of the activities if you are working in a criminal justice setting. For example, if scissors are prohibited, you may need to have the women tear items out of magazines for their collages.

You will need a watch or clock for timing many of the activities. You also may want to bring a small bell or chime to use as a way to let the women know when the time is up for completing an activity. It is a soothing way to get their attention.

The timing suggested for each part of a session is a guideline, but each group will have its own personality, and different groups will move through the materials at different speeds. You may need to adapt a session by using fewer activities or substituting optional activities, shortening the lectures, or leading discussions in different directions.

The best room setup for most parts of the group session is a circle of movable chairs (one chair for each participant, including you). Circular settings foster a sense of respect and equality, as well as allow each woman to make eye contact with others in the group. Try to avoid standing in front of a row of chairs (as in a classroom) or sitting at a desk in the front of the room. When you are delivering a lecture or leading a discussion, you may want to stand by the flip chart, which will be positioned just outside of the circle where all can see it, so that you can write down things that you particularly want the women in the group to remember. At other times, such as when the women are sharing sensitive information about themselves, it is best if you sit in the circle. This will make it easier for the women in the group to accept you, identify with you, and share their feelings and opinions.

For some of the activities, you will need to move the chairs. For others, you may need tables or desks or floor space for the women to work on. Some groups like having round tables or desks in a circle for all of the sessions so it is easier for them to write in their workbooks.

Adjusting the Timing

The program is designed for twelve sessions, each lasting two hours. The group sessions can be held once or twice per week. This generally depends on the size of the group and how much sharing the group members want to do.

Adapting the Sessions for Use with Girls

The *Beyond Trauma* program can be used with adolescent girls with some adaptations. In some settings, especially juvenile justice settings, the case records of girls may be filled with diagnostic labels, with little said about the girls' experiences of trauma. Many girls have accumulated multiple diagnoses, and their treatment primarily has been medication and/or behavior management. When traumatic events begin at an early age and remain unresolved, a girl's most immediate reaction may be a desperate attempt to cope. What are often labeled as self-destructive behaviors actually can be tension-reducing behaviors, such as aggression, substance abuse, bingeing and purging, suicide attempts, self-inflicted violence, and indiscriminate/reckless sexual behavior. With our greater understanding of trauma, we can see that the behaviors we are most concerned about often are responses to trauma.

One study in the District of Columbia compared girls who had experienced sexual abuse by a family member with a matched comparison group of girls who had not been abused. The average starting age was eleven; the girls were followed for twenty years and they were assessed six times. Compared with girls of the same ages, races, and social circumstances, sexually abused girls had suffered more often from depression, dissociative symptoms, troubled sexual development, obesity, and self-harm. They had dropped out of high school at a higher rate, had more major illnesses, and had been diagnosed with a host of different psychiatric labels (Trickett, Noll, and Putnam 2011). This is one of many examples of developmental trauma.

Because so many girls have experienced traumatic events in their lives (especially interpersonal violence), it is important that they learn some of the basic information about trauma, its effects, typical responses, and ways to regulate their emotions and feel connected to their bodies.

Although *Beyond Trauma* was not written specifically for girls, it has been used effectively in many settings that serve girls. It often is used as a companion to or continuation of *Voices: A Program of Self-Discovery and Empowerment for Girls* (Covington 2004). Each session in this *Beyond Trauma* program contains notes at the end about adapting the group material for use with teenage girls and young women (ages fifteen to twenty-one). If you will be facilitating the sessions with girls, you will want to go through the contents of the sessions with a pen and delete anything that is inappropriate for girls. As you delete material that you feel will not work with the particular girls you are helping, add language (information, examples, and activity topics) that *will* resonate with their experiences and needs. In addition, there are specific handouts for girls. They can be used with some of the adapted exercises and are located in appendix 4.

Studies have shown that even simple interventions can make a difference. When university students wrote about their trauma fifteen minutes per day for four days, it decreased their student health visits, increased their positive moods, created more optimistic attitudes, and improved their physical health (when compared to students writing about their days) (Pennebaker 2012). (For more information on treating complex trauma in girls, see Ford and Courtois 2013.)

Special Considerations for Criminal Justice Settings

There are many unique challenges to being a facilitator in a criminal justice setting. Often there is a "culture clash" in these settings. Historically, the criminal justice system has been based on a control model, while the treatment field is based on a change model. *Beyond Trauma* is based on a change model. Some treatment providers struggle to work in a setting that feels unsupportive. If you work in such a setting, you may sense the conflict between these two cultures. For example, confidentiality is more difficult to ensure in a setting in which security is prioritized and trust is not the norm.

The facilitator in a criminal justice setting needs to think through the following issues before the sessions begin (Bloom, Owen, and Covington 2003). Some challenges are:

- Space and setting: Can chairs be moved? Is music allowed? Is privacy allowed or must correctional staff be present? Are there other security issues that affect the setting and environment you are trying to create?

- Confidentiality: Is confidentiality more difficult to ensure in a setting where security is prioritized and trust is not the norm?

- Interruptions: These may include the offender "count," observations by correctional officers, inflexible times when women are called out for court or medication, and special security issues.

- Attitudes of group members: Are some mandated to be there? Are women resistant to being there? Are women attending only because they do not want to be somewhere else?

- Using the program videos: Is it possible to play videos in this setting? Can the participant video segments be used?

- Other materials and workbooks: Are women allowed to have program materials in their cells? Do women have the time and permission to do the activities away from the group setting?

- Support: Often, there is no counseling staff available in the evenings. Be sure to help the women anticipate who their support people will be. As the group develops, the women often become supports for one another.

- Support for the facilitator: The correctional environment can be harsh for the facilitator as well as for the participants. Getting support from someone within the institution or correctional setting can help the facilitator navigate the system more easily as well as provide an emotional sounding board for her concerns.

- Standard operating practices: Things such as searches, restraints, and isolation may traumatize and/or retraumatize women.

It is particularly important in this setting for the facilitator to provide confidentiality and emotional safety as best she can, as well as be an advocate for the women and the group.

Suggestions for Conducting Group Sessions

As previously mentioned, *Beyond Trauma* is designed as a group process. However, the activities found in each session can be adapted for individual work. Facilitated groups help the women see that their problems are not unique and help reduce the shame and isolation that is common to trauma survivors.

Creating Safety

Some women are fearful of coming to a trauma group. A few facilitators have changed the name of the group to something without *trauma* in the title, such as "Growth Group," "Chasing Butterflies," or "Finding Myself."

It is possible that many of the women in the group have never felt safe. These women spend a great deal of energy trying to keep themselves safe or being anxious when they do not feel safe. The emotional environment is critical to the success of the session and the comfort of all group members. Therefore, it is important to create a sense of safety in the group—both internal safety and external safety. Judith Herman calls trauma "the disease of disconnection" (1997). A caring group can help establish connection and healing. You will encourage mutual, respectful, and compassionate connections among the women. The group setting also needs to be free from physical and emotional discomfort and fear. Setting limits, ground rules, and boundaries can help the women feel safe.

Group Agreements

Group agreements or ground rules are crucial to the smooth running of a group. Basic guidelines for group participation and confidentiality need to be discussed early on with all women in the group. Defining the agreements right from the start serves to create a safe group culture. This provides the foundation for women to feel comfortable sharing their feelings, asking questions, and fully engaging with the others and with the materials.

Group agreements should be clear, short, simple, and direct. Confidentiality, nonviolence, and not coming to sessions under the influence of alcohol or other drugs are three agreements that are nonnegotiable. Have the group come up with other ground rules and do your best to get group consensus. Sample agreements include the following:

1. *Group members need to honor confidentiality.* What is said in the room and the group stays in the room and the group. You might want to ask group members: "What does confidentiality mean to you? What happens when it is violated? How does that feel? What do you want to do, as a group, to maintain confidentiality?" At the end of the first session, the facilitator reminds the group members of the confidentiality commitment. (In criminal justice settings, confidentiality can be particularly complicated. Discussing specifics about crimes may impact women's sentencing, probation, or paroles.)

2. *No physical, emotional, or verbal abuse will be tolerated in the group.* Violence and aggressive behavior are not permitted. Intimidating, abusive, or belittling language is not permitted.

3. *Sessions will start on time and end on time.*

4. *Regular attendance and participation is important for everyone in the group.* Stress that making the commitment to attend is something that the women are doing for themselves as well as for the group as a whole. Their contributions are greatly valued. Group members should contact the facilitator if they are unable to attend a session. If someone misses a session, she needs to complete the homework and then review the information from the session with the facilitator. (In criminal justice settings, the fact that women may be court-ordered to attend may change the atmosphere, and it may be necessary to emphasize the importance of them being there in a different way. Tell the group members that

although attendance may have been court-ordered, if they keep an open mind, the group may be helpful to them.)

5. *Contact with other group members outside the regular group session is permitted.*

6. *Share the floor with others.* Everyone in the group should have the time to talk and share what is on her mind.

7. *There will be no smoking during the group sessions.*

8. *No member may come to a group session under the influence of alcohol or other drugs.*

9. *Having feelings is okay.* Crying in the group is okay. Laughing is okay. Getting angry is okay. Being abusive to another group member is not okay.

10. *Group members may decline, or "pass," when asked a question or asked to do an activity that requires verbal participation.* If a woman repeatedly passes up an opportunity to speak, you may want to take time after the session to privately ask the woman why she passed. Often, those who do not speak have a great deal to say but do not feel comfortable sharing in a group setting. Find out how you may be able to assist the women in feeling safe enough to share.

11. *Cellular phones.* All cell phones will be turned off and put away. No ringing or vibrating, checking for text messages, calling, or texting.

Facilitating Group Interaction

Part of the facilitator's job is to stimulate and encourage participation by and interaction among group members. Some ways to do this are as follows:

- To minimize disruption to group communication, ask participants in community-based settings to turn off the ringers on cellular phones and put them away. It is preferable to have no cell phone visible during the sessions. Some facilitators have a basket or box where cell phones are placed during the group session.

- Encourage the women to speak about their personal experiences, not give generalizations or abstractions, while keeping the pace moving along. Sharing personal experiences increases connection and closeness with others. It also enables the women to learn from one another's experiences.

- Encourage participation by all women, yet respect their comfort levels, need for contemplation, and healing. It is important to understand a woman's resilience as well as her struggles with a painful event. Disclosing and listening to the stories of other women may be upsetting for a woman. Some group members may feel too vulnerable and at risk to share personal information. A woman who has experienced trauma will need enough time to observe and assess the facilitator's and other group members' abilities to create an environment in which she can feel safe.

- At the same time, the women get to set their own limits with respect to self-disclosure. Let the women know they can "pass" when debriefing activities in the group. As noted earlier, if a woman chooses to pass, you may want to follow up with her after the group session to discuss her need to pass. Do not make this feel intrusive or punitive. The objective is to help her feel more comfortable sharing in the group.

- The process of talking about a trauma may restimulate the trauma memories. Even though this may stir up physiological distress, the goal is to focus on how the traumatic experiences have affected the women's minds, bodies, and spirits and not to uncover or retrieve traumatic memories. If women retell the stories of their trauma, the facilitator needs to emphasize their strengths, coping capabilities, and resilience. Focusing on the women's personal strengths rather than solely on the trauma pain is more helpful in this stage of the healing process. In general, it is more useful to focus on understanding the impact of the memories of the trauma, to connect with other survivors, and to learn new, healthy coping strategies.

- If you are a trauma survivor yourself, be sure you have done some of your own healing work before you facilitate *Beyond Trauma*. You may be triggered by events in the group and will want to have your own support person. This is especially important for facilitators who are also survivors of abuse. If you feel overwhelmed, seek help from a colleague, supervisor, or other professional.

- Many of the topics covered are emotionally draining, even for the facilitator. Clinical supervision for a facilitator is very important. Share with a colleague what topics impact you personally.

- Be aware that too much disclosure on the facilitator's part may be inappropriate and may derail the group process. It is also detrimental to use the group as a sounding board for your personal concerns. If you are considering self-disclosing, always ask yourself, "What would be most helpful for the women in the group?" Remember, in a support group, the important discoveries will come from the group members. Your self-disclosure should be kept at a minimum, except when you are sharing at the beginning of session 1.

- If you find that some women are not sharing regularly, you can have the participants work in duos for the preliminary sharing as part of an activity. (The word *duos* is used in the sessions to avoid the sense of women "pairing up" or "partnering" to the exclusion of others.) Some women feel more comfortable sharing with one person than with a whole group. This also may help increase the more silent members' feelings of security. You then can follow up by having the duos summarize their discussions for the whole group.

- Some facilitators may intervene during a conflict between group members because of their own discomfort rather than allowing the women to explore the depths of the issue at hand. Be sure you understand the motivation behind your actions. If you are acting on an impulse, it is more likely to be about you than the group process.

- Keep the group focused on the relevant topics in the curriculum.

- Confidentiality is a value that must be adhered to by the facilitator as well as the group members. There are two exceptions: (1) you may communicate with treatment team members as part of a woman's ongoing care, and (2) you may break confidentiality when someone's personal safety or the safety of others is at stake.

- Ask the women to listen to one another attentively, without interrupting. Each woman has an important experience to relate, which should not be judged or challenged. All feelings are real for the person feeling them. No one should be told how to feel.

- Strive for complete honesty. Honesty need not be in conflict with privacy or protecting the feelings of others. Remind yourself and the women in the group that honesty without sensitivity can hurt feelings, decrease connection, and appear mean-spirited.

- Encourage the women to share all comments, questions, and opinions with the group. This may help others with the same issue. Side conversations can alienate and divide group members.

- If some women have difficulty reading or writing, allow them to draw instead of writing during assignments or have them work with others who can read and write, and can help them do assignments. Women often have shame regarding their writing skills and sometimes drop out of a group because of it. Explain words, concepts, and after-session assignments carefully. Do not assume that a person's level of literacy equates with her level of intelligence.

- Discussing common issues and problems can help alleviate women's feelings of isolation. Explore ideas about how to make personal life changes. Explore what keeps each woman from making personal changes and what kind of support she needs from the group or others.

- When appropriate, inject humor and lightness into the conversation. If everything is intense and serious, group members may become too overwhelmed.

- If possible, encourage each woman to find a safe support person (a trustworthy friend or mental health provider) to be available for her between the sessions. This may be another challenge in settings or communities where support is not easily available.

Emphasizing Resilience

Facilitators will find that, among women with histories of trauma, some are more wounded than others. Some are more resilient. Resilience is the ability to adapt well in the face of difficult life events. It is the ability to recover from or adjust easily to misfortune or change. The word *resilience* stems from a Latin word meaning "leap back." Although some people are more naturally resilient, a way to develop resilience is in working through the emotions and effects of stress and painful events. Resilience develops as people develop better coping skills. It also comes from supportive, caring relationships with others. *Beyond Trauma* is designed to help women (and girls) become more resilient through:

- building close relationships
- developing a positive view of the self

- learning to manage strong feelings

- feeling more in control

- finding resources

- seeing the self as resilient (as a survivor rather than as a victim)

- coping with stress

- finding positive meaning in life despite traumatic events

Dealing with Challenging Situations

A good facilitator allows everyone a chance to speak and creates opportunities for less vocal women in the group to be heard. Start a session by saying, "I would like to start this discussion by inviting people who have not spoken to give us their thoughts and feelings." If women do not participate in discussions or appear to have their minds elsewhere, you may want to call on them by name to give an answer or recount an experience. Always give them the option not to speak if they prefer not to. Always praise a person for responding.

Politely manage each discussion and do not let certain group members dominate. It is important that different viewpoints can be expressed. Possible responses to difficult or domineering people include the following:

- Politely interrupt the person with a statement such as "Can we put that on the back burner for the moment and return to it later?" or "If it is all right, I would like to ask if we can discuss that after the session. There's another important point we still need to discuss, and we are running a little short of time."

- You can also jump in at a pause with "That is a good point. Have others felt this way?" or redirect the conversation, as in "We have had several comments in support of this idea; are there different thoughts or feelings about this?" This approach brings the focus back to the group as a whole and encourages others to speak.

- If a discussion escalates and becomes highly emotional, divert the conversation away from the people participating before it gets out of hand. "I think we all know how Latisha and Susanne feel about this. Now, does anyone else have a comment?" Or, validate their feelings or emotional reactions by saying something such as "Clearly this is a very emotional and difficult issue with differing viewpoints." Intense emotions can be a good indicator of major issues just underneath the surface. You may want to give extra time for discussion to see if some clarity or understanding can come out of it.

- All along register steps of agreement and disagreement with participants. Say, "Am I correct in assuming we all agree (or disagree) on this point?" or "You may simply agree to disagree on certain issues, because each person is unique."

- If you need to rein in the person who "knows it all," acknowledge the person's contribution and then ask others in the group for their opinions of the person's statement.

- When a discussion gets off track, say, "Your point is an interesting one, but it is a little different from the main issues here; perhaps we can address your issues after the session," or "We will be talking about that later in session X. Your points are very interesting; could you hold those thoughts until we get to that session?"

- If a person speaks in broad generalizations, ask, "Can you give us a specific example on that point?" or "Your general idea is a good one, but I wonder if we can make it even more concrete. Does anyone know of a situation where . . . ?"

- If a person in the group states something that is incorrect (yet no one addresses the misinformation), avoid direct or public criticism. You can graciously correct the information or use indirect methods to set the record straight, such as analyzing a similar situation in which the correct information is given. You may also want to talk to the person after the session and share the correct information.

- If a person is difficult in a group session, next time be sure to sit next to her. This proximity of the facilitator often can help mediate difficulties.

- Generally, try not to interrupt participants. Be respectful and listen. Be open yet firm and manage the discussion, keeping in mind what is best for the whole group.

Asking and Answering Questions

- Anticipate the types of questions the women might ask and plan how to handle them. As you get ready for the session, consider the questions you are most likely to be asked and think about your answers. You can use these questions to stimulate group discussions throughout your session. Make sure your questions are designed to elicit thoughtful reactions to specific points. Do not ask questions that can be answered by yes or no. Open-ended questions generate better participation.

- Questions from participants are good indicators of their levels of awareness, attention, and interest in the subject. Questions have value in helping you clarify, modify, or fortify points or test an idea for its potential. Remember that answering a question is impromptu. Pause if you need to, relax, maintain your poise, keep your answers short and to the point, and give the short answer first (e.g., yes or no); then explain why.

- Some questions involving women's specific situations may border on giving legal advice (e.g., "Can I sue the person?"). Be clear about what questions are legal matters and when it is more appropriate to refer the question to legal aid or a lawyer.

- If you do not know the answer to a question, acknowledge that fact; then offer to find the information. Not all questions have to be answered. Sometimes the most effective response is one that allows the participants to keep thinking about the issue or concern.

- After you answer a question from a woman, ask her, "Does that answer your question?" "Do you agree?" or "Has that been your experience as well?"

- Rephrase questions that are unclear or rambling.

- Avoid a one-to-one conversation or argument with a participant. Many women have come from harsh environments, and the group is one place in which they should feel safe and supported.

- The curriculum includes data that were current at the time of publication of the reference. You are encouraged to update or find local statistics before a session.

Sharing Reading and Writing Tasks

In each session, there are opportunities for the group members to read some of the material aloud. Often this helps the women to have "ownership" of the content and to feel more involved with the program. Each time you ask the women to read, it is important to allow anyone to decline, or "pass." Reading is a challenge for some women. Literacy issues often are hidden out of shame. So being able to pass is very important. If members of the group seem to be engaged with reading the material aloud, expand the reading and include additional sections for them to read.

There also are opportunities to have the women in the group write the session goals, responses to discussion questions, and other items on the flip-chart paper, rather than having the facilitator do this. The more the women choose to participate, the more empowered they will feel and the more invested in the program they are likely to become.

In any book or program that includes information from other sources, it is necessary to include reference citations in order to give credit to the original sources. When you or the women are reading content items, remember that the reference citations, which are enclosed in parentheses—for example (Covington 2000)—are not meant to be read aloud.

Adjusting the Timing

As mentioned previously, the program is designed for twelve sessions, lasting two hours each. The group sessions can be held once or twice per week. However, some facilitators have indicated that there is enough content for longer sessions. This generally depends on the size of the group and how much sharing the group members want to do. Feel free to schedule the amount of time your particular group needs to cover the content. Some facilitators conduct two group meetings per week to cover each session: In the first, the group goes through the session as set out in this facilitator's guide; in the second (approximately one hour), the women do their Between-Sessions Activities and then share them.

Assessing Current Trauma

In addition to past trauma, some of the participants may be experiencing trauma, particularly abuse in current relationships. It is important that each woman in recovery be assessed for risk of current abuse. The facilitator will be teaching the women several questions to ask themselves if they are not sure if an incident was abusive.

1. Was there full consent?
2. Was there an element of betrayal or loss of trust?
3. Have you ever feared for your physical safety in your relationship?
4. Have you felt afraid in other ways?
5. Have you ever been forced to do things against your will?
6. Have you ever been hit or threatened?
7. Have you ever been kicked or choked?
8. Have you ever sustained bodily injuries, such as bruises, cuts, or broken bones?
9. Have your children been hit or threatened?
10. Was there violence, pain, restriction, force, or bodily harm?
11. Have you been verbally put down?
12. Have you been harassed, stalked, or monitored?
13. Did it feel like abuse to you?

It is helpful to know how to respond to current domestic violence. It occurs in same-sex as well as heterosexual relationships. The most important messages are that family violence is a crime, that help is available, and that the facilitator respects a woman's right to choose when she is ready and able to leave a relationship. The women in the group need to know it is safe to talk about what they are experiencing, even if they do not feel ready to leave their relationships or take legal action. Even when a woman has a safe place to go, she may fear for her life. Often, when a woman tries to leave an abusive relationship, the violence escalates.

If it appears that a woman is in an abusive relationship, the facilitator may respond by saying:

1. I am afraid for your safety.

2. I am afraid for the safety of your children.

3. The abuse or violence could get worse.

4. You deserve better than this.

5. I am here for you when you are ready.

6. There are safe places for you to go and people who will help you.

We know that a woman's greatest risk for being severely hurt or killed is when she tries to leave an abusive relationship. Careful plans must be laid and resources put in place to help her leave when she deems it is the right time to do so. We also know that the brains of victims of domestic abuse can be impacted, based on the duration and severity of the abuse, and that it can be very difficult for the women to make decisions in their best interest, especially if they grew up in abusive environments. You will be discussing this with the women in your groups.

Finding Local Resources

The facilitator can affirm a woman's right to decide when to leave and, at the same time, offer her a glimpse of a different life she could create for herself. You can make available the resources to which the woman may turn (a shelter or safe house, legal assistance, or a hotline number). It will be helpful if you have the women fill out the resource charts on page 38 in their workbooks, should any of them need such information. It is also important to know the state and local laws regarding mandated reporting of abuse.

If it appears that a woman is going to return to an abusive or violent relationship, the following statements from you may be helpful:

1. Do you feel apprehensive about returning to your relationship?

2. Is the apprehension related to a fear of being physically hurt or emotionally hurt?

3. We need to find some local resources to help you. Some possibilities are a hotline for domestic violence, a domestic violence shelter, and a mental health clinic. If we make plans about these now, you can call on them when you are ready or decide that you need them. There are also books you may want to read or other women who have gone through similar situations you may want to talk to.

Using the Workbooks

Ideally, each woman will have her own workbook to use both for writing in during the group sessions and for work outside the group. Workbooks are used instead of reproducible handouts as they help create another level of safety. With workbooks, the women know where all their work is, and it isn't loose and "floating" around. It also allows them to have a record of their group experiences. Many women talk about the value of being able to reread the workbook materials and their responses. The workbook also serves as a reminder of the tools they have learned.

Using the Videos

There are two videos that accompany the *Beyond Trauma* facilitator guide and workbook. One of these is to be used for facilitator training. It contains discussions and demonstrations of many of the activities included in the sessions. This video should be watched by every facilitator prior to implementing the program. It can be watched individually or in a group setting with other facilitators. This training video can also provide "refresher" training for facilitators who are returning to the program or need a review of the basic content.

The second video, divided into video segments, is designed to be shown to the participants throughout the twelve sessions. In the sessions, there are directions as to when each video segment should be shown. The content of the video segment is also provided in the facilitator guide for review prior to the session, or it can be read aloud together with the participants if it is not possible to show the video. The video is an optional activity because some settings (particularly criminal justice programs) may not have the necessary equipment. Many facilitators like to use the video as a way to connect the women to the author of the program, Dr. Covington. It is also particularly helpful if a facilitator is just beginning to use this material and it feels new to her. However, you have the option of presenting the content yourself, rather than using the participant video.

Using Guided Imagery

This program uses guided imagery, or visualization, in some sessions. Its goal is to allow women the opportunity to imagine scenarios that are different from their own realities. It offers them an opportunity to safely envision using different behaviors. It allows them to break through boundaries or barriers that may be hindering their healing processes. It opens up their world to possibilities.

The facilitator should practice to become familiar and comfortable with this approach, as her relaxed style in explaining the visualization will help the women in the group feel relaxed.

It is important in a visualization activity to slowly bring the women out of the experience and into the "here and now." Once you have finished the visualization and asked the women to open their eyes, remember to indicate that the visualization has ended.

For some trauma survivors, closing their eyes for an activity can be very difficult. This is why the instructions give the women the choice of closing their eyes or lowering their eyelids. They may need to keep their eyes open until there is a deeper sense of safety and trust.

Completing the Collages

During some sessions, the women are asked to create collages. Twenty or twenty-five minutes are allotted for the women to create each collage, and this is sufficient time for each woman to create at least a partial collage. Some women would like to take one or two hours to create their collages. This usually is not possible in a group setting. However, you can suggest to the women that the time allotted in the group can be used to get a good start on their collages (and some will be completed), and that they can complete the rest between the group sessions. (You will need to plan to have the collage materials available to them between sessions.)

Mindfulness

Mindfulness is one of the therapeutic techniques that is shown to be helpful to trauma survivors, and it is used in *Beyond Trauma*. Mindfulness is a state of active, open attention on the present. When you are mindful, you observe your thoughts and feelings from a distance, without judging them as good or bad. Jon Kabat-Zinn (2012) defines mindfulness as paying attention in a particular way: on purpose, in the present moment, and nonjudgmentally. Mindfulness is also a form of meditation practice used as a way of reducing stress and developing greater balance, control, and fuller participation in life. When you notice your thoughts and feelings, instead of judging them or reacting to them, you simply notice them and let them pass. It is a gentle effort to be present with the experience of the moment.

Yoga Poses and the Mind-Body Connection

Our bodies respond to the ways in which we think, feel, and act. This is called the "mind-body connection." When a person is stressed, anxious, or upset, her body may try to tell her that something isn't right. The body can do this with aches, pains, and even symptoms of illness. If feelings of stress, sadness, or anxiety are causing physical problems, keeping the feelings inside can make a person feel even worse. The findings of the Adverse Childhood Experiences (ACE) research (see session 5) demonstrate the mind-body connection.

In addition to the many activities and exercises provided in this program, there are certain yoga poses that can help with the release of emotions stored in the body. *Yoga* is the Sanskrit word for "connection." These poses help people to be more consciously aware of their bodies and their breathing. This is particularly important for women who have histories of trauma, particularly abuse. The four poses suggested for use in this setting are the Breath of Joy, the Seated Pigeon, the Modified Triangle, and the Twisted Branches to Open Wings. These poses are simple to teach, and the women can learn to do them by themselves in their living spaces. The poses are highly recommended as activities in various sessions, and appendix 2 provides complete instructions and photographs (developed by Machelle Lee).

Staff Training

One of the best ways to learn this material is to have the staff members (facilitators, supervisors, and administrators) complete the *Beyond Trauma* program as a group prior to implementation with participants. You can meet each week in a scheduled staff meeting or over a long lunch hour, with a different staff member doing the facilitation for each session. For the program director, these sessions offer a team-building tool and also help reveal staff members' strengths, skills, and challenges. Program directors who have used this approach consistently report the effectiveness of this method. It also helps them assess who the best people are to facilitate the groups.

When planning to implement this process, it is important to be able to explain the differences between a training (learning) group and a therapy group. This method of training on *Beyond Trauma* utilizes the principles and structure of a learning-training group.

Training Group	Therapy Group
The focus is on	*The focus is on*
Learning as a group	Individual growth
Using the group for experiential learning by means of activities	Using the group to recreate family-of-origin dynamics
Having support from outside the group (for individual issues)	Using the group for support for individual issues
Sequential learning	Process

Conclusion

The first part of this facilitator guide was designed to give you some background information about the process and treatment of trauma in women's lives, the *Beyond Trauma* curriculum, and group facilitation. For some of you this material was new, and for others it was a review.

The second part of the facilitator guide is the session outlines or lesson plans. These outlines create the structure and content of the program. They provide the process that the women will experience.

Although in-person training in the use of the curriculum is available, the facilitator guide and video are designed to provide self-instruction. The video elaborates on the information in the facilitator guide by providing additional explanations, examples, and demonstrations of many of the activities. You will find that the combination of reading the materials (including the participant workbook) and viewing the facilitator video before you start the process will be very helpful.

We hope that you find the *Beyond Trauma* experience to be insightful and rewarding. Thank you for your commitment to helping women grow and heal.

PART 2

Session Outlines

MODULE A

Violence, Abuse, and Trauma

Introduction to the Program

▧ Time

Two hours

▧ Goal of the Session

To introduce the program *Beyond Trauma: A Healing Journey for Women*

▧ Participant Objectives

At the end of this session, participants will be able to:

1. Describe the goals and structure of the program
2. Define trauma
3. Explain the prevalence of trauma
4. Demonstrate some grounding and self-soothing activities

▧ Materials Needed

- Name tags for the facilitator and each woman in the group
- Relaxing music and equipment to play music
- A participant workbook for the facilitator and each woman
- A pencil or pen for the facilitator and each woman
- A piece of flip-chart paper (or poster) showing the Spiral of Trauma and Healing (see page 89)
- *Optional: A DVD player and monitor and* Beyond Trauma *Participant Video Segment 1: Welcome and Segment 2: The Spiral of Trauma and Healing*
- A sheet of blank paper for each woman
- A newsprint flip-chart pad, an easel, and felt-tip pens
- Masking tape
- Facial tissues
- *Optional: Five Senses cards (found in appendix 1), which can be printed on card stock or laminated.*

continued

INTRODUCTION TO THE PROGRAM

■ **Session Overview**

- Facilitator Welcome and Introduction
- Group Introductions
- Quiet Time
- *Optional:* Beyond Trauma *Participant Video (Segment 1: Welcome)*
- Overview of the Program
- Group Agreements
- Session Format
- Lecture: What Is Trauma?
- *Optional:* Beyond Trauma *Participant Video (Segment 2: The Spiral of Trauma and Healing)*
- Lecture: The Spiral of Trauma and Healing
- Lecture: Triggers
- Activity: Five Senses
- Activity: Breathing and Exhaling
- Lecture: How Often Trauma Occurs
- Check-In
- Discussion: What Would You Like to Get from This Group?
- Activity: Palms Down, Palms Up
- Between-Sessions Activity
- Closing

continued

INTRODUCTION TO THE PROGRAM

Background Information for the Facilitator

Workbooks

If you are conducting this program in a residential setting, the women who are participating in the program can keep their workbooks with them between the sessions. To ensure confidentiality is maintained, make sure the women feel their workbooks will be safe in their rooms. If maintaining the privacy of the workbooks is an issue, you can provide each woman with a clear plastic envelope with a string to close the flap. Having sticky seals to put over the flap also can increase a woman's sense of privacy. If you are conducting this group in a correctional setting, you may need to store the workbooks for the women between the sessions and arrange a time and place for them to do their Between-Sessions Activities in their workbooks.

Language and Tone

Focusing on trauma in a group setting requires sensitivity. Advise the women that they are not required to discuss their specific trauma experience(s) in order to participate in the group. This has enabled many women to complete the *Beyond Trauma* program. As the trust in the group develops, most women will share their stories, but this is not a requirement.

You may want to review some of the information in the introduction and chapter 1 of this guide before leading this session. The group setting must be an environment of trust, mutuality, and collaboration. The facilitator is not there to "fix" the women.

Throughout the program, the facilitator(s) must keep the environment free from confrontation, harshness, humiliation, and/or judgmental language. This includes the language used by both the facilitator(s) and the group members. Trust, respect, honesty, and social connection can flow from an atmosphere of mutual support and validation.

continued

INTRODUCTION TO THE PROGRAM

Confidentiality

Early in this session (under Group Agreements), the facilitator explains the need for everyone involved in the group to keep what happens in the group confidential. The facilitator needs to be specific about the policy regarding confidentiality, about this being a joint agreement between the group members and the facilitator(s), and about the consequences determined and agreed on by group members, if the confidentiality agreement is not kept. However, if someone does break the agreement, it can be used as a learning tool. (For example, the first time a woman breaks confidentiality, she could be asked to write an essay on trust.) Or there could be a warning and then a consequence. It does not necessarily have to mean dismissal from the program. If the problem continues, a solution can be determined through group consensus.

Involving Participants

Whenever time and circumstances allow, try to involve the group members in the session content and experience. Some of this is built into the sessions, but as you get to know the group members, you can often find additional ways to increase their involvement and responsibility. For example, you can invite group members to volunteer to write the things being introduced or discussed on the flip-chart pad (or whiteboard), rather than have a facilitator do it. You can also ask the group members to help set up the room, distribute materials, and lead grounding activities.

References for Lecture Materials

When statistics and assertions are presented about the topics in the sessions, reference citations are included, both to indicate the source of the material and to let you know where more information can be found on the topic. These reference citations are enclosed in parentheses: for example, (Covington 2015). When you are reading the lecture material or statistics in the group sessions, you do *not* need to read the reference citations.

continued

INTRODUCTION TO THE PROGRAM

Use of Video

It is highly recommended that you use the opening welcome message (Participant Video Segment 1: Welcome) and the closing message (Segment 11: Closing) from Stephanie Covington. Other parts of the video are optional for the facilitator.

Preparing for the Lecture on the Spiral of Trauma and Healing

Prior to the session, prepare a piece of flip-chart paper (or a poster) with a drawing that shows the Spiral of Trauma and Healing (see the sample drawing below). You will be showing this to the women and explaining it during the session. (As an option, you may show segment 2 of the participant video.)

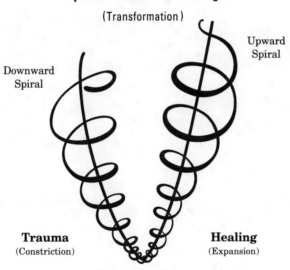

Spiral of Trauma and Healing

(Transformation)

Upward Spiral

Downward Spiral

Trauma
(Constriction)

Healing
(Expansion)

Adapted from the Spiral of Addiction and Recovery in *Helping Women Recover*.
Copyright 1999, 2008 by Stephanie S. Covington.

Preparing for the Five Senses Activity

In appendix 1, you will find multiple copies of the Five Senses drawing. You may wish to print this out on card stock and then cut the cards out so group members can take a card with them. Some facilitators laminate the cards.

The Session

TIME & TOPIC	FACILITATOR NOTES	DISCUSSION WITH WOMEN
3 min. **Facilitator Welcome and Introduction**	*Describe your background and your interest in working with the women. This is your first opportunity to establish trust, credibility, and connection with the women in the group.* *Share some personal information about how you came to be part of this program and why you believe the program is important.* *If desired, you could read aloud together the program introduction on page 5 in the participant workbook.*	Welcome, everyone. Today we've come together as a group to start a new program. Its title is *Beyond Trauma: A Healing Journey for Women*. My name is _____, and I will be the facilitator for this group. This group is designed to help you gain insight and skills in order to better manage the difficult experience of dealing with the effects of trauma in your life. Traumatic experiences can cause distress in the mind, the body, and the spirit. Understanding and dealing with the effects of trauma in your life will help you understand more about yourself and help you discover how to have a healthy relationship with yourself and with others. Our goal at this stage of healing from trauma is to help you establish a sense of safety—both internal and external safety. We will talk more about that soon. After today's session, we will be meeting for eleven more sessions. Our group will meet on _____ [day] at _____ [time].

TIME & TOPIC	FACILITATOR NOTES	DISCUSSION WITH WOMEN
12–15 min. **Group Introductions**		Now let's go around the room and introduce ourselves. Look on page 6 of your workbooks for things to include in your introductions. My name: _____ When and where I was born: _____ _____ _____ How I identify myself (including culture, ethnicity, race): _____ _____ The people in my family (can include a spouse or partner, children, mother, father, brothers, sisters, or whomever you consider your immediate family): _____ _____ _____ One thing I like about myself or a special gift that I have: _____ _____ _____
2–3 min. **Quiet Time**	*Begin playing the soft music.*	From now on, we will start the beginning of each session with some quiet time, with soft music playing, to help us calm our minds and bodies. This also helps us turn our attention away from what is going on outside this room and helps us focus on this group. Some of you may find that you can relax by sitting still and focusing on your breathing or focusing on your feet touching the ground and your hips touching the chair. For others, standing up and slowly walking may be the best way to focus their attention here in this room. Some people find that "tapping" helps them to focus on the present moment. You may want to try this. With the fingertips

TIME & TOPIC	FACILITATOR NOTES	DISCUSSION WITH WOMEN
	After one and a half to two minutes, ask the women to take a deep breath and return their focus to the group.	of both your hands, tap on the top of your head, then on your forehead, and then on your cheeks. Then cross your arms and tap on your shoulders, alternating one side and then the other. This is called a "butterfly hug." Another thing that works for some people is to find a focal point in the room and just look at it for the next few minutes. You may even want to try one technique today and then try another the next time we meet. Whichever you choose, let's be quiet now and bring our attention to the present, here in this room.
6 min. Optional: **Beyond Trauma Participant Video** Segment 1: Welcome		As part of our first session today, I'd like to play a brief video for you. This is a message from the developer of the program, Stephanie Covington.
10 min. **Overview of the Program**	*Describe your role as the program facilitator. The following are some possible points:* • *Each session will be based on the program materials.* • *The facilitator's job is to maintain the focus and help the group move through the program content.* • *Each woman will have her own experience of the group.*	

TIME & TOPIC	FACILITATOR NOTES	DISCUSSION WITH WOMEN
	Discuss who will be available between group sessions if the women have questions or concerns. This is particularly important if you're conducting this group in an outpatient setting or a correctional facility.	
	Provide information on site logistics, such as the location of bathrooms, parking or public transportation issues, and the availability of bottled water.	Remember, each session will take two hours, without a break. Please be sure to allow time to go to the bathroom before each session starts. Most women like to arrive about ten minutes early to get settled.
	Provide information on group rules, such as the following: • *Each session will begin on time and end on time.* • *All cell phones are to be turned off and put away during the group sessions.* • *No food or drinks (other than bottled water) are allowed in the group room.*	
	If the women have not received the participant workbooks prior to the start of this session, distribute them now. Make sure everyone has a pencil or pen as well. Explain that the workbooks are for the women's use in reviewing the content of the sessions, writing their thoughts and reactions, and completing activities during and after the sessions.	What is going to be most important is for the members of this group to feel safe and to know that we are supports for one another. Feeling safe with others is often difficult when you've been harmed by another person. But having safe connections with other people is important in having meaningful and satisfying lives. We'll be doing a variety of things to help you all feel safe here with one another.

TIME & TOPIC	FACILITATOR NOTES	DISCUSSION WITH WOMEN
	Explain that they will be able to keep their workbooks to work on between sessions and that they should bring their workbooks to each group session. It's their responsibility to remember to do this. *As you read the following information, you could have participants follow along on page 7 in their workbook.*	Now let's look at the goals of the *Beyond Trauma* program. They are: • to provide a safe place to reflect and learn more about ourselves • to learn about trauma and its effects on women • to learn skills in dealing with trauma and taking care of ourselves • to identify the lives we want to live These sessions will include: 1. Information about trauma in our world 2. How trauma can affect your thoughts, feelings, and behaviors 3. How to better manage your feelings, especially the powerful and painful ones 4. The effects of families and relationships on your life 5. Information about abusive and healthy relationships 6. Ways to "ground" yourself and soothe yourself 7. Ways to deal with things that "trigger" traumatic responses 8. Ways to enhance healing and well-being We'll be looking at many areas of our lives in order to better understand ourselves and our responses to trauma. For example, many women have difficulty with their feelings. One of the things you'll learn in our group sessions is how to manage feelings and not be overwhelmed or derailed by them.

TIME & TOPIC	FACILITATOR NOTES	DISCUSSION WITH WOMEN
	Advise each woman to use the group to focus on what is most important for her. For example, some women may be struggling with issues related to anger. Other women may be struggling with shame, remorse, guilt, or denial. Some women may be struggling with a poor self-image. Assure them that a variety of pertinent issues and topics will be covered. Remind them that they won't be required to discuss the details of any traumatic event. What's important is that they can learn to tolerate the feelings they feel and to trust what they know.	How many of you have participated in one of Stephanie Covington's other programs, maybe *Helping Women Recover,* or *Beyond Anger and Violence,* or *A Woman's Way through the Twelve Steps*? You may find that some of the activities we'll do are similar to some in those programs. Stephanie deliberately includes a few of the same activities in all of her programs, because they're so valuable, and many women have reported the value of repeating them. Some women actually ask to participate in the same program more than once because of this.
10 min. **Group Agreements**	*Have the participants generate a list. Write their ideas on the flip-chart pad.* *There are three things that must be included in the group agreements: (1) maintaining confidentiality, (2) not attending group sessions*	One way to help everyone feel comfortable is to have some agreements about how we will act in the group. Now that you have an idea of what this group is about, these are agreements about behaviors you believe are important to make sure the group remains a safe and supportive place for each person. Let's develop a list of things we can agree to as group members. An example is agreeing to show up for each session on time. What are some other group agreements you can think of?

TIME & TOPIC	FACILITATOR NOTES	DISCUSSION WITH WOMEN
	under the influence of alcohol or other drugs, and (3) no verbal or physical abuse. *If the members do not suggest these, do so yourself.* *1. In describing the need for confidentiality, explain that the group members need to know they can trust one another, and there can be no trust if information about a group member is shared with outsiders or if group members gossip about one another outside the group. Explain that there may be two exceptions to this: (a) the facilitators have to communicate with other members of a woman's treatment team as part of her ongoing care; and (b) the facilitators are required by law to break confidentiality if a group member's personal safety or the safety of another person, including children, is at stake.* *2. In discussing sobriety, explain that a woman will be asked to leave the session (not the program) if she comes to group under the influence of alcohol or other drugs. Say that part of the reason for abstinence is for safety in the group. Many women have experienced abuse by a person who was under the influence*	

TIME & TOPIC	FACILITATOR NOTES	DISCUSSION WITH WOMEN
	of alcohol or other drugs. Therefore, their feelings of safety are affected by others who are drinking or using drugs. *3. In discussing safety, explain that it's important that all members feel safe in the group so they can share and learn and grow. In order for this to happen, everyone needs to agree there will be no verbal or physical abuse in the group.* *Examples of typical group agreements follow:* *1.* Timing. *Our sessions will start on time and end on time.* *2.* Attendance. *Regular group attendance is important. We all agree to show up at all the sessions. If there's an emergency, and you can't attend, please contact me [the facilitator].* *3.* Confidentiality. *Group members need to honor one another's confidentiality. What is said in this room stays in this room. No personal information revealed in this room may be repeated outside this room.* *4.* Sobriety. *No one may attend a group session while under the influence of alcohol or another drug.*	

TIME & TOPIC	FACILITATOR NOTES	DISCUSSION WITH WOMEN
	5. Safety. *There will be no physical or emotional abuse. Part of safety is showing respect for one another and for the uniqueness of every person's thoughts, feelings, experiences, and responses. Respect is essential. We will let people express themselves in their own ways. Being rude or abusive to another group member is not okay.* 6. Eating or drinking. *There will be no eating or drinking during the group sessions* [except, perhaps, for bottled water; be specific about this]. 7. Cellular phones. *All cell phones will be turned off and put away. No ringing or vibrating, checking for text messages, calling, or texting.* 8. Sharing. *Everyone in the group should have the time to contribute and share their experiences. We will try to let everyone have a chance to talk. We will not interrupt other group members but will let them finish before we respond or add something.* 9. Participation. *We'll try to assist one another in feeling safe enough to share and participate.*	

Duplicating this page is illegal. Do not copy this material without written permission from the publisher.

99

TIME & TOPIC	FACILITATOR NOTES	DISCUSSION WITH WOMEN
	We'll ask questions to help us learn and grow. However, everyone is entitled to "pass" when asked a question or when asked to do an activity that requires participation.	
	10. Socializing. Contact with other group members outside the regular group session is permitted.	
	When the participants have generated a list, and you've suggested any other agreements that you think are important, tape the list onto the wall. Ask if the women all agree the items listed are important and they agree to them. Have the women write additional agreements from their group on page 9 in their workbooks. When the list is finalized, display it on the wall at each group session.	
	Mention that, as the facilitator, you may privately ask a woman after the session why she passed. Often, those who don't speak have a great deal to say but may not feel comfortable sharing in a group setting. Do not push for participation.	
	Ask the group members what they want to do if someone does not honor the group agreements.	

TIME & TOPIC	FACILITATOR NOTES	DISCUSSION WITH WOMEN
	For example, say, "What would you like to have as a guideline if someone breaks the agreement about confidentiality? What do you think is the best way to handle this? What would be a useful learning experience?" or "What if someone is consistently late or misses sessions?" The women can set policies, such as "Group members need to contact the facilitator if they're unable to attend a session." When the facilitator and the participants agree on an item, record it on the flip-chart pad. When all guidelines have been listed, post this list next to the list of group agreements.	
5 min. **Session Format**		Let's look at how the *Beyond Trauma* program is set up: • The program contains three modules or content areas. Within each are a number of sessions that address different pieces of the content. • In each module, we'll practice some self-soothing and grounding activities. We may use the same activity in several sessions, to allow you time to feel comfortable using it in your daily lives. • We'll then discuss the Between-Sessions Activity from the previous session and talk briefly about the goals of the current session.

TIME & TOPIC	FACILITATOR NOTES	DISCUSSION WITH WOMEN
		• In each session, there will be information presented on specific topics, followed by activities and discussions based on the information. • There will be questions to help guide our discussions. • At the end of each group session, we'll talk about new Between-Sessions Activities that will be things to practice and activities to do in your workbooks before the next session. Some of the content we'll be covering in these sessions may be difficult for you to think about and talk about. We'll continue to work on making this group a safe and supportive place where you can experience your feelings and learn from them, learn a number of calming and soothing activities, and practice supporting one another in this healing journey. We'll be looking at the links between violence, abuse, and trauma while also considering the role power plays in the continuation of abuse in women's lives. To help us understand the impact that trauma has on our lives, we'll discuss the physical, mental, emotional, and social effects of trauma. We'll do this in part by looking at two spirals: the Spiral of Addiction and Recovery and the Spiral of Trauma and Healing. We'll practice some techniques you can use in your day-to-day lives that will help you ground and soothe yourselves. These techniques may help you as you go through the process of learning to cope with the effects of trauma.

TIME & TOPIC	FACILITATOR NOTES	DISCUSSION WITH WOMEN
		Each session will begin with a time to settle in, soothe ourselves, and begin to turn inward to prepare to do what we need to do during this time together. We'll end with a reflection on what we've shared and learned from one another. Today you each received a workbook. Please bring your workbook to each group session, as it will be an important part of your personal work and our work together. This is your workbook, so what you write is confidential and just for you.
5–10 min **Lecture: What Is Trauma?**		Before we discuss trauma in more detail, let's define it. A definition of *trauma,* based on a publication by the American Psychiatric Association, is exposure to actual or threatened death, serious injury, or sexual violence in one or more of four ways: 1. Directly experiencing the event; 2. Witnessing, in person, the event occurring to others; 3. Learning that such an event happened to a close family member or friend; and/or 4. Experiencing repeated or extreme exposure to aversive details of such events, such as with first responders (American Psychiatric Association 2013, 271–80). This experience causes significant distress or impairment in social relationships, capacity to work, or other important areas of functioning. Violence and other trauma have many forms, including:

TIME & TOPIC	FACILITATOR NOTES	DISCUSSION WITH WOMEN
		• natural disasters, such as hurricanes, earthquakes, tornadoes, fires, floods, and volcanoes
		• the oppression of an entire group of people, such as economic and religious persecution and genocide
		• immigration, which often can be traumatic
		• discrimination based on race, poverty, gender, sexual orientation or gender identity, disability, or age
		• child abuse (emotional, physical, and/or sexual)
		• elder abuse
		• domestic violence, such as physical abuse and rape
		• abandonment (especially for children)
		• witnessing violence, such as a parent harming another parent
		• being the victim of a crime, such as burglary, robbery, mugging, assault, or rape
		• street and gang violence
		• witnessing murder
		• automobile accidents
		• catastrophic injuries and illnesses
		• extremely painful and frightening medical procedures
		• the loss of a loved one, including a pet
		• war and combat
		• terrorism and torture
		• kidnapping

TIME & TOPIC	FACILITATOR NOTES	DISCUSSION WITH WOMEN
		In the case of a natural disaster, people often gather around the victims, there's usually acknowledgement of what happened, and sympathy and comfort are offered. That's very different from what happens after traumas such as assault, incest, rape, and domestic violence. These forms of trauma often are hidden, and the survivors rarely get to publicly acknowledge what took place and rarely get the support they need to move on in their lives. Too often, the victim of a private trauma ends up with a deep sense of shame and invisibility, along with silent rage about not being acknowledged or protected.

Trauma also is defined as a *reaction* to an event that overwhelms people physically and psychologically. *Beyond Trauma* is designed for women who have experienced threatening events that have overwhelmed their psychological and/or physiological coping mechanisms—especially suffering inflicted by others. |
| 4 min.

Optional:

***Beyond Trauma*
Participant
Video**
Segment 2 | **Segment 2: The Spiral of Trauma and Healing**

Rather than deliver the next lecture yourself, you may choose to convey this information by showing segment 2 of the video. | I'd like to show you another video segment about trauma and healing. |

TIME & TOPIC	FACILITATOR NOTES	DISCUSSION WITH WOMEN
5–10 min. **Lecture:** **The Spiral of Trauma and Healing**	*You can present this content to the group or have the group members volunteer to read sections of the information on pages 10–11 in their workbooks aloud.* *Post the flip-chart paper (or poster) showing the Spiral of Trauma and Healing.*	There is a model for what happens in reacting to the trauma in one's life and then learning to heal from the trauma. This model is the basis for the *Beyond Trauma* program. The model is called the Spiral of Trauma and Healing. **Spiral of Trauma and Healing** (Transformation) Downward Spiral Upward Spiral **Trauma** **Healing** (Constriction) (Expansion) Adapted from the Spiral of Addiction and Recovery in *Helping Women Recover.* Copyright 1999, 2008 by Stephanie S. Covington. The downward spiral represents the limitations and constrictions that trauma can create in a woman's life. Constriction can include a person pulling away from relationships and becoming isolated, stuffing feelings, feeling afraid of people and places, etc. The line through the middle represents the traumatic event. It becomes the organizing principle in the woman's life.
	Give a sheet of blank paper to each woman. Ask the women to imagine that each sheet of paper is a person before any abuse or trauma occurs in her life. Then ask the women to crumple their papers into balls. Say this	This paper is another way to see the limitations and constrictions in the downward Spiral of Trauma. Sometimes a person looks okay on the outside but feels crumpled on the inside. Can anybody relate to that?

TIME & TOPIC	FACILITATOR NOTES	DISCUSSION WITH WOMEN
	is what can happen to someone who has had many experiences of abuse or trauma. Allow a few people to respond to the question on page 106.	This program represents a turning point, a place of change, at the bottom of the downward spiral. Here a woman steps onto a new path, the upward spiral. The upward spiral represents the process of healing, in which a woman's life begins to expand. Her world becomes larger as she includes more people in her daily life, becomes more involved in activities, and feels more confident in the world. The trauma is still the line through the middle, but it has less of an influence; it has loosened its grip. There is space now for new activities and new relationships. The trauma becomes a thread in the tapestry of her life; it is no longer the core. The image of the spiral helps us see that healing is a transformative process.
2–3 min. **Lecture:** **Triggers**		Imagine a path created by someone who is moving in deep snow. Once there is a path, it's easier to move forward if you stay in that path. Our life experiences cause pathways to develop in our brains. When you have a traumatic experience, particularly one that occurs more than once, a pathway is made in your brain. Then, if you experience what we call a "trigger"—something that reminds you of the traumatic event—you react in the same way because of the existing pathway. A trigger can be something you see, hear, smell, or feel. It can be a person, a place, or anything that reminds you of the traumatic event. When a woman is triggered, she is pushed back in time to the painful event and may feel all the old

TIME & TOPIC	FACILITATOR NOTES	DISCUSSION WITH WOMEN
		feelings connected to that event. These feelings can affect her thoughts and behavior. Some survivors of trauma never really feel safe. One of our goals in this program is to provide some ways to cope with overwhelming thoughts and feelings related to the trauma. You can learn some grounding and self-soothing activities that you can use to create new pathways when you are stressed or triggered. These activities can help us stay in the present so we don't lose ourselves in the past. As we continue in this program, we'll be discussing more information about trauma and its effects. This may act as a trigger for some of us because of our life experiences. It may create some anxiety or other uncomfortable feelings. So it's important that we have tools we can use when this happens. Let's practice two types of coping or grounding tools you can use: the Five Senses activity and a deep-breathing and exhaling exercise. We'll be learning another coping tool at the end of our time today, and in future group meetings we'll learn others.
3–5 min. **Activity: Five Senses**	*Read the instructions that follow in a calm, soothing voice. Allow enough time between each instruction to allow the participants to experience what they can see, feel, hear, smell, and taste.* *Trauma survivors often have difficulty closing their eyes, so make it optional for the participants to leave their eyes open with their*	We'll start with the activity called Five Senses. 1. Please close your eyes or lower your eyelids. 2. Relax for a few moments. Take a few deep breaths and exhale slowly. 3. Open your eyes when you are ready 4. Silently, identify five things you can see around you.

TIME & TOPIC	FACILITATOR NOTES	DISCUSSION WITH WOMEN
	lids lowered for step 1. Tell them that some women may have difficulty closing their eyes.	5. Now identify four things you can feel or touch. 6. Identify three things you can hear. 7. Identify two things you can smell. 8. Finally, identify what you can taste right now.
	Allow several participants to respond or, if there is time, have participants write their thoughts in their workbooks on pages 12 and 13 before responding. *A template containing multiple copies of the Five Senses drawings is found in appendix 1. You may wish to print this template out on card stock and then cut the cards out so group members can take a card with them.* From *Healing Trauma: Strategies for Abused Women* by Stephanie Covington (Center City, MN: Hazelden, 2011; rev. 2016 as *Healing Trauma: A Brief Intervention for Women*).	How do you feel after doing this activity? At the end of this session, you may want to look at page 13 in your workbook. There is a drawing of the Five Senses there to remind you of this activity. I also have a card for each of you to take with you. **Five Senses** 5 things 4 things 3 things 2 things 1 thing
3–5 min. **Activity: Breathing and Exhaling**		Let's all stand up. 1. Place your feet a little distance apart so you feel stable. Take a few deep breaths. 2. Relax your shoulders and drop your hands to your sides. Let your arms and hands just dangle, relaxed. 3. Take in a deep breath through your nose and blow it out through your mouth like a big gust of wind.

TIME & TOPIC	FACILITATOR NOTES	DISCUSSION WITH WOMEN
	Ask each woman to share one word that describes how she felt when she first walked into the room and one word to describe how she feels now. Or have the women write their answers in their workbook on page 14 before responding aloud.	4. Now inhale again and let the air out by blowing it out through your mouth. 5. Remember to relax your shoulders and arms. 6. Let's do the inhaling and exhaling three more times. This is another grounding tool we can use. Grounding is something we can do when we feel overwhelmed by our feelings. Grounding helps us get back into the present. We're now going to cover some heavy information that may be upsetting or bring up some uncomfortable feelings. We're going to pay attention to how everyone is doing and how they feel. Later, we'll go over some more ways to self-balance when you're stressed or upset.
10–15 min. **Lecture: How Often Trauma Occurs**	*Read the following statistics aloud. (Remember that you don't need to read the reference citations enclosed in parentheses. Participants could follow along in their workbooks on pages 14–16, where some of the statistics are presented.)*	Here are some statistics to give us an idea of how often relationship violence, a form of trauma, occurs in women's and girl's lives. It's important to know how common relationship violence is for women and girls because they often feel isolated, alone, or at fault for the violence. **Violence against Women and Children** • Each year in the United States, more than 1.25 million children experience maltreatment, including 44 percent experiencing abuse and 61 percent experiencing neglect.

TIME & TOPIC	FACILITATOR NOTES	DISCUSSION WITH WOMEN
		Of those who are abused, 58 percent experience physical abuse, 24 percent experience sexual abuse, and 27 percent experience emotional abuse. Girls are at a higher risk of abuse than boys and are more than five times more likely to experience sexual abuse. In more than 70 percent of cases of child abuse, the abuser was the child's parent (Sedlak et al. 2010).
		• Approximately 75 percent of child sexual abuse is perpetrated by a family member or someone known and trusted by the child (U.S. Department of Health and Human Services 2007).
		• One out of every four girls in the United States is sexually abused before the age of eighteen (U.S. Department of Health and Human Services 2011). One in every six boys in the United States is sexually abused before the age of eighteen (Stoltenborgh et al. 2011).
		• The National Crime Victimization Survey found that, from 2006 to 2010, more than two-thirds of the rapes and sexual assaults committed in the United States remained unreported (Langton et al. 2012).
		• Children from violent homes have a higher tendency to commit suicide, abuse alcohol or other drugs, and continue the cycle of domestic violence by committing violence against their own partners or children (Whitfield et al. 2003).
		• Approximately one in three adolescent girls in the United States is a victim of physical, emotional, or verbal abuse from a dating partner (Bonomi et al. 2013).

TIME & TOPIC	FACILITATOR NOTES	DISCUSSION WITH WOMEN
		Relationship Violence • On average, twenty-four people per minute are victims of rape, physical violence, or stalking by an intimate partner in the United States. Over the course of a year, that equals more than twelve million women and men (Black et al. 2011). • Each year, women experience close to 4.8 million physical assaults and rapes by intimate partners (Davidov, Larrabee, and Davis 2015). • Nearly one in four women will experience violence by a current or former spouse (Centers for Disease Control and Prevention 2008). • In 2005, 1,181 women in the United States were murdered by their intimate partners. This was more than three women murdered per day (Catalano 2007). • Globally, approximately 40 percent of murdered women have been killed by their intimate partners. Across the world, almost a third of women experience intimate-partner violence during their lifetimes. The exposure to violence often starts at ages fifteen to nineteen, suggesting that violence in women's intimate relationships starts early and continues throughout their lives (World Health Organization 2013). • Individuals who experience sexual abuse are more likely to have anxiety, depression, eating disorders, and posttraumatic stress disorder, and they are more likely to attempt suicide than are those who have not experienced sexual abuse (Chen et al. 2010).

TIME & TOPIC	FACILITATOR NOTES	DISCUSSION WITH WOMEN
		• The negative effects on a child who witnesses violence against his or her mother (called "secondary victimization") appear to be higher rates of aggression, anxiety, and social withdrawal (Howell et al. 2010).
	If you are working with women in the criminal justice system, you may want to add these statistics:	**Optional: Additional Statistics** • Women who are involved in the criminal justice system are three times more likely to have traumatic experiences than are women in the general population (Grella, Lovinger, and Warda 2013). • Compared with men in correctional facilities, incarcerated women are seven times more likely to have histories of sexual abuse and physical abuse prior to incarceration (Center on Addiction and Substance Abuse 2010). • Women in correctional facilities who have a history of sexual abuse are more likely to have physical and mental health concerns than are women without such histories. Women with extensive histories of sexual assault have higher rates of depression, chronic health concerns, and suicide attempts (Aday, Dye, and Kaiser 2014). • Approximately 40 percent of women and 22 percent of men involved in the criminal justice system have mental health and substance use concerns (Center on Addiction and Substance Abuse 2010). • Fifty percent of women involved in the criminal justice system have experienced sexual abuse, and 75 percent have experienced physical abuse (Staton-Tindall et al. 2007).

TIME & TOPIC	FACILITATOR NOTES	DISCUSSION WITH WOMEN
		• Women can be traumatized (or retrau-matized if they have already experienced trauma in their lives) by the standard operating practices in criminal justice settings, such as denial of privacy, body searches, restraints, and isolation (Bloom, Owen, and Covington 2003).
		All these statistics can be overwhelming. That is a normal reaction to this infor-mation. However, it's important that we acknowledge the relationship violence in women's lives. Many abused women feel isolated. They may not reveal their abuse to others because of shame or fear of reprisal. However, if a problem isn't acknowledged, a solution can't be found. A quotation from Helen Keller can help empower women to take steps to acknowledge and overcome their abuse: *"Although the world is full of suffering, it is also full of the overcoming of it."* —Helen Keller This is the core of *Beyond Trauma: A Healing Journey for Women*.
2–5 min. **Check-In**		How is everyone doing? Let's all stand up and take a few deep breaths. Often, we hold our breath when we hear or see or think about painful things. This infor-mation on violence and other abuse may remind you of experiences in your lives. Our goal is to get through this together. Please count off by ones and twos, so everyone is either a "one" or a "two."

TIME & TOPIC	FACILITATOR NOTES	DISCUSSION WITH WOMEN
		Each "one," please turn and make eye contact with the person standing next to you on your right side. Take a deep breath. Now, each "two," turn toward the person on your right side and make eye contact. Take a deep breath. Let's sit down again and talk more about this program.
5–10 min. **Discussion: What Would You Like to Get from This Group?**	*Allow each participant to share one or two things she would like to get out of this group. Allow people to pass if they are not comfortable sharing. If desired, you could have participants take a minute or two to make some notes in the space provided on page 17 of their workbooks before they share with the group.*	This group will be meeting for a number of weeks and covering a variety of topics that are important in women's lives. When we meet, each of you will have the opportunity to share feelings and experiences that are unique to you. The stories and wisdom that you will bring to the group are of great value and will contribute to the richness of our experience together. Each of you will contribute to making this group supportive and meaningful for yourself and others. You will find commonalities and differences and, most importantly, a place to share your voice, to be heard, and to be supported by other women. Now I'd like each of you to think about what you'd like to get out of this group. The most important thing to think about in answering this question is what you really want, not what anyone else wants for you. Who will start?

TIME & TOPIC	FACILITATOR NOTES	DISCUSSION WITH WOMEN
2 min. **Activity: Palms Down, Palms Up**	*Read the following slowly:*	In our sessions, we'll be exploring different techniques for dealing with our thoughts and feelings by practicing self-soothing and calming activities. Let's do one technique called Palms Down, Palms Up. 1. Sit comfortably with your back straight. Close your eyes or lower your eyelids and focus on your breathing. Take a slow, deep breath while counting to four. Then exhale slowly, counting to four. 2. Do this four more times until your breathing is slow and relaxed. 3. Keep breathing slowly and evenly. Hold your hands gently in front of you with your palms up and imagine them holding all the negative or upsetting thoughts and feelings you've had today. 4. Now turn your palms down. Imagine yourself emptying your hands of all the negative or upsetting things you've been carrying today. Let go of them. 5. Keep breathing slowly. Now, turn your palms up. Your palms are up and open to receive positive energy, thoughts, and feelings. Your palms are open to receive support and help. 6. Now slowly open your eyes. Anytime you need to let go of something negative and receive the positive, you can take a few minutes to do this activity.
1 min. **Between- Sessions Activity**		The activity for you to do between now and our next session is to practice the two grounding exercises you learned today: Five Senses and Breathing and Exhaling. Try to do each of them at least once each day between now and our next session.

TIME & TOPIC	FACILITATOR NOTES	DISCUSSION WITH WOMEN
1 min. **Closing**	*If there is time, encourage the women to spend a few minutes writing their thoughts on the session in the Reflection section on page 18 of their workbook. Or this can be done as part of the their Between-Sessions Activity.*	Thank you all for coming today. It takes a lot of courage to try something new. Today, we're starting on a journey together, and I look forward to our explorations and discoveries in the coming weeks. I know we've covered a lot of difficult material today. How is everyone doing as we end? Remember your self-soothing exercises if you are feeling distressed. Please also remember to bring your workbooks to the next session.

Session Notes

ADAPTING THE SESSION FOR USE WITH GIRLS

You may want to consider creating sessions for girls that are one hour in length (maximum one and one half hours).

When facilitating this introductory session with girls, you often will want to change the use of the words *woman* and *women* to *girl, girls,* or *young women.*

It's more complex to lead a trauma group with girls than with women. Many girls are very connected to their friends and find a group with strangers to be uncomfortable. Some girls are isolated and feel uncomfortable in any group situation. This is magnified because of the topic of these sessions. It may help the girls relax a bit if you offer food either before or just after the group session. The food should be healthy things that their age group likes.

In introducing the program to girls, you can say something about how there have been trauma groups for women for years, and that it has been learned that there are many girls (or young women) who have had traumatic experiences, and these young women would like to understand and deal with these experiences earlier in their lives and not wait until adulthood. Many women have said they wish this had been possible for them. Acknowledge that the topic is difficult.

Ask the girls how they would like to refer to their trauma (for example, as an "event," a "situation," or a "bad time in my life").

You may want to turn the group introductions into an art activity. You can provide colored pencils and crayons and ask the girls to draw on the inside covers of their workbooks. Each girl will draw something that represents her. Then have the girls go around the group and show and/or describe their drawings as a way to introduce themselves. Or you may want to conduct an icebreaker activity and make it light, active, and fun.

continued

ADAPTING THE SESSION FOR USE WITH GIRLS

It's important to review the group agreements with the girls. You may want to have a discussion with them to see if they all can agree to the list. The issue of confidentially is particularly important. Make confidentiality a big focus of discussion and discuss ways that it might be broken without a group member meaning to. You can choose to provide two or three sheets of poster board and markers so they can split into two or three subgroups and work together to create posters of the agreements. When the girls engage in working on a project together, they're more likely to "buy in" to the group. Likewise, you may want to make the end of the Five Senses activity an art project and have the girls decorate their Five Senses cards.

Questions for this first session might include "What were you told about this group?" Expand on the questions about their personal goals and ask about their expectations: their hopes for and their fears about the group. Some facilitators devise an incentive system for completing homework assignments.

The Crisis Text Line (operative in February 2015) is the first and only national 24/7 crisis intervention hotline to conduct its conversations (the majority of which are with teenagers) exclusively by text message. Adolescents use text messaging almost exclusively to contact their friends, and text messages are four times more likely to be read than emails. A girl can contact the Crisis Text Line without even looking at her phone. The number, 741741, traces a simple path down the left column of the keypad. Be sure to explain this information to the girls in your group and ask them to put this number into their contact lists.

MODULE A: SESSION 2

The Connections between Violence, Abuse, and Trauma

▦ Time

Two hours

▦ Goal of the Session

To understand the connections between violence, abuse, and trauma.

▦ Participant Objectives

At the end of this session, participants will be able to:

1. Describe examples of traumatic events in a woman's life
2. Explain the different responses to trauma

▦ Materials Needed

- Name tags for the facilitator and each woman in the group
- Relaxing music and equipment to play music
- Each participant's and the facilitator's workbook
- A pencil or pen for the facilitator and each woman
- A variety of crayons or colored pencils for the women
- A newsprint flip-chart pad, an easel, and felt-tip pens
- *Optional: A DVD player and monitor and Segment 3: The Effects of Toxic Stress and Trauma from the* Beyond Trauma *Participant Video*
- Masking tape
- Facial tissues

continued

THE CONNECTIONS BETWEEN VIOLENCE, ABUSE, AND TRAUMA

■ Session Overview

- Welcome, Review of Introductions, and Logistics
- Quiet Time
- Review of Group Agreements
- Goal of the Session
- Discussion and Reading: What Causes Trauma?
- Check-In
- *Optional Activity: Breathing and Exhaling*
- Lecture and Discussion: The Effects of Toxic Stress and Trauma
- *Optional:* Beyond Trauma *Participant Video (Segment 3: The Effects of Toxic Stress and Trauma)*
- Lecture: Substance Use and Trauma
- Lecture: How Violence and Abuse Are Different for Men and Women
- Lecture: Different Responses to Trauma
- Lecture: Posttraumatic Stress Disorder
- Activity: Creating Safety
- *Optional: Between-Sessions Activity: Finding Our Symbols*
- Reflection
- Between-Sessions Activity
- Activity: Palms Down, Palms Up
- Closing

continued

THE CONNECTIONS BETWEEN VIOLENCE, ABUSE, AND TRAUMA

Background Information for the Facilitator

Preparing for the Session

Prepare for each session ahead of time, so you don't need to read the lectures and discussion points word for word. Also decide if you're going to present the lectures or show the corresponding video segment.

Remember, these are some of the things you are responsible for:

- beginning and ending each session on time

- keeping the group activities and discussions on track

- moving the group through the content of each session

- leading by example by having appropriate boundaries and containing your feelings

- allowing each woman to have her own experience of the group

Preparing for the Lecture on the Effects of Toxic Stress and Trauma

You have the option of delivering the lecture yourself or using the *Beyond Trauma* Participant Video (segment 3) to present it.

The Session

TIME & TOPIC	FACILITATOR NOTES	DISCUSSION WITH WOMEN
5–10 min. **Welcome, Review of Introductions, and Logistics**	*Welcome the women to the group. Reintroduce yourself, briefly review your background and your interest in working with women and trauma, and briefly review your role as the facilitator.* *Allow each participant to share. If someone wants to pass, allow her to do so. Thank the women for sharing.*	Let's go around the group so you can introduce yourselves again. In Session 1: Introduction to the Program, you shared things you like about yourselves. This time, after you give your name, I'd like each of you to briefly share something you would like us to know about you. It could be that you are a mother or a recovering alcoholic, that you just finished some type of schooling, that you are happy to be here in the group, or even that you have a new puppy! Everyone has about one minute maximum to speak. We'll be meeting for a total of twelve sessions—this one and ten more—and covering a variety of topics that are important in our lives. For the period of time we meet, each of you will have the opportunity to share feelings and experiences that are unique to you. The stories and the wisdom you bring to the rest of the group are invaluable. Each and every one of you will contribute greatly to making the collective group a rich and supportive environment. Here you'll find commonalities and differences, but most importantly, a space to find your voice, to be heard, and to be supported by other women. Each session will take two hours, without a break. Please be sure to make time to go to the bathroom before each session starts. Most women like to arrive about ten minutes early to get settled.

TIME & TOPIC	FACILITATOR NOTES	DISCUSSION WITH WOMEN
3–4 min. **Quiet Time**	*You may want to play some soft music during this quiet time.* *Allow one to two minutes for this.*	In our last session, we tried various techniques for becoming present: sitting still and focusing on our breathing; focusing on our feet and feeling the chair; slowly walking around the room; tapping our head, forehead, cheeks, and shoulders with our fingers; and finding a focal point in the room and just looking at it for a few minutes. Whichever you choose, let's be quiet now and bring our attention to the present, here in this room. Now let's scan the room, scan our surroundings. If we were cats or dogs coming into this room, we wouldn't just sit down and start paying attention, we'd check out our space and check out the people in the room. Notice the colors, the light, and the objects. When you've done that, close your eyes or lower your eyelids and begin to settle yourself inside. Note any places of tension or discomfort and try to send them some loving attention. Become aware of your breathing. Try to breathe more deeply from your belly, maybe even sighing. Now slowly focus on the room and the group and, when you're ready, open your eyes. Welcome back!
3–5 min. **Review of Group Agreements**	*Post the list of group agreements and consequences generated during session 1.* *Answer any questions the women may have.*	These are the group agreements that we came up with during session 1. These agreements will help to ensure the group remains a safe and supportive place for each of you. Does anyone have any questions about these?

TIME & TOPIC	FACILITATOR NOTES	DISCUSSION WITH WOMEN
1 min. **Goal of the Session**		The goal of this session is to understand the connections between violence, abuse, and trauma. Personal growth, recovery, and healing can be part of our life journey. The trauma we've experienced may always be with us at some level. However, if we take the risk of learning about trauma and give ourselves the opportunity to explore the process of healing, we can grow and cope and live happy and healthy lives after a traumatic experience.
15–20 min. **Discussion and Reading: What Causes Trauma?**	*Have the women share their thoughts about what some traumatic events might be and what else might cause trauma. Write their responses on the flip-chart pad. This list may include some things that were discussed in the last session and some new things. Participants could also write down ideas in their workbook on page 19 during this discussion.* *Thank the women for responding. If they haven't mentioned any of the following, add them to the list:* *• natural disasters, such as hurricanes, earthquakes, tornadoes, fires, floods, and volcanoes* *• the oppression of an entire group of people* *– economic or religious persecution* *– genocide*	

TIME & TOPIC	FACILITATOR NOTES	DISCUSSION WITH WOMEN

	• *discrimination based on*
	   – *race*
	   – *poverty*
	   – *gender*
	   – *sexual orientation or*
	     gender identity
	   – *disability*
	   – *age*
	
	 • *emotional abuse*
	 • *physical abuse*
	 • *sexual abuse*
	 • *abandonment*
	 • *witnessing violence or*
	   murder
	 • *being the victim of a crime*
	 • *street or gang violence*
	 • *automobile accidents*
	 • *immigration*
	 • *catastrophic injuries and*
	   illnesses
	 • *painful and frightening*
	   medical procedures
	 • *the loss of a loved one*
	 • *war and combat*
	 • *terrorism and torture*
	 • *kidnapping*
		A particular source of trauma is called *stigmatization.* This is a form of discrimination based on something that other people can see about you, such as your race, class, or sexual orientation. Let me read an excerpt written by a noted black writer to help us understand how stigmatization can be traumatizing. This is from Audre Lorde's book *Sister Outsider.*

TIME & TOPIC	FACILITATOR NOTES	DISCUSSION WITH WOMEN
	Excerpted from: EYE TO EYE: Black Women, Hatred, and Anger – from the Essay Collection SISTER OUTSIDER, published by Crossing Press/Random House Inc. © 1984, 2007 by Audre Lorde.	"The AA subway train to Harlem. I clutched my mother's sleeve, her arms full of shopping bags, Christmas-heavy. The wet smell of winter clothes, the train's lurching. My mother spots an almost seat, pushes my little snowsuited body down. On one side of me a man reading a paper. On the other, a woman in a fur hat staring at me. Her mouth twitches as she stares and then her gaze drops down, pulling mine with it. Her leather-gloved hand plucks at the line where my new blue snowpants and her sleek fur coat meet. She jerks her coat closer to her. I look. I do not see whatever terrible thing she is seeing on the seat between us—probably a roach. But she has communicated her horror to me. It must be something very bad from the way she is looking, so I pull my snowsuit closer to me away from it, too. When I look up the woman is still staring at me, her nose holes and eyes huge. And suddenly I realize there is nothing crawling up the seat between us; it is me she doesn't want her coat to touch. The fur brushes past my face as she stands with a shudder and holds on to a strap in the speeding train. Born and bred a New York City child, I quickly slide over to make room for my mother to sit down. No word has been spoken. I'm afraid to say anything to my mother because I don't know what I've done. I look at the sides of my snow-pants, secretly. Is there something on them? Something's going on here I do not understand, but I will never forget it. Her eyes. The flared nostrils. The hate."

TIME & TOPIC	FACILITATOR NOTES	DISCUSSION WITH WOMEN
1–3 min. **Check-In**	*Check with the women in the group now (and periodically throughout the session) to see how they're doing. If anyone is experiencing difficulty, you might ask her to concentrate on the age that she is now, focus on the chair she is sitting in, and notice her feet touching the ground. You may want to use the Breathing and Exhaling activity for a minute or so. Some women may want to get up and walk around for a minute or so.*	
3–5 min. Optional Activity: **Breathing and Exhaling**		Let's all stand up. 1. Place your feet a little distance apart so you feel stable. Take a few deep breaths. 2. Relax your shoulders and drop your hands to your sides. Let your arms and hands just dangle, relaxed. 3. Take in a long, deep breath through your nose and blow it out through your mouth like a big gust of wind. 4. Now inhale again and let the air out by blowing it out through your mouth. 5. Remember to relax your shoulders and arms. 6. Let's do the inhaling and exhaling three more times. Remember, you can do this to ground yourself whenever you feel overwhelmed by your thoughts or feelings. Grounding can help bring you back into the present.

TIME & TOPIC	FACILITATOR NOTES	DISCUSSION WITH WOMEN
20 min. **Lecture and Discussion: The Effects of Toxic Stress and Trauma**	*Allow participants to share their answers. If people want to pass, let them.* *Allow participants to share. It's okay if participants choose to pass. Thank the women who have volunteered to share.*	What were some of your thoughts and feelings as I read the story? Have you experienced or observed similar situations? If you haven't experienced the trauma of stigmatization yourself, try to imagine the effect of those few minutes on a child's life, then to be repeated over and over throughout her life. During the previous discussion and as I read the story, you may have noticed your own body's response. You may have experienced tingling, muscles tightening or loosening, an increased or decreased heart rate, numbness, paralysis, temperature changes, different colors or shapes appearing in your inner field of vision, fleeting images, thoughts or emotions, or maybe you felt nothing in your body. Pay attention to these things that occur automatically or almost unconsciously. We'll be addressing these things first by becoming aware of them and then by learning strategies for coping with them. What did you notice happening in your body? Who is willing to start?
9 min. Optional: ***Beyond Trauma* Participant Video** Segment 3	**Segment 3: The Effects of Toxic Stress and Trauma** *Rather than deliver the lecture on the next few pages yourself, you may choose to show segment 3 of the video.*	Let's watch a video segment that will talk more about toxic stress and trauma.

TIME & TOPIC	FACILITATOR NOTES	DISCUSSION WITH WOMEN
		We need to understand that trauma and stress are not the same thing. Certainly, all traumatic events are stressful, but not all stressful events are traumatic. Removing the causes of stress can reverse the symptoms of stress. Learning how to cope with adversity, with difficult life experiences, is an important part of our developing and growing. Moderate, short-lived stress in our bodies can promote growth. However, toxic stress is a strong, unrelieved experience that can adversely affect healthy development, particularly in a child. Without caring adults to buffer children, the unrelenting stress caused by extreme neglect, poverty, or abuse can weaken the developing brain and have long-term consequences on both physical and mental health (National Scientific Council on the Developing Child 2007). There's a difference between routine and traumatic stress.

The symptoms of trauma must be addressed differently because trauma has a deeper and more far-reaching impact. Women who've experienced traumatic events describe feelings of intense fear, shame, helplessness, anger, and horror. These are normal reactions to abnormal or extreme situations. Trauma can affect our inner and outer selves:

• Our inner selves include our thoughts, feelings, beliefs, and values. For example, some women who have experienced the trauma of abuse believe that "You can't trust anyone," or "The world is a very unsafe place," or "There must be something wrong with me."

• Our outer selves—our outer lives—are our relationships and behaviors. Many women who have experienced trauma struggle with their relationships with their family |

TIME & TOPIC	FACILITATOR NOTES	DISCUSSION WITH WOMEN
		members, their friends, and their sexual partners. For example, parenting can become more complicated by the experience of trauma. Some women who've experienced the trauma of childhood abuse may be triggered by their children to remember or re-experience that abuse. The risk for this happening is greatest when a woman's child becomes the age she was when the abuse first occurred. In terms of behavior, some women become numb, isolated, and asexual. Other women's behavior is at the opposite end of the continuum; they may become agitated, loud, and often hypersexual.

One woman described her experience this way: "I often feel really ashamed and depressed about all of the abuse I have seen and experienced and wonder if I will ever be able to be happy. The strange thing is I am so good at putting on a smile when I see people. Even when people could see the bruises, I would pretend like nothing was happening, even though I knew they knew. Really, on the inside I just wanted to cry or talk about it, but I was too afraid—it made me feel crazy, like I was living in two different worlds or something."

A major part of the healing process is becoming congruent. This means having our inner selves (our thoughts, feelings, beliefs, and values) connected to, and consistent with, our outer selves (our relationships and behaviors). This is the wholeness, the integration, reflected in the Upward Spiral we saw in the first session. One example is whether your face (your outer self) reflects how you're feeling (your inner self). |

TIME & TOPIC	FACILITATOR NOTES	DISCUSSION WITH WOMEN
		In discussing trauma, we also need to make a distinction between the suffering that we encounter as a natural part of life and the suffering that we, as human beings, create. We can't avoid the suffering that comes from natural disasters, such as earthquakes, floods, and tornadoes. We also often experience pain during the normal course of life, as we grow up, get an education, move into the workplace and relationships, age, and experience illness and death. Although these life passages can be difficult, they're the foundation stones of our identities. These are normal stressors. They challenge us, helping us define who we are and what we want from our lives. We can see these kinds of experiences as part of life's journey and use them to help us grow and create meaning in our lives.

Then there's the suffering that we, as human beings, have created: the pain and destruction generated by greed, abuse of power, and violence. Wherever we look, around the world and at every level of our society, we can see the pain and destruction that results from abuse, violence, and other crimes. Every day in the United States, women are sexually harassed in the workplace; raped; and beaten by their husbands, boyfriends, and strangers. Significant numbers of our children are neglected and abused, which creates toxic stress. Some are even killed by their parents and caretakers. There has been, and still is, suppression of Native Americans, African Americans, and Native Alaskans and Hawaiians. Violence is widespread in our society, and many have become numb to it. Similar trauma is created all over the world. No person, institution, or country is free from the effects of created suffering. |

TIME & TOPIC	FACILITATOR NOTES	DISCUSSION WITH WOMEN
	Check with the women to see if any of them are having trouble concentrating and staying present. If any of them have emotionally left the discussion, ask them where they went. Remember, dissociation is a defense mechanism that you may have to cope with continually in the process of facilitating this program. Also, you can have the women breathe and be conscious of their breath for a moment. This is one way to help women ground themselves.	
		Some of the questions that women who have experienced trauma often struggle with are:
		• Why did this happen to me?
		• What did I do wrong?
		• Why do I feel so ashamed?
		• Why did people hurt me?
		• Why is life such a struggle?
		• What do I do now?
		Are these questions any of you have asked yourself?
	Allow participants to respond. If people don't want to share, they can pass.	
		One woman who was in prison wrote: "I was very shocked when the police confided in my attorney that they believed I was an abused woman. Who, me, abused? My husband had a quick temper and some personality quirks, and, yes, he had dropped me on the floor, knocked me out cold, and pushed me down the stairs, but, gee, I never had to go to the hospital. Little did I know that I would

TIME & TOPIC	FACILITATOR NOTES	DISCUSSION WITH WOMEN
		discover what constitutes abuse and how this affected me and my children." It may sound amazing that a woman might not know that she was abused, but it's not uncommon.
		Women often feel ashamed about the abuse they've suffered. They may think the abuse is their fault. It may hurt so much to think about the abuse in their past that women in recovery may consider using addictive substances to deal with the pain. So it's important to know that abuse is never the victim's fault. Even if a child disobeys, the parent is never justified in doing things that harm the child. Even if a woman is drunk or flirtatious, a man is never justified in hitting her or forcing her to have sex.
		Two things I hope you'll take away from this group are that you are not alone in your experience with trauma and that any violence you have suffered is not your fault. There are many ways to deal with difficult interpersonal situations, but violence is never acceptable.
		Women need support to heal from trauma. Part of the process is developing connection with and receiving support from others. This group provides a safe space to explore your own thoughts and feelings. You may find that many of the questions you have are similar to those of other women in the group. The healing journey can be challenging, but it's also filled with hope.

TIME & TOPIC	FACILITATOR NOTES	DISCUSSION WITH WOMEN
2 min. **Lecture: Substance Use and Trauma**		We have seen how common abuse and other forms of trauma are in women's lives. For some women, there's a link between trauma and substance use. For these women, alcohol and other drugs (or other addictive behaviors, such as overeating, gambling, and overworking) help ease the pain of the abuse. Studies show that women who abuse substances have higher rates of childhood physical and sexual abuse than men and non-substance-abusing women (Covington and Surrey 1997; Mason et al. 2014; Ullman et al. 2013). Also, women who abuse alcohol and other drugs are more vulnerable to being abused. The connection between interpersonal violence and substance use and abuse is often complex, especially for women. Survivors of abuse can become dependent on alcohol and/or other drugs, in part as a way of managing trauma symptoms and reducing the tension and stress of living in violent situations. Men who abuse substances are more likely to use violence against women and children, and women who use substances are also more vulnerable to violence because of relationships with others who abuse substances, their impaired judgment while using alcohol or other drugs, and their presence in risky and violence-prone situations.
2–3 min. **Lecture: How Violence and Abuse Are Different for Men and Women**	*You can present this information or have the women volunteer and take turns reading this information aloud from page 22 in the workbook.*	Girls and boys are both at risk of experiencing physical, sexual, and emotional abuse. But the victimization rate changes as girls and boys grow older. In adolescence, girls are more likely than boys to continue to be abused, often by someone close to them, such as a relative or a date. Boys are less likely to be abused, but, if they are, it's less

TIME & TOPIC	FACILITATOR NOTES	DISCUSSION WITH WOMEN
		likely to happen in an intimate relationship than it is from peers or rivals, such as gangs. When males are assaulted or abused, it's more likely to be committed in public and by strangers or by people who dislike them. Females are assaulted or abused more often in private and by someone they know. This pattern carries on into adulthood. Women are at risk from people they know, and men are at risk from strangers and in war.
		Of all the forms of trauma, women are at greater risk of interpersonal violence than men are. Males don't have the same experience of abuse throughout the course of their lives. In the United States, women are nine times more likely than men to be victims of crime in the home, as opposed to on the street (Donziger 1996). For women and girls, the people who say "I love you" to them often are their abusers. This dynamic can be emotionally crazy-making for females. It breaks down a woman's sense of trust, safety, and security in the world, because she may not know if she's safe even within her intimate circle. "If you hurt me and say you love me, what sense can I make of this?"
2–3 min. **Lecture: Different Responses to Trauma**	*You can present this information or have the women volunteer to read this information aloud from pages 22–23 in the workbook.*	No two people experience trauma in the same way. Many factors influence how a woman responds to a traumatic event: her age, history with other trauma, family dynamics, support systems, and more. What may be a traumatic event for one person may not be for another. One woman may feel an event was life threatening—making her feel vulnerable and afraid. Another

TIME & TOPIC	FACILITATOR NOTES	DISCUSSION WITH WOMEN
		woman may experience that same event differently, perhaps as a challenge. Women may have different responses to violence and abuse because they do or do not have coping skills that are effective for a specific event. Sometimes the trauma from an event is not recognized immediately because the violent event may have been perceived as normal. It's important to remember that each woman's experience and her feelings surrounding her experience need to be honored. This will help us be supportive and nonjudgmental toward one another.
4–5 min. **Lecture: Posttraumatic Stress Disorder**		The terms *trauma, abuse,* and *posttraumatic stress disorder* or *PTSD* are often used interchangeably. Sometimes people use the word *trauma* to describe an event, sometimes to describe a response to an event. Abuse is one type of traumatic event, and PTSD is a common response to trauma. The effects of traumatic victimization often result in posttraumatic stress disorder. The symptoms of PTSD can be grouped into four categories (American Psychiatric Association 2013): 1. *Re-experiencing* an event may occur as disturbed sleep, distressing dreams, nightmares, intrusive memories, flashbacks, and reliving the event. 2. *Numbing and avoidance* may occur as not feeling anything physically or emotionally and avoiding any thoughts, feelings, people, places, or reminders of the traumatic event.

TIME & TOPIC	FACILITATOR NOTES	DISCUSSION WITH WOMEN
		3. *Changes in mood and thoughts* may result in low self-esteem, neglect of health, dissociation, the ability to remember events or feelings but not both, memory loss for certain events, loss of faith and hope, mistrust of others, and isolation and disconnection.
		4. *Hyperarousal* may involve intense emotions, difficulty sleeping, panic and anxiousness, self-harm, risky behaviors, irritability, anger, and difficulty concentrating.
		There are two types of posttraumatic stress disorder: simple and complex. Simple PTSD stems from a single incident, such as an earthquake or automobile accident, usually in adulthood. Complex PTSD stems from repeated incidents, such as childhood sexual abuse and domestic violence. Generally, there are more symptoms and a more complicated recovery process with complex PTSD (Herman 1997; Najavits 2002; Williams and Sommer 2013).
		In our group sessions, we'll explore together our responses to different traumatic situations, understand why we respond in the ways we do, and learn new ways of responding.
20–25 min. **Activity: Creating Safety**		Safety is an important issue for every woman. If you've been abused or have experienced other forms of trauma, the need for safety can be even more of a priority. Safety can be viewed on two levels: external safety and internal safety.

TIME & TOPIC	FACILITATOR NOTES	DISCUSSION WITH WOMEN
	Write the women's responses on the flip-chart pad. *Write the women's responses on the flip-chart pad.* *Remember that some women may feel too anxious to close their eyes. Have them lower their eyelids or focus on an object with their eyes open. Give the following directions slowly.*	External safety involves actions we take in our surroundings. We do things to try to keep ourselves physically safe in our environment. We may lock our doors, choose not to go out alone at night, or have unlisted telephone numbers. What are some of the other things we do to keep ourselves safe in the world? Internal safety is how we take care of our thoughts and feelings. When we feel overwhelmed, sad, angry, lonely, frightened, or stressed, we need to have ways to take care of ourselves. What are some ways to do that? Sometimes it's harder to take actions to protect our internal safety. But our internal safety is just as important as our external safety. We'll be learning techniques in this program to help comfort and nurture ourselves and to help us pay attention to our internal safety. We can also learn new self-soothing techniques from one another. Some women find it helpful to have an object that they keep with them to focus on when they need to comfort themselves. Let's do an activity that will help you find your own self-soothing object. 1. Close your eyes. Relax. Take a few deep breaths. 2. Think of a place that makes you feel comfortable and secure. It might be a new place or some place you have been to. It might be a favorite chair, or it might be your bed. It might be a place you've created in your imagination: at the beach, in the water, in a garden or at a lake, in a beautiful meadow, in a

TIME & TOPIC	FACILITATOR NOTES	DISCUSSION WITH WOMEN
		hammock hanging from a tree, in the snow, or at the top of a hill. If you can't think of any place where you really feel good, think of a place where you've felt free from fear, relaxed, or maybe even bored. This may be a real place or a place in your imagination.
		3. Keep your eyes closed and notice all the details in that picture of the place. What do you see?
		4. What do you hear?
		5. What do you smell?
		6. What do you feel?
		7. What do you taste?
		8. What is the quality of the light, the air, the temperature? Experience every part of it.
	Pause for one to two minutes to let the women totally experience their pictures.	
		9. Now make any changes to your picture that will enhance the serenity and security of the experience. You can take things out or add things. Nod your head when you've changed the picture in your mind.
		10. Enjoy this place and embrace the peacefulness of it. Keep your eyes closed or your eyelids lowered.
		11. Now, let your mind choose a souvenir or symbol that will remind you of this experience in the future. The symbol can be an object, sight, sound, or sensation. Take a minute to receive your symbol. When you have it, take time to look at it, feel it, and stay connected with it.

TIME & TOPIC	FACILITATOR NOTES	DISCUSSION WITH WOMEN
	Give the women four to five minutes to draw their self-soothing symbols in their workbooks. *Have the women write their feelings in their workbooks in the space provided. Responses might include comfort, security, and safety.* *Ask the women to share their symbols with the group. Allow people to pass if they don't want to share.*	12. When you're familiar with your symbol, slowly open your eyes and begin to focus again on the here and now. When you're fully present, think back to the symbol. Turn to page 24 in your workbook. You will find a space to draw a picture of the symbol that you visualized. What feelings do you have when you think of your symbol? Even though we're all unique and probably had different pictures in our minds, sharing our images with the group can give us ideas of places and symbols to use for comfort.
1 min. Optional: **Between-Sessions Activity: Finding Our Symbols**	*Note that it may be difficult for women in correctional settings to find and/or carry objects.*	For the next session, find an object that will remind you of the symbol you chose. Maybe it'll be something you can easily carry with you. Look at it when you want to bring back those safe, comforting feelings. If you can't find an object, keep copies of your drawing in places where you can easily get to it, such as in your purse or pocket, on your refrigerator, in your locker, or on your mirror.
5 min. **Reflection**	*Allow participants to respond. People can pass if they want to. If there is time, also have the women take a few minutes to write in the Reflection section of their workbook on page 25.*	How does it feel to have created a safe place for yourself? What was meaningful for you in this session?

TIME & TOPIC	FACILITATOR NOTES	DISCUSSION WITH WOMEN
5 min. **Between-Sessions Activity**		Your Between-Sessions Activity, on pages 26–27 of the workbook, gives you an opportunity to practice ways to calm and soothe yourselves. There are some questions you can start to answer before our next session. We'll start that session by talking about your experiences and thoughts. **Between-Sessions Activity** This gives you an opportunity to practice ways to calm and soothe yourself. Here are some questions you can start to answer before the next session: 1. *Name some ways in which you've calmed yourself when you have been afraid.* _____ _____ 2. *What are some other ways of calming yourself that you can imagine doing in the future?* _____ _____ 3. *Write about an experience when you calmed yourself, or write about the ways you've seen or heard other women calm themselves.* _____ _____ 4. *Finish drawing your symbol (on page 24), if you felt you didn't have enough time during the session. You might want to make copies of it to keep in your pocket or purse, hang on your mirror, or keep in your locker.*
	Allow participants to ask questions.	Are there any questions about the Between-Sessions Activity?
1–2 min. **Activity: Palms Down, Palms Up**	*Read the following directions slowly:*	So far, we've done three activities for calming and grounding ourselves. Let's do the Palms Down, Palms Up activity again. 1. Sit comfortably with your back straight. Close your eyes or lower your eyelids and focus on your breathing. Take a slow, deep breath while counting to four. Then exhale slowly, counting to four.

TIME & TOPIC	FACILITATOR NOTES	DISCUSSION WITH WOMEN
		2. Do this four more times until your breathing is slow and relaxed. 3. Keep breathing slowly and evenly. Hold your hands gently in front of you with your palms up and imagine them holding all the negative or upsetting thoughts and feelings you've had today. 4. Now turn your palms down. Imagine yourself emptying your hands of all the negative or upsetting things you've been carrying today. Let go of them. 5. Keep breathing slowly. Now, turn your palms up. Your palms are up and open to receive positive energy, thoughts, and feelings. Your palms are open to receive support and help. 6. Now slowly open your eyes. Remember, any time you need to let go of something negative and receive the positive, you can take a few minutes to do this activity.
1 min. **Closing**		What a lot of strength and courage we have in this room! Isn't it amazing that with all the hard things each of you has been through, you've survived, you've been able to get through what life has given you, and you have the courage to be here now making choices about your future. All of these things are assets that will help you in your process of recovery. Thank you for your courage and hard work today, and I'll see you *[announce the date and time of the next session]*.

ADAPTING THE SESSION FOR USE WITH GIRLS

You may find the girls in your group have difficulty with the quiet time that opens each session. You may need to create a different opening activity. One suggestion is to rotate and have each girl bring some of her favorite music to the group. It may not be "quiet," but it may help the girls get settled into the group. The objective of the quiet time is to get their attention focused in the room. Perhaps you can find something else more soothing and actually quiet, rather than their music.

Ask the girls to name their group ("What would you like to call this group?"). Then have them create a poster (on poster board) for the group. Explain that it's like a sign that represents the group. This can be done by creating a drawing (distribute colored markers or crayons) or a collage (have old magazines, scissors, and glue available) that represents the group.

With girls, you can expand the information on gender differences. Ask them who is more at risk for abuse in a dating relationship? What do girls share about their dates and what are they silent about? Do most girls feel they can tell their parents or their friends about any abuse they suffer?

After you've explained what posttraumatic stress disorder (PTSD) is, ask if they know anyone (friend or family member) who has this.

Be aware of their emotional affect as well as what you can observe about their bodies during the session.

Power and Abuse

▧ Time

Two hours

▧ Goal of the Session

To recognize the connection between power and abuse in our society.

▧ Participant Objectives

At the end of this session, participants will be able to:

1. Explain how social messages impact women's lives

2. Compare and contrast gender roles and expectations

3. Explain the connection between power and abuse

▧ Materials Needed

• Name tags for the facilitator and each woman in the group, if needed

• Relaxing music and equipment to play music

• Each participant's and the facilitator's workbook

• A pencil or pen for the facilitator and each woman

• A newsprint flip-chart pad, an easel, and felt-tip pens

• *Optional:* Life Prayers from Around the World: 365 Prayers, Blessings, and Affirmations to Celebrate the Human Journey *(Roberts and Amidon 1996, page 266, by Jamie Sams, and pages 274–75, by Alla Renee Bozarth)* or Circle of Stones *(Duerk 1993)*

• *Optional: A DVD player and monitor and Segment 4: Role Reversal from the* Beyond Trauma *Participant Video*

• A blank sheet of paper for each woman

• Masking tape

• Facial tissues

continued

Duplicating this page is illegal. Do not copy this material without written permission from the publisher.

147

POWER AND ABUSE

■ **Session Overview**

- Quiet Time
- *Optional: Reading*
- Check-In
- Review of Between-Sessions Activity
- Goal of the Session
- Discussion: Gender Expectations
- *Optional:* Beyond Trauma *Participant Video (Segment 4: Role Reversal)*
- *Activity: Role Reversal*
- Lecture: The Connection between Abuse and Power
- Activity: Grounding
- Lecture: The Power and Control Wheel
- Lecture: Local Resources
- Reflection
- Between-Sessions Activity
- Activity: Five Senses
- Closing

continued

POWER AND ABUSE

Background Information for the Facilitator

Preparing for the Role Reversal Activity

You have the option of reading the role reversal fantasy or using the *Beyond Trauma* Participant Video segment 4 to present it. Then plan to debrief after either with participants.

Preparing for the Lecture on the Power and Control Wheel

Create a poster-sized copy of the Power and Control Wheel (see example below) and post it on a wall. It should be large enough that all the women in the group can read it from their chairs.

Power and Control Wheel

Duluth Domestic Abuse Intervention Project, 202 East Superior Street, Duluth, MN 55802, www.theduluthmodel.org, 218-722-2781.

continued

POWER AND ABUSE

Also, prior to the session, make a list on the flip-chart pad of the various forms of abuse, as follows:

- emotional abuse
- physical abuse
- economic abuse
- sexual abuse
- coercion and threats
- intimidation
- isolation

- using children
- using male privilege
- minimizing
- denying
- blaming

Post this list when you begin the lecture.

Preparing for the Lecture on Local Resources

As every community has different resources for dealing with domestic violence, violence against children, other forms of abuse, and stalking, you'll need to compile a list of the resources available in your area. In appendix 3 there is a template for such a list (see sample). Have this list printed and make it available to the women in the group. It's also important to know your state and local laws regarding mandated reporting of abuse.

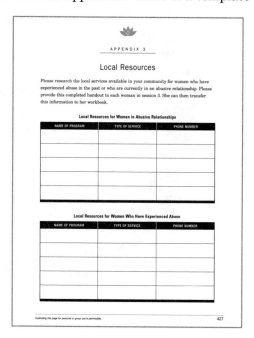

The Session

TIME & TOPIC	FACILITATOR NOTES	DISCUSSION WITH WOMEN
2 min. **Quiet Time**	*Begin playing the soft music.*	Welcome to session 3 of *Beyond Trauma: A Healing Journey for Women.* Let's be silent for a minute or two to give ourselves time to unwind, relax, and focus on where we are now. While we're silent, let's scan the room. Look at the space. Notice the colors, the light, and the objects in the room. Notice the people in the room. When you've done that, close your eyes or lower your eyelids and begin to settle yourself inside. Note any places of tension or discomfort and try to send them some loving attention. Notice your breathing. Try breathing deeper from your belly, maybe even giving a big sigh. Allow yourself to be present in an intentional way with yourself. Maybe use the technique that has worked best for you in one of our earlier sessions. Now slowly bring your attention back into the room and, when you're ready, open your eyes. Welcome back!
1–2 min. **Optional: Reading**	*You may want to read excerpts from either of two excellent sources:* Life Prayers from Around the World: 365 Prayers, Blessings, and Affirmations to Celebrate the Human Journey *(Roberts and Amidon 1996, especially page 266, by Jamie Sams, and pages 274–75, by Alla Renee Bozarth) or* Circle of Stones *(Duerk 1993).*	

TIME & TOPIC	FACILITATOR NOTES	DISCUSSION WITH WOMEN
10–15 min. **Check-In**	*Encourage the women to talk about how they've been doing since the last group session. You can use the technique of the "weather report" to ask the women how they are. Are they sunny, cold and rainy, or is there an impending storm? You may also want to ask specific questions or raise issues based on what was discussed in session 2.* *It's important that check-ins be kept brief. Any major individual issues will require individual appointments, to be set right after the session.* *Allow participants to respond. If people want to pass, allow them to.*	What have you been feeling and thinking about coming to this session? Let's do our check-in today like a weather report. Are you sunny? Cold? Rainy?
10–15 min. **Review of Between-Sessions Activity**	*Have the women share their Between-Sessions Activity, including describing the following:* 1. *Some ways in which they've calmed themselves when they've been afraid.* 2. *Some ways to calm themselves that they can imagine doing in the future.* 3. *Their writings about experiences when they calmed themselves or ways they've seen or heard of other women calming themselves.*	

TIME & TOPIC	FACILITATOR NOTES	DISCUSSION WITH WOMEN
	If they found symbols of their safe places, ask the women to show them to the group. If they found objects and didn't bring them, they can explain or describe them.	
	Allow participants to respond.	Also, who duplicated her drawing of her symbol? Where did you place it?
1 min. **Goal of the Session**		The goal of session 3 is to recognize the connection between power and abuse in our society.
10–15 min. **Discussion: Gender Expectations**	*Write each question on the flip-chart pad as you ask it. Write the women's responses under each question. The women can also write their answers in their workbooks on pages 29–31.*	Today we'll look at some of the differences between women and men—what we call gender differences. Gender is the experience of being raised as a female or a male. This experience is affected by the messages we receive from our families, our friends, the media, and society. Let's start by discussing some questions: 1. How are boys and girls treated differently as children? 2. What are the social messages boys get? 3. How are boys supposed to be? 4. What are the social messages girls get? 5. How are girls supposed to be? 6. How are these different in the various cultures in the United States? One's sex is determined by nature, but gender expectations are defined by a person's society, religion, ethnicity, family, peers, place of work, and so on.

TIME & TOPIC	FACILITATOR NOTES	DISCUSSION WITH WOMEN
	The answers may include be quiet, be polite, be nurturing, be a caregiver, don't talk back, don't be too smart, be dependent, be pretty, be sexy, be a good housekeeper, always be available for men, and so on. *The answers may include be aggressive, be the breadwinner, be emotionally unavailable, be mean, be tough, don't cry, be successful, be strong, be in control, be dominant over women, and so on.* Optional: *You may want to comment on how difficult this is for people who are born with the body of one sex but feel they are the other.*	7. How do we learn these gender expectations and roles? 8. What does it mean to "act like a woman"? 9. What does it mean to "act like a man"? 10. How is this different for different ethnicities? Just by the fact that we're female, we're taught certain ways of acting or being (taking on particular roles) in our culture. Gender expectations begin when we're infants and influence the ways we act and the choices we make throughout our lives. Now let's think about what it would be like if our roles were changed.
8 min. Optional: ***Beyond Trauma Participant Video*** Segment 4	**Segment 4: Role Reversal** *Rather than read the role-reversal fantasy (on the next page) yourself, you may choose to show segment 4 of the video to present it. Then you can proceed to debrief the role reversal with the women using the guided questions on pages 161–162.*	

TIME & TOPIC	FACILITATOR NOTES	DISCUSSION WITH WOMEN
20 min. **Activity: Role Reversal**	*Read the "It's a Woman's World" fantasy slowly, so the fantasy aspect is reinforced and there is time for the images it conjures up to be realized by the listeners.*	I'm going to read a fantasy scenario about role reversal . . . a scenario in which female and male roles are reversed. Remember this is an imaginary situation. Just listen carefully and notice how you begin to feel. It takes about three minutes or so. As you listen, try to feel what this world would be like for a woman and for a man. Think of it as always being that way, every day of your life. Absorb what it tells you about the importance and value of being a woman— or being a man. Feel your feelings through each description. If you start thinking too much, try to become aware of your feelings again. Now please close your eyes or lower your eyelids. As I read, put yourself into this fantasy world. **It's a Woman's World** You are invited to enter a world in which women are the leaders, the power brokers, the prime movers. Women are the heads of countries, legislatures, police departments, courts, corporations, religions, and the media—especially when important events are covered. Therefore, women are respected, honored, and obeyed. Because they are the leaders and rulers, women are on the move from morning to night. They "own" the streets. They can walk alone anywhere they want—on city streets, in parks, in the country—and they take it for granted that they will be safe. Men, on the other hand, are cautious about

TIME & TOPIC	FACILITATOR NOTES	DISCUSSION WITH WOMEN
		venturing out alone without their powerful female companions. Especially at night, they are worried about their safety and cautious when they are alone. They lock their doors and they scan the environment for danger when going to their cars or when they are in unfamiliar surroundings. Men who go out alone or in small groups, especially at night, often are subjected to comments from women about their sexual desirability. The obvious biological explanation for the superiority of women is their genital construction. A female's genitals are compact and internal, protected by her body. A male's genitals are so exposed that he is vulnerable and must be protected from outside attack to ensure that he can perform his function of getting a female pregnant. In addition, because the genitals of males are visible, they invite comparison and ridicule. Even young girls may jeer at boys' genitals because they "flop around." Because males envy females, they learn to strap up their genitals. Women feel more secure in their bodies. A girl can run, climb, and ride horseback unencumbered. Because she can move freely, she is encouraged to develop her body and mind to prepare for her womanly responsibilities. In addition to her work, she is more suited to engage in sports and other physical activities. Female athletes are honored and respected role models, and many earn huge incomes. Because girls grow up feeling secure, they learn to

TIME & TOPIC	FACILITATOR NOTES	DISCUSSION WITH WOMEN
		be comfortable with and supportive of one another. Women are proud of their achievements, and it gives them an incredible bond. Because women feel secure about their bodies, they aren't focused on how they look. Their clothes are comfortable, and they can move easily. Because males are less secure, they compete with one another for female attention throughout life and can be highly emotional. Men are very concerned with staying thin, toned, and sexy so that women will be attracted to them, support them, and protect them. They often post photos of themselves looking provocative, so they are subject to cyberbullying. Thus, males are more passive than females and have a desire to be symbolically and physically engulfed by the protective body of the woman. If a male denies these feelings, he is unconsciously rejecting his masculinity. Therapy is needed to help him adjust to his own nature. Of course, therapy is administered by a woman who has the education and wisdom to facilitate the male's growth and self-actualization. Because the male needs female protection, historically men were sold or given to women as helpmates. As the man's natural role is husband and father, he is taught to fulfill himself through nurturing children and making the home a refuge for the woman. This is only natural to balance the biological role of woman, who devotes her

TIME & TOPIC	FACILITATOR NOTES	DISCUSSION WITH WOMEN
		body to perpetuating the race through pregnancy.

If a woman chooses to have children, they (and her husband, if she has one) carry her name. A man longs to be married to a woman who will support him and deliver a girl child to carry on the family name. He knows that if the first child is a boy, he has disappointed her.

Women are more financially secure, so they determine the family budget and make the final decisions about how money is spent. Men provide child care services so that women's work is rarely interrupted. Men are the day care teachers, caretakers, and assistants. Their role is nurturing and helping others. Some men work outside the home, of course, but they must find jobs that allow them to balance the responsibilities of caring for children and coordinating the children's activities and transportation, as well as other household tasks. This enables women to concentrate on their careers, on current events (about which their opinions are needed), and on sports or other activities, which help them relax after work.

Men are often tired from all their roles, but a man knows that it is his responsibility to provide sexual pleasure whenever his woman is in the mood for it and to give her space when she is tired or preoccupied. |

TIME & TOPIC	FACILITATOR NOTES	DISCUSSION WITH WOMEN
		Of course, there is some criticism of sexism in this society. For example, there are more restrooms for women than for men, so busy women never have to wait in line. Medical research has made having a period easy and comfortable for women, as it is important for the survival of the race, so there are plenty of supplies available to help with periods, especially in schools, workplaces, public arenas, subways, and airplanes. There are also many products to help make sure women get the sexual stimulation and pleasure they need and desire. As men age, they often feel undesirable and invisible. However, women celebrate menopause as a time when they come into their ultimate power and wisdom.
	Note: A special thank-you to the late Theodora Wells. Her original idea for this type of role reversal (which she titled "Woman—Which Includes Man, of Course") in 1970 provided the impetus for this updated version. Unfortunately, over forty-five years later, gender roles and their effects are still very much a part of our society.	

TIME & TOPIC	FACILITATOR NOTES	DISCUSSION WITH WOMEN
	For some women, this is very enlightening. For others, it's annoying because it seems so unequal. Although this was originally written a long time ago and recently updated, a lot of things in it have not changed. In our society, men (especially white men) still have more power. *You can debrief this exercise with your group as per the following directions.* *On the flip-chart pad, draw a line down the middle of the paper. Write "Woman" at the top of one column and "Man" at the top of the other column. As you ask the discussion questions, write the women's responses on the pad. After the discussion, the women can also write some of their answers in the space provided on pages 32 and 33 in their workbooks.*	As you leave this fantasy, take your time coming back, and hold on to the feelings you are having. When asked, say what you feel inside you. Let's talk about the role reversal scenario.

TIME & TOPIC	FACILITATOR NOTES	DISCUSSION WITH WOMEN
		1. How do you think a woman in this fantasy might feel? What do you think it would be like to live in this fantasy world as a woman?
	Women typically respond with answers such as in charge, strong, powerful, respected, not vulnerable, responsible, important, and safe.	
		2. How do you think a man in this fantasy might feel? What do you think it would be like for a man to live in this fantasy world?
	Answers often include dis-empowered, angry, vulnerable, scared, emasculated, not valued, and unimportant.	
	It was pretty obvious that the women did.	3. In the fantasy, who had the most power?
	Most women see that men would have the greater risk of depression.	4. Who do you think is at greater risk for depression in this fantasy?
	Most women recognize the man is more likely to have lower self-esteem.	5. Who do you think will have lower self-esteem?
	You may need to explain that codependent *means having one's life revolve around another person's addiction. Most see the man as falling into this role in the fantasy.*	6. Who is more likely to be considered "codependent"?

TIME & TOPIC	FACILITATOR NOTES	DISCUSSION WITH WOMEN
	Most women say the man.	7. Who is more likely to feel guilt and shame?
	Most women say the man.	8. Who is more likely to feel negative about her or his body?
	Most women say the men are at the greatest risk for abuse.	9. Who is more likely to be abused?
		This is an important point. Those who have less power are at greatest risk for being abused. When men have the most power, women are at greatest risk for abuse. When women have more power, men are at risk. This fantasy helps us see how our social structure is based on a dominant and subordinate model. The dominants are the strongest and/or the ones in charge. The subordinates are considered lower and "less than" the dominants. If you're a person in a less powerful group, you probably know quite a bit about the dominant culture. But the dominant group tends not to know as much about what it's like to be in a subordinate role. One example is that women tend to know a lot more about men than men know about women. Blacks know a lot more about whites than whites know about blacks. Lesbians and gay men know more about straight people than straight people know about lesbians and gay men. Subordinates learn as much as possible about the dominant culture in order to survive in that world. Dominants don't need to know about subordinates to survive and, in fact, may feel they have nothing to learn from subordinates.

TIME & TOPIC	FACILITATOR NOTES	DISCUSSION WITH WOMEN
	Sometimes young women do not relate to the role reversal at all.	There is a myth in a dominant-subordinate culture that says dominants will protect subordinates. Men are supposed to protect women, and adults are supposed to protect children. In reality, dominant people frequently abuse and devalue subordinates. Think about your experience as a woman, a child, a person of color, an employee, or another subordinate role. Now think about what it's like to be the adult, the white person, or the rich person who can take advantage of someone with less power. This fantasy can help us imagine and feel what it's like to have power and control. Powerlessness is a huge issue for women and one we will explore together in the coming sessions. Some of you may not like the fantasy because it describes a world that still involves power over others. I agree: An imbalanced system in which some people are dominant and some are subordinate is not good for anyone.
5 min. **Lecture: The Connection between Abuse and Power**		Let's revisit the messages that women are often given and talk about how these messages help or harm a woman's sense of power and her sense of self in the world. Part of this is how power and roles relate to abuse, violence, and trauma. Many women who experience or witness violence, particularly actions that threaten their lives and safety, are traumatized by events that "overwhelm the ordinary system of care that give people a sense of control, connection, and meaning" (Herman 1997). In other words, a woman's sense of self, self-worth, and self-power are decreased by abuse.

TIME & TOPIC	FACILITATOR NOTES	DISCUSSION WITH WOMEN
	Elicit responses to this from the group and write them on the flip-chart pad. Examples might include the following: • *The abuser uses power over the victim.* • *Abuse takes power away from the victim.* • *The victim feels powerless against the abuser and in many aspects of her life.* • *The victim feels trapped or locked in a role.* • *The victim feels isolated, so there's no strength or power from others who could help.*	What are some of your thoughts about what happens when someone who has power abuses another person? What are the effects on the victim?
5 min. **Activity: Grounding**	*You may find that some of the women are uncomfortable, distracted, or having negative feelings in response to this content. A grounding technique can help women detach or disconnect from their emotional discomfort by focusing on the outer world.* *Give the following instructions very slowly, to allow time for the women to respond to each part.*	In dealing with this content, you may find yourself feeling uncomfortable or distracted or having negative feelings. Grounding techniques are ways to detach or disconnect from our emotional discomfort by focusing on the outer world. Grounding is one way to become empowered. With your eyes open, remind yourself of your name, your age, where you are now, the day of the week, the date, and the city you are in. Then notice the environment you are in—the size of the room, the color of the walls, the furniture in the room, the pictures on the wall, the height of the ceiling, and so on. This is a technique you can use in or out of the group setting.

TIME & TOPIC	FACILITATOR NOTES	DISCUSSION WITH WOMEN
		Now let's look at the workbook, at the grounding skills we learned in session 1. Let's review these: the Five Senses on page 12, the Breathing and Exhaling exercise on page 14, and Palms Down, Palms Up on page 17. The grounding activity we just did is also in your workbook on page 34. You can use these activities anytime to soothe and comfort yourself.
20–25 min. **Lecture: The Power and Control Wheel**	*Post the Power and Control Wheel on a wall where all the women can see it.* *Post the list you made on the flip-chart pad of the various forms of abuse:* • *intimidation* • *emotional abuse* • *isolation* • *minimizing* • *denying* • *blaming* • *using children* • *using male privilege* • *economic abuse* • *coercion and threats* • *physical abuse* • *sexual abuse*	Professionals who deal with domestic violence developed this graphic of the various forms of abuse. It shows that power and control are at the center of violence. We'll be working with this now and then using it as part of the Between-Sessions Activity. You can see that the Power and Control Wheel is divided into parts or segments. Each of these represents ways someone can be abusive to another. **Power and Control Wheel** Duluth Domestic Abuse Intervention Project, 202 East Superior Street, Duluth, MN 55802, www.theduluthmodel.org, 218-722-2781.

TIME & TOPIC	FACILITATOR NOTES	DISCUSSION WITH WOMEN
	Have the women form duos (groups of two). Distribute sheets of blank 8½ × 11-inch paper to the women (one sheet per duo). Ask the duos to spend five to ten minutes developing examples of how each form of abuse might look in a relationship. You may want to have each group of two start at a different place on the wheel and work clockwise. This helps to get information on all the spokes. *Then have them come back into the group circle and begin to share their examples with the rest of the women.* *After they complete their descriptions of how these behaviors look in a relationship, thank them for sharing and then do a check-in. Ask the women what they're feeling emotionally and in their bodies. Allow participants to pass if they don't want to share. If there is time, they can start to add the descriptions of abusive behavior in their workbooks on pages 34 and 35.*	Now look at page 36 in the workbook. There is a more detailed copy of the Power and Control Wheel showing how the various forms of abuse may play out. Let's go around the group and take turns reading each of the segments of the wheel.

TIME & TOPIC	FACILITATOR NOTES	DISCUSSION WITH WOMEN
		Let's see if there were things that we didn't list. Remember, you have the right to "pass" if you don't want to read aloud at this time. Who will volunteer to start reading the segment on intimidation? **Power and Control Wheel** One serious problem in dealing with personal abuse is that many women who are in abusive relationships have difficulty acknowledging it. They may think, "This can't be happening to me," or they may be ashamed to let their friends and family members know what's going on, or they may be afraid to report their abuser to anyone.

Duluth Domestic Abuse Intervention Project, 202 East Superior Street, Duluth, MN 55802, www.theduluthmodel.org, 218-722-2781.

TIME & TOPIC	FACILITATOR NOTES	DISCUSSION WITH WOMEN
		If you've been or currently are in such a situation or have a friend or family member in such a situation whom you'd like to help, here are some questions you can ask that may identify whether the incident or relationship was or is abusive. Remember, domestic violence occurs in same-sex relationships as well as in relationships between women and men, and it occurs across all age groups and relationships in a family.
	As you ask each question, have women follow along on page 37 in their workbook.	1. Was there full consent? 2. Was there an element of betrayal or loss of trust? 3. Have you ever feared for your physical safety in your relationship? 4. Have you felt afraid in other ways? 5. Have you ever been forced to do things against your will? 6. Have you ever been hit or threatened? 7. Have you ever been kicked or choked? 8. Have you ever sustained bodily injuries, such as bruises, cuts, or broken bones? 9. Have your children been hit or threatened? 10. Was there violence, pain, restriction, force, or bodily harm? 11. Have you been verbally put down? 12. Have you been harassed, stalked, or monitored? 13. Did it feel like abuse to you?

TIME & TOPIC	FACILITATOR NOTES	DISCUSSION WITH WOMEN
		Remember that violence is a crime, help is available, and a woman has to choose when she's ready and able to leave. Even if you don't feel ready to leave a relationship or take legal action, it's safe for you to talk with me or another member of the staff or another counselor outside our group sessions about what you're experiencing. Sometimes, plans must be made carefully to leave an abusive relationship. Often, when a woman tries to leave an abusive relationship, the violence escalates. Even if a woman has a safe place to go, she may fear for her life. If you're in such a relationship, know that: 1. I am afraid for your safety. 2. I am afraid for the safety of your children. 3. The abuse or violence will just get worse. 4. You deserve better than this. 5. I am here for you when you are ready. 6. There are safe places for you to go and people who will help you. If a woman decides to leave an abusive relationship but is afraid for her safety, she needs to make careful plans and have resources in place to help her leave when it's the right time to do so.
5–8 min. **Lecture: Local Resources**		Taking advantage of the resources available in the community for counseling for abuse and for help getting out of an abusive relationship can help a woman decide when to leave and, at the same time, offer her a glimpse of a different life that she may create for herself. Such resources may include a hotline number, a mental health clinic, a shelter or safe house, and legal assistance.

TIME & TOPIC	FACILITATOR NOTES	DISCUSSION WITH WOMEN
	Distribute the list of local resources that you have compiled: Local Resources for Women in Abusive Relationships and Local Resources for Women Who Have Experienced Abuse.	Please turn to page 38 in your workbook. Later, you can fill out these resource charts with the information I just gave you.
5–8 min. **Reflection**	*Allow participants to respond. Also allow people to pass if they don't want to share anything. If there is time, have women write their thoughts in the Reflection section on page 39 in their workbook, after they share with others.*	In this session, we discussed power and abuse and how those without power are at greatest risk for abuse. Those with power may use their privilege to abuse others. What is one thing you learned today that surprised you or perhaps felt particularly challenging?
3–5 min. **Between-Sessions Activity**		For your Between-Sessions Activity, work on filling in more examples of abuse in relationships on pages 34 and 35 in your workbooks. You may work in groups of two if you would like and use the notes you made in group. Second, fill in the lists of local resources in the resource charts provided on page 38 in the workbook, so you don't have to worry about losing the pages I gave you. Also, use each of the grounding techniques you've learned before our next session. The more often you repeat these, the easier they are to use when you really need them. Let's close our group by doing the Five Senses activity.

TIME & TOPIC	FACILITATOR NOTES	DISCUSSION WITH WOMEN
3 min. **Activity:** **Five Senses**	*Read the adjacent instructions in a calm, soothing voice. Provide enough time between each question to allow the participants to experience what they can see, feel, hear, smell, and taste.*	1. Please get comfortable in your chairs. 2. Now close your eyes or lower your eyelids. 3. Relax for a few moments. Take a few deep breaths and exhale slowly. 4. Open your eyes when you're ready. 5. Silently, identify five things you can see around you. 6. Now identify four things you could feel or touch. 7. Identify three things you can hear. 8. Identify two things you can smell. 9. Finally, identify what you can taste right now. How do you feel now?
1 min. **Closing**		I know this content has been really heavy for some of you. It can bring up a lot of old negative feelings for many women. Thank you for your courage and being willing to stay in the group. As I mentioned before, when we can acknowledge our experiences, we have an opportunity to heal from them. I'll see you at our next session on *[state the day and time]*.

Session Notes

ADAPTING THE SESSION FOR USE WITH GIRLS

Another way to work with gender differences is to use popular songs and switch the language, or use songs that switch genders, such as *Like a Boy* by Ciara. You can ask questions such as "What does it mean to be 'like a boy' in this song? How does that make girls feel? Why would a girl want to act like a boy? Is it okay for boys to act like this? How does it affect girls to stereotype boys in this way?"

The role-reversal fantasy may not work well with girls and often not well with young women. In order to provide some examples and generate a discussion on gender differences, you may wish to have the girls create a collage. Provide poster board, a variety of different types of magazines (several types of magazines designed for women, business magazines, celebrity magazines, etc.), glue sticks, and scissors (if allowed). Ask the girls to cut (or tear) out words and pictures to reflect the messages given to girls and to boys. They can use half of the paper for the girl messages and half for the boy messages. If they create a collage, you can still ask which group they believe is at greater risk for depression, low self-esteem, eating disorders, body-image issues, and abuse.

The Power and Control Wheel and the questions about abuse in relationships are important for girls.

Developed from the Duluth Domestic Abuse Intervention Project, 202 East Superior Street, Duluth, MN 55802, www.theduluthmodel.org, 218-722-2781. Produced and distributed by National Center on Domestic and Sexual Violence, www.ncdsv.org, Austin, Texas.

PHYSICAL VIOLENCE SEXUAL

TEEN POWER AND CONTROL WHEEL

Peer Pressure
Threatening to expose someone's weakness or spread rumors • Telling malicious lies about an individual to peer group

Anger/Emotional Abuse
Putting him/her down • Making him/her feel bad about him or herself • Name calling • Making him/her think he/she's crazy • Playing mind games • Humiliating him/her • Making him/her feel guilty

Using Social Status
Treating her like a servant • Making all the decisions • Acting like the "master of the castle" • Being the one to define men's and women's roles

Isolation/Exclusion
Controlling what another does, who he/she sees and talks to, what he/she reads, where he/she goes • Limiting outside involvement • Using jealousy to justify actions

Intimidation
Making someone afraid by using looks, actions, gestures • Smashing things • Destroying property • Abusing pets • Displaying weapons

Sexual Coercion
Manipulating or making threats to get sex • Getting her pregnant • Threatening to take the children away • Getting someone drunk or drugged to have sex

Threats
Making and/or carrying out threats to do something to hurt another • Threatening to leave, to commit suicide, to report him/her to the police • Making him/her drop charges • Making him/her do illegal things

Minimize/Deny/Blame
Making light of the abuse and not taking concerns about it seriously • Saying the abuse didn't happen • Shifting responsibility for abusive behavior • Saying he/she caused it

PHYSICAL VIOLENCE SEXUAL

continued

ADAPTING THE SESSION FOR USE WITH GIRLS

However, their experiences are different from those of older women. On the previous page is a Power and Control Wheel for girls that is more appropriate to their ages.

(This is in appendix 4 so you can use it as a handout.) You'll need to adapt the lecture and discussion accordingly.

Many girls don't have positive models of what a healthy relationship should look like or what power equality means in a relationship. The Equality Wheel for Teens is an important complement to the Teen Power and Control Wheel. (This is also in appendix 4.)

NONVIOLENCE

NEGOTIATION AND FAIRNESS:
Seeking mutually satisfying resolutions to conflict. Accepting changes. Being willing to compromise.

NON-THREATENING BEHAVIOR:
Talking and acting so that she feels safe and comfortable expressing herself and doing things.

COMMUNICATION:
Willingness to have open and spontaneous dialogue. Having a balance of giving and receiving. Problem solving to mutual benefit. Learning to compromise without one overshadowing the other.

RESPECT:
Listening to her non-judgmentally. Being emotionally affirming and understanding. Valuing her opinions.

TEEN EQUALITY

SHARED POWER:
Taking mutual responsibility for recognizing influence on the relationship. Making decisions together.

TRUST AND SUPPORT:
Supporting her goals in life. Respecting her right to her own feelings, friends, activities, and opinions.

SELF-CONFIDENCE AND PERSONAL GROWTH:
Respecting her personal identity and encouraging her individual growth and freedom. Supporting her security in her own worth.

HONESTY AND ACCOUNTABILITY:
Accepting responsibility for self. Acknowledging past use of violence. Admitting being wrong. Communicating openly and truthfully.

NONVIOLENCE

Developed from the Duluth Domestic Abuse Intervention Project, 202 East Superior Street, Duluth, MN 55802, www.theduluthmodel.org, 218-722-2781. Produced and distributed by National Center on Domestic and Sexual Violence, www.ncdsv.org, Austin, Texas.

The most recent statistic is that one out of every three girls in a dating relationship is being abused emotionally, physically, and/or sexually (Bonomi et al. 2013). Provide the girls/young women with the following warning signs of abuse (suitable for their age group) (this is also in appendix 4):

continued

ADAPTING THE SESSION FOR USE WITH GIRLS

Ten Warning Signs of Abuse

1. Checking your cell phone or email without permission
2. Continually putting you down
3. Extreme jealousy or insecurity
4. Explosive temper
5. Isolating you from family or friends

6. Making false accusations
7. Mood swings
8. Physically hurting you in any way
9. Possessiveness
10. Telling you what to do

If you need help with dating abuse, contact the National Teen Dating Abuse Helpline:

www.loveisrespect.org   Call: 1-866-331-9474

Chat: 24/7/365   Text: love is to 22522

"The Signs" presented by Center for Nonprofit Leadership at Adelphia University, School of Social Work and produced by Digital Bodega. Reprinted with permission. Available online at https://vimeo.com/85676862.

Also talk to the girls about the types of abuse girls do to one another or experience in their relationships:

- *Intimidation:* bullying; making her afraid by using looks, actions, and gestures
- *Emotional abuse:* calling her names, being mean, making her feel bad about herself
- *Isolation:* controlling what she does, who she sees, and whom she talks to
- *Minimizing, denying, etc.:* making light of the abuse, saying the abuse didn't happen, shifting responsibility for abusive behavior

continued

ADAPTING THE SESSION FOR USE WITH GIRLS

- *Using children:* making her feel guilty about her children, threatening to take children away

- *Using privilege:* not letting her make her own decisions

- *Economic abuse:* taking her money

- *Coercion and threats:* pressuring her to use drugs or have sex

It's important to complete the Local Resources sheets with information about agencies that provide services to girls and young women. You can find the adapted page that says "Local Resources for Girls in Abusive Relationships" (instead of women) in appendix 4.

MODULE A: SESSION 4

The Process of Trauma and Reactions to Trauma

▥ Time

Two hours

▥ Goal of the Session

To understand different types of abuse, the process of trauma, and common reactions to trauma.

▥ Participant Objectives

By the end of the session, participants will be able to:

1. Identify the different types of interpersonal abuse (emotional, physical, and sexual)

2. Explain the process of trauma

3. Describe the biological nature of reactions to trauma

4. Identify the responses associated with trauma

▥ Materials Needed

- Relaxing music and equipment to play music
- Each participant's and the facilitator's workbook
- A pencil or pen for the facilitator and each woman
- A newsprint flip-chart pad, an easel, and felt-tip pens
- Masking tape
- Three sheets of blank paper for each woman
- Small bottles of bubble soap (one bottle for every two women)
- A bubble wand for each woman
- A small brown paper lunch bag with various items in it for each woman
- *Optional: A DVD player and monitor, Segment 5: The Process of Trauma from the* Beyond Trauma *Participant Video, and Segment 6: The Effects of Trauma on the Brain from the* Beyond Trauma *Participant Video*
- Facial tissues

continued

Duplicating this page is illegal. Do not copy this material without written permission from the publisher.

177

THE PROCESS OF TRAUMA AND REACTIONS TO TRAUMA

■ **Session Overview**

- Quiet Time
- Check-In
- Review of Between-Sessions Activity
- Goal of the Session
- Activity: Types of Abuse
- *Optional:* Beyond Trauma *Participant Video (Segment 5: The Process of Trauma)*
- Lecture: The Process of Trauma
- Activity: Listing Calming Strategies
- Activity: Mindful Breathing
- Lecture: Responses Associated with Trauma
- Activity: Slowed Exhalation
- Lecture and Discussion: The Effects of Trauma on the Brain
- *Optional:* Beyond Trauma *Participant Video (Segment 6: The Effects of Trauma on the Brain)*
- Activities: Reconnection with the Body
- Reflection
- Between-Sessions Activity
- Closing

continued

THE PROCESS OF TRAUMA AND REACTIONS TO TRAUMA

Background Information for the Facilitator

Session Content

The content in this session may be difficult for some of the women. Be aware of your group members and suggest grounding activities for anyone who becomes distressed. Also assist anyone who becomes dissociated to come back into the present (using the Five Senses activity often is helpful).

Preparing for the Lecture on the Process of Trauma

You have the option of delivering the lecture on the Process of Trauma yourself (based on the provided chart) or using the *Beyond Trauma* Participant Video (Segment 5: The Process of Trauma) to present it. You could also have the group read the information aloud together from pages 42–45 in the workbook.

Preparing for the Slowed Exhalation Activity

Remember to obtain containers of bubble soap (one for each duo) and wands (one for each woman in the group) before the session. Small individual bubble containers with wands are inexpensive and readily available at some dollar stores, party stores, and online.

Preparing for the Lecture on the Effects of Trauma on the Brain

You have the option of delivering the lecture yourself or using the *Beyond Trauma* Participant Video (Segment 6: The Effects of Trauma on the Brain) to present it.

Preparing for the Texture and Sensation Activity

It may take some time, prior to the session, to gather the items to put into the bags for this activity (one bag per woman; a brown paper lunch bag is preferred). These items should be of various textures that feel different from one another (for example, a small stone, a feather, a piece of velvet or satin, a piece of fur, something made of plastic, something made of smooth metal, and sandpaper), and/or they can be items with strong, distinct odors (for example, a piece of lemon peel, a garlic clove, or a rose petal).

The Session

TIME & TOPIC	FACILITATOR NOTES	DISCUSSION WITH WOMEN
2 min. **Quiet Time**	*Begin playing the soft music.* *Call time after a minute or so and ask the women to redirect their attention to the group.*	Welcome to session 4 of *Beyond Trauma: A Healing Journey for Women*. We'll start with our quiet time to help us calm our minds and bodies, turn our attention away from what's going on outside this room, and focus on this group. Some of you may find you can relax by sitting still and focusing on your breathing. For others, standing up and slowly walking may be the best way to focus your attention here in this room. Some people find that "tapping" helps them focus on the present moment. You may want to try this. With your fingertips, tap on the top of your head, then on your forehead, and then on your cheeks. Then cross your arms and tap on your shoulders. Another thing that works for some people is to find a focal point in the room and just look at it for the next few minutes. Whichever technique you choose, let's be quiet now and bring our attention to the present, here in this room.
5 min. **Check-In**	*Allow participants to briefly respond. Keep this check-in short.*	How is everyone doing today?

TIME & TOPIC	FACILITATOR NOTES	DISCUSSION WITH WOMEN
5–10 min. **Review of Between-Sessions Activity**	*Post the Power and Control Wheel (from session 3) where all the women can see it.* *Allow participants to share their thoughts. Also allow people to pass if they don't want to share.*	In the last session, we talked about power and control and their connection to abuse. In your workbooks, you filled in sections of the Power and Control Wheel. What were your realizations from studying the Power and Control Wheel? What are some of the additional things you added? Who'd like to share first?
1 min. **Goal of the Session**		The goal for this session is to learn about the different types of abuse (one form of trauma), the process of trauma, and some common reactions to trauma.
15 min. **Activity: Types of Abuse**	*Distribute three pieces of paper to each woman and make sure all the women have a pencil or pen. Direct the women in the group to form duos (groups of two). Ask each duo to identify various examples of emotional abuse, physical abuse, and sexual abuse. They should each write examples of each type of abuse on a separate piece of paper. Allow four to five minutes for duos to complete this activity.* *Call time. Ask the duos to report their answers. Write their responses on the flip-chart pad. The following information is for you to add to their descriptions if any of it is not covered.*	One of the greatest risks for women is the abuse and violence that happens in relationships. We have been looking at the Power and Control Wheel, and each of you has given examples of various forms of abuse. Let's look more specifically at emotional, physical, and sexual abuse. As we know, these are common in many women's lives.

TIME & TOPIC	FACILITATOR NOTES	DISCUSSION WITH WOMEN
	1. Emotional abuse includes: *– name-calling* *– continual criticism* *– withholding approval or affection as punishment* *– using silence as punishment* *– isolating (depriving someone of access to family members, children, or friends)* *– depriving someone of money needed for necessities* *– humiliating someone publicly or privately* *– playing "mind games"* *– trying to coerce someone to do something she doesn't want to do* *– blaming* *– belittling* *– embarrassing* *– breaking promises* *– being inconsistent or unpredictable* *– threatening* *– threatening or abusing children or pets* *– manipulating by using children* *– deliberately intimidating* *– breaking things*	

TIME & TOPIC	FACILITATOR NOTES	DISCUSSION WITH WOMEN
	2. Physical abuse *includes:* – *pushing* – *shaking* – *spitting* – *slapping* – *kicking* – *biting* – *pinching* – *choking* – *burning* – *restraining (such as holding someone down or pinning the person's arms)* – *locking someone out of the house* – *threatening with a weapon* – *shooting, stabbing, tasing, or using another type of weapon on someone* – *harassing someone to the point of physical illness* – *depriving someone of sleep or food* – *leaving someone alone or withholding treatment or medication when she is sick* – *deliberately giving someone a sexually transmitted disease*	

TIME & TOPIC	FACILITATOR NOTES	DISCUSSION WITH WOMEN

	3. Sexual abuse includes:
	
	    – rape
	
	    – coercion (such as forced participation in acts that a person objects to)
	
	    – unwanted sexual photographing or recording
	
	    – unwanted or inappropriate touching
	
	    – sexual harassment (including unwanted sexual comments)
	
	    – demanding sex after a beating or an illness
	
	    – sexual criticism
	
	    – forcing sex in front of others
	
	    – treating others as sex objects
	
	    – nonconsensual sadistic sexual acts.
	
	When the lists are complete, thank the women for participating. Discuss any participant's questions.
		Does anyone have any questions?
		
		Each of you has a choice about what to do with your lists. You may want to get rid of them, so they don't remind you of things in your past. Or you may want to add to the lists in your workbook on pages 41 and 42.

10 min. Optional: **Beyond Trauma Participant Video** Segment 5	**Segment 5: The Process of Trauma** *Rather than deliver the lecture on the Process of Trauma yourself (on page 186), you may choose to show segment 5 of the video to present it.*	Let's look at a video segment now that talks about the process of trauma.

TIME & TOPIC	FACILITATOR NOTES	DISCUSSION WITH WOMEN
30 min. **Lecture: The Process of Trauma**	*While you are presenting this information, have the women follow along by looking at The Process of Trauma chart on page 43 in their workbooks.*	We talked about trauma in our earlier sessions. Please turn to page 43 in the workbook. You will see a diagram titled The Process of Trauma. This illustration shows how the events in our lives affect our emotional, psychological, and physical selves and our behaviors. It also reminds us of the relationships between how we think, feel, and behave and our physical and mental health. Let's go through the process step by step. As you know, trauma results from an experience that overwhelms a person's normal coping abilities. The first response a person has when threatened or frightened is to either fight, run away, or freeze. The brain sends a signal to the body to be on alert. There is an increase in heart rate, an increase in blood pressure and muscle tension, dilation of the eyes, shallow breathing, flushed skin, tunnel vision, and a flow of adrenaline—the release of certain chemicals from the brain into the body. These reactions are called the *fight-or-flight* response. Freezing is when a person becomes immobile. Think of what happens when a deer is caught in your headlights on the road at night. At the point of greatest danger, it freezes. Opossums also play dead to avoid getting hurt. Sometimes the best response to prevent further harm is to freeze. Then there are other physical and psychological reactions, including altered states of consciousness, bodily sensations, numbing, hypervigilance, hyperarousal, and collapse. *Altered consciousness* is often experienced as being in a daze. Some *body sensations* are tingling or getting hot or cold. *Numbing* can happen physically in the body and also

The Process of Trauma

Traumatic Event

Overwhelms our physical and psychological coping skills

Response to Trauma

Fight, flight, or freeze

Altered state of consciousness, Body sensations, Numbing

Hypervigilance, Hyperarousal, Collapse

Sensitized Nervous System
Changes in the Brain
Brain-Body Connection

Psychological and Physical Distress

Current stressors, Reminders of trauma (triggers)

Sensations, Images, Behavior, Affect (emotions), Memory

Emotional and/or Physical Responses

Retreat	Harmful Behavior to Self	Harmful Behavior to Others	Physical Health Issues
Isolation	Substance use disorders	Aggression	Lung disease
Dissociation	Eating disorders	Violence	Heart disease
Depression	Deliberate self-harm	Rages	Autoimmune disorders
Anxiety	Suicidal actions	Threats	Obesity

Trigger list adapted from *In an Unspoken Voice: How the Body Releases Trauma and Restores Goodness*
by Peter Levine (Berkeley, CA: North Atlantic Books, 2010).

TIME & TOPIC	FACILITATOR NOTES	DISCUSSION WITH WOMEN
		in feeling mentally numb. *Hypervigilance* is always scanning the environment; feeling a sense of constant threat, like living in a war zone; and always being on guard. *Hyperarousal* is one of the most common reactions to trauma. Hyperarousal is when the body is agitated and you feel like you are on edge. Some women have difficulty breathing (such as panting or shallow, rapid breaths), an increased heart rate, cold sweats, tense muscles, racing thoughts, and worry. The blood vessels in the skin, arms, legs, and internal organs may constrict and cause your muscles to tense. Sometimes a person experiences both hyperarousal and freezing, and a feeling of overwhelming helplessness and powerlessness results. Peter Levine, a well-known expert in the field of trauma, says that if hyperarousal is the nervous system's accelerator, immobility is its brake (Levine 1997). The body feels truly paralyzed. Remember, these are things that happen when the body is overwhelmed. All of these are normal responses to abnormal or extreme situations. The person's nervous system then becomes sensitized and is vulnerable to any future stressors. Stress is the body's alarm system. When stress occurs too often or for too long, it creates wear and tear on the body. Some stressors are routine or normal, and others can be overwhelming and toxic, creating traumatic stress. A woman may experience triggers in her current life by reminders of the traumatic event that happened in the past. These triggers may come from physical sensations in the body, images, behavior that she does or someone else does, feelings and emotional responses to situations,

TIME & TOPIC	FACILITATOR NOTES	DISCUSSION WITH WOMEN
		and memories of the traumatic experience. There may be nightmares and flashbacks to the earlier experience. This creates a painful emotional state and subsequent emotional and/or physical responses. Trauma can also cause changes in a person's brain chemistry and how the brain functions. The human brain is the most complex organ in the body and is the center of all human activity. Your brain is a communications center consisting of billions of neurons, or nerve cells. Different parts of the brain are responsible for coordinating and performing different functions. It coordinates and regulates everything you think, feel, and do. The brain's functions enable you to move, breathe, talk, eat, drive a car, create or enjoy art, and engage in everyday activities. Your brain enables you to interpret and respond to everything you experience. Your brain can also influence how your body works and can affect your physical health. People who are under stress often process and organize information differently. For example, physical, emotional, or sexual abuse can set off a series of physical changes that alter the structure and functioning of a child's brain in order for it to cope with a dangerous world. Flashbacks (including fear and terror) and confusion (such as racing or jumbled thoughts) both may stem from the effect of trauma on the brain. Many women talk about frightening thoughts "invading" their minds, sometimes after something triggers memories of traumatic events. Some victims of trauma have nightmares or "night terrors," from which they wake up screaming and sweating, even though they can't remember their dreams.

TIME & TOPIC	FACILITATOR NOTES	DISCUSSION WITH WOMEN
		This can create a feeling that they're never safe. Sometimes these things make a person feel like she's going crazy or losing control of her mind. Remember the discussion of pathways in the brain in session 1? Once there is a path, it's easier to move forward if you keep to the path. When there's a traumatic experience, particularly one that occurs more than once, a pathway is made in the brain. Then, if you experience a trigger that reminds you of the event, you may react in the same way because of the existing pathway. Triggers can activate the nervous system. Some women shut down, and others become anxious. Our bodies also respond to the ways in which we think, feel, and act. This is called the *brain-body connection*. When a person is stressed, anxious, or upset, her body may try to tell her that something isn't right. The body can do this with aches, pains, and even symptoms of illness. If feelings of stress, sadness, or anxiety are causing physical problems, keeping the feelings inside can make things even worse. This is why it's important to create some new pathways by doing grounding and self-soothing activities to counteract the triggers. As in learning a new sport, it'll take practice, and it isn't likely to happen in just a few sessions of this program. But these sessions are the beginning of your healing journey. The fourth section in the Process of Trauma chart mentions current stressors. These can be from life events, such as being arrested; from one's lifestyle, such as living on the streets or using; and from triggers.

TIME & TOPIC	FACILITATOR NOTES	DISCUSSION WITH WOMEN
		Now let's examine the emotional and physical responses to trauma. The stress of trauma can cause a person to exhibit behaviors that are adaptations to the stress. These include retreat, harmful behavior to the self, harmful behavior to others, and physical health issues. Retreat responses include isolation, dissociation, depression, and anxiety. Isolation is different from making time to be alone and quiet. Although we all need some alone time, isolation occurs when a woman keeps to herself, avoids interacting with others, and may not even make eye contact with people. In group settings, she'll rarely share her feelings or experiences. She has shut herself off from others. Dissociation is a split between the mind and the body. It occurs when your mind disconnects from the event or physical reality of what is happening. It can be experienced as physical or psychological numbing. It can be experienced as losing time. It also can include loss of memory. Women who have experienced trauma, particularly in childhood, often learn how to separate themselves from the distress. When they dissociate, they seem to watch from a distance in order to not have to be part of the experience. They may feel lost, overwhelmed, abandoned, and disconnected from the world. They may feel they're unloved, empty, helpless, trapped, and weighted down. Dissociation as a defense mechanism is very useful when a person is being abused, but it doesn't help a person function in the real world. The grounding and self-soothing techniques you learn in this

TIME & TOPIC	FACILITATOR NOTES	DISCUSSION WITH WOMEN
		program can help you manage your stress and your triggers and help you stay in the present so you don't lose yourself.

Denial is like dissociation, only not as severe. A woman ignores or fails to acknowledge the abuse and its related feelings, or acts as though they aren't important. Dissociation and denial are psychological responses that act as coping mechanisms. Sometimes it may seem as if a woman is denying her abuse when actually she isn't sure she has been abused.

The third retreat response is depression. It is diagnosed twice as often in women as in men and is one of the most common illnesses among women in the United States. When women turn their anger inward, they're at risk of becoming depressed. Some people say that depression is another face of anger. Depression is a condition of feeling persistently sad, having difficulty sleeping and having little energy, experiencing the loss of hope or joy, having trouble concentrating, experiencing changes in appetite, and/or having frequent thoughts of suicide. The symptoms are present for at least two weeks (usually longer). When someone has severe, chronic depression, she may feel that death is the only solution to the pain. If you're experiencing some of these feelings or have any thoughts about suicide, please come and talk with me after the session.

Depression is different from grief. Grief occurs naturally as a result of loss. Grief can also be traumatic when the loss comes from a traumatic event. |

TIME & TOPIC	FACILITATOR NOTES	DISCUSSION WITH WOMEN
		Another retreat response is anxiety. Women are two to three times more likely to experience anxiety disorders than men. The most common anxiety disorders for women are panic and phobia (which means intense fear). Another common trauma- and stress-related diagnosis for women is posttraumatic stress disorder, or PTSD. Some of the symptoms of PTSD (American Psychiatric Association 2013) are:

• *intrusive symptoms,* such as nightmares, flashbacks, and intense or prolonged distress

• *avoidance symptoms,* such as isolation and disconnection from others; emotional numbness; and avoiding people, places, and situations that are triggers or reminders

• *negative emotions and thoughts,* such as blaming, excessive negativity, fear, anger, shame, and diminished interests

• *arousal and reactivity,* such as angry outbursts, reckless and dangerous behaviors, hypervigilance, difficulty sleeping, and an increased startle response

Other behaviors that result from trauma are harmful behaviors to oneself and harmful behaviors to others. Harmful behaviors to oneself include alcohol and other drug abuse; eating disorders; cutting, burning, and other self-injury; and suicidal actions. Women are more likely to turn their feelings inward and retreat or hurt themselves, while men are more likely to engage in aggression and violence as well as to be self-destructive in response to trauma. Women often turn their feelings inward, and men often turn their feelings outward toward |

Duplicating this page is illegal. Do not copy this material without written permission from the publisher.

193

TIME & TOPIC	FACILITATOR NOTES	DISCUSSION WITH WOMEN
		others. However, some women's responses to trauma are aggression and violence, including rages and threats. There is another program for women by Stephanie Covington that deals with these issues more directly; it's called *Beyond Anger and Violence: A Program for Women.*
		In summary, trauma can affect a person in multiple ways. It can affect the inner self—the person's thoughts, feelings, beliefs, and values. It can also affect the outer self—the person's behavior. This, in turn, can affect her relationships. Many people who've experienced trauma struggle with their relationships with their family members, friends, and sexual partners. As the chart shows, trauma also affects the body, and many people who are trauma survivors struggle with physical health problems. We will learn more about this later in this program.
	Allow participants to discuss the following questions. People can choose not to share if they don't want to.	
		What is your response to seeing and hearing about this chart? Is there something new you have learned about yourself? Or maybe you have a better understanding of the connection of things in your life. Who will share first?
	Have participants answer this question by writing their answers in their workbooks on page 45. If the women are comfortable, they could then share from their list. Don't force anyone to share.	Have you experienced any of these symptoms of trauma?

TIME & TOPIC	FACILITATOR NOTES	DISCUSSION WITH WOMEN
5 min. **Activity: Listing Calming Strategies**	*Write the techniques that the women identify on the flip-chart pad as they call them out. Then have the women turn to page 46 in their workbooks to see a list of calming strategies. Ask them to identify any from this list that they have used or could use. Have them place an X next to those activities. The list includes* • *reading a book* • *listening to music* • *dancing* • *pacing* • *hugging a stuffed animal or toy* • *coloring* • *taking a bubble bath* • *deep breathing* • *exercising* • *writing in a journal* • *doing a craft or creative activity* • *eating* • *taking a shower* • *doing yoga or tai chi* • *watching television* • *talking to friends or relatives* • *going for a walk in a garden or park* *Allow the women a few minutes to write the other ideas generated by the group in their workbooks on page 46. That way, they have these ideas with them when they leave.*	If we've experienced trauma, we need a toolbox filled with techniques for calming, soothing, and grounding ourselves, especially if we experience triggers. These are things that help relax us and keep us in the present moment. Not all calming strategies are exercises such as deep breathing or the Five Senses activity. There are many things you can do to calm and soothe yourself. Some of them work better for different people. Now let's make a list of simple, basic ways to calm and ground ourselves. Just call out your ideas.

TIME & TOPIC	FACILITATOR NOTES	DISCUSSION WITH WOMEN
5 min. **Activity: Mindful Breathing**	*Read the following slowly.* *Allow several participants to respond. Some people may choose not to share. Show the women that this exercise is in their workbook on page 47. They can use these directions to use this exercise outside of group or at home.*	Now we're going to do a calming activity called Mindful Breathing. 1. Slowly take a breath in through your nose. Notice how the breath moves into your lungs and how it feels in your belly, ribs, chest, and shoulders. Notice your belly filling up like a balloon. 2. Exhale slowly. Let the breath move out of your lungs slowly, like a balloon losing air, until they're empty. 3. Repeat this three times. When you are mindful of your breathing, you can notice whether it's smooth or uneven or barely there. When we pay attention to our breathing, our minds become calmer. Let's do this again for three breaths, while each of you just notices your body's reactions. Who is willing to share her experience with mindful breathing?
5 min. **Lecture: Responses Associated with Trauma**		Now let's continue to look at what can happen if a woman is traumatized by abuse. Traumatic reactions that are experienced both in the inner self—a person's thoughts, feelings, beliefs, and values—and the outer self—a person's relationships and behaviors—are normal responses to abnormal or extreme situations. People respond to danger and threats in a variety of ways:

TIME & TOPIC	FACILITATOR NOTES	DISCUSSION WITH WOMEN
		instinctively, physically, and psychologically. For example, if a woman is overwhelmed by a threat and unable to fight, flee, or faint, she may instinctively freeze. Or perhaps her nervous system is highly aroused and her consciousness seems to leave her body, as with dissociation. Let's talk more specifically about some of the responses associated with trauma. Some responses show up immediately following a traumatic event, and some show up later. Please turn to page 47 in the workbook. Let's go around the group and read the list of typical early responses. Who will volunteer to start?

TYPICAL EARLY RESPONSES TO TRAUMA

- ☐ Disturbed sleep and/or nightmares
- ☐ Exaggerated emotional and startled reactions to noises, quick movements, etc.
- ☐ Restlessness
- ☐ Hyperactivity
- ☐ Hypervigilance
- ☐ Fear of losing control
- ☐ Abrupt mood swings
- ☐ Flashbacks
- ☐ Sensitivity to sound, light, smell, taste, and touch
- ☐ Fear of going crazy
- ☐ Desire for alcohol or other drugs

As mentioned earlier, PTSD is a way of describing a cluster of symptoms. It is a diagnosis often given to survivors of trauma who begin to experience many of these responses a month or more after the traumatic event.

TIME & TOPIC	FACILITATOR NOTES	DISCUSSION WITH WOMEN
		There also are responses that typically take longer to develop. These are listed on page 48 in the workbook. Who will volunteer to start reading these?

TYPICAL LATER RESPONSES TO TRAUMA

☐ Panic attacks, anxiety, and phobias

☐ Mental blankness or being "spacey"

☐ Avoidance behaviors (avoidance of people, places, and things that are reminders of the traumatic event; isolating oneself from people; avoiding talking to others)

☐ Attraction to dangerous situations

☐ Frequent anger or crying

☐ Exaggerated or diminished sexual activity

☐ Amnesia and forgetfulness

☐ Diminished emotional responses

☐ Inability to love, nurture, or bond with other individuals

☐ Fear of dying or having a shortened life

☐ Self-harming behavior

☐ Cravings (particularly if the person has a substance use disorder)

☐ Fatigue or low energy

☐ Physical health problems, such as a depleted immune system or thyroid dysfunction

☐ Other illnesses, such as neck and back problems, asthma, digestive distress, spastic colon, and severe premenstrual syndrome

☐ Eating disorders

☐ Inability to make commitments

☐ Depression

☐ Feelings of isolation, detachment

☐ Reduced ability to make decisions, formulate plans, and carry them out

TIME & TOPIC	FACILITATOR NOTES	DISCUSSION WITH WOMEN
	Allow the women a few minutes to look at these lists in their workbooks and identify any responses they've experienced. Have them place a check mark next to these responses. If they feel comfortable sharing, ask people to share examples from their list. Don't force anyone to share.	It is important to listen to our bodies and to understand how one or more of these responses show the effect that trauma has had on our lives.
5 min. **Activity: Slowed Exhalation**	*Ask the women to form duos. Distribute a bubble wand to each woman and have each duo share a bottle of bubble solution.* *Pace the instructions to the rate of breathing you desire.* *Have the women repeat the breathing and blowing five to ten times.*	Now let's do another mindful-breathing activity. One way to become more aware of our breathing is to slow down when we exhale our breaths. First, we'll breathe in deeply and exhale. With the next breath, we'll blow a bubble as we exhale. You can dip your bubble wand into the solution as you breathe in. Each time you exhale, try to slow down your outgoing breath and blow an even longer bubble. Let's try it. 1. First, breathe in deeply and then exhale. 2. Now dip your wand into the bubble solution, breathe in, and blow a bubble as you exhale. 3. Keep going, but try to slow down your exhalation each time. Blow longer bubbles each time. 4. Focus your breathing as you inhale and exhale. Most of us breathe too shallowly. This exercise is a way to learn how to slow down your breath to about six breaths per minute. Learning how to breathe deeply and mindfully helps you to be physically relaxed and is an essential tool for recovery from trauma.

TIME & TOPIC	FACILITATOR NOTES	DISCUSSION WITH WOMEN
10 min. **Lecture and Discussion: The Effects of Trauma on the Brain**		Now we're going to discuss the effects of trauma on the brain. We've already talked about the human brain being the center of all human activity. Our brains enable us to interpret and respond to everything we experience. We know trauma affects how the brain functions and that the stress of trauma can result in brain changes. People under stress often process and organize information differently. Trauma can cause a person to exhibit various behaviors that are adaptations to stress. In our last session, we discussed things such as dissociation, flashbacks, and nightmares. Confusion, such as racing or jumbled thoughts, also may stem from the effects of trauma on the brain. Some women feel angry a lot of the time. Many women think they're crazy and don't realize that what's going on in their brains may be the result of earlier trauma. I wonder if any of you have experienced some of these effects of trauma. What was this like for you? Did you understand what was happening?
	Allow the women to spend a few minutes writing their thoughts in the workbook on page 50. Then ask if anyone would like to share their thoughts with the group. Help the women describe and share their responses but don't speak for them. Allow people to pass if they don't feel comfortable sharing.	Today we understand that one of the first steps in the healing process is sharing one's story and having other people listen who can understand and show empathy. Many children who are abused don't get this experience, and then their traumatic experiences and their feelings get buried. Later in life, there's the risk of having these things come to the surface stronger and more confusing than they may have been years ago.

TIME & TOPIC	FACILITATOR NOTES	DISCUSSION WITH WOMEN
10 min. Optional: **_Beyond Trauma_ Participant Video** Segment 6	**Segment 6: The Effects of Trauma on the Brain** _Rather than deliver the next lecture yourself, play the video segment._	Let's watch a video segment that discusses the effects of trauma on the brain.
		Research on the brain has shown that child abuse, one form of trauma, can cause serious damage to the structure and functioning of the developing brain. As mentioned earlier, physical, emotional, or sexual abuse or extreme neglect or any other form of toxic stress can set off a series of physical changes that alter a child's brain in order for it to cope with a dangerous world. Extreme stress can change the brain to cause a person to exhibit various antisocial behaviors. When trauma affects the brain, it can result in brain changes. Problems such as dissociation, flashbacks, and racing or jumbled thoughts, which we discussed earlier, may all stem from the effect of trauma on the brain. Fear from a traumatic event is experienced in the mind. Some people experience and re-experience these thoughts even though they don't want to have them and try not to have them. This can make them feel that they're not safe anywhere or that they're going crazy. Have any of you experienced this kind of thing?
	Allow the women to share, but if people choose to pass, let them.	

TIME & TOPIC	FACILITATOR NOTES	DISCUSSION WITH WOMEN
		Sometimes the information on the brain can be frightening because we are afraid we can't "fix it." However, one neuroscientist who studies the impact of trauma on the brain has developed the concept of SEEDS (Arden 2014). These are the five factors that can help heal the brain and help us all stay vital, productive, and happy for a lifetime:
		S—social connectivity—being in connection and relationship with others. **E**—exercise—thirty minutes a day can make a big difference. **E**—education—learn something new each day. **D**—diet—the food we eat either nourishes or starves our brain. **S**—sleep—our brains and our bodies need to rest and regenerate each day.
		These things can help you reduce your risk of having physical and mental health problems. Think about how to begin to plant these SEEDS in your life. What information about the brain has been useful or important to you?
	Discuss the women's responses to what they have learned. As you discuss this question, have women write their answers in the space provided on page 51 in their workbooks.	
	Discuss participants' responses. Typical responses are that others tell the women to "just put it all behind you" or "move on."	If you have told others that traumatic events have affected your lives, what have their reactions been?

TIME & TOPIC	FACILITATOR NOTES	DISCUSSION WITH WOMEN
		Trauma can also cause problems with addiction. Understanding that trauma can change brain chemistry—just as substance abuse can change brain chemistry—can help you see the connection between trauma and what's going on physically and emotionally.
20 min. total **Activities: Reconnection with the Body**		In this session, we've learned that dissociation and disconnection from the body are some reactions to trauma. Now we'll do two activities that'll allow you to explore your connection to your body. We'll learn ways to begin the reconnection—to help you learn to get better acquainted with what's happening in your body.
10 min. **Activity 1: Four Sensations**	*Remember, some women may need to keep their eyes open and just lower their eyelids.* *After about thirty seconds, ask the women to open their eyes.*	1. First, please close your eyes or lower your eyelids. 2. Then slowly touch your face, arm, or hand. Continue touching for the rest of this exercise. 3. Focus on the body part's temperature. Is it warm or cold? 4. Then focus on the pressure of your touch. Is it light or firm? 5. Now focus on the texture of your skin. Is it smooth or rough? 6. Finally, focus on the presence or absence of moisture. Is it absolutely dry or is there some moisture? 7. Just try to relax into the sensations that you are feeling.

TIME & TOPIC	FACILITATOR NOTES	DISCUSSION WITH WOMEN
	Then ask them the adjacent questions. Allow them a few minutes to write their answers in their workbooks on page 52 and then discuss their answers as a group.	1. What was your experience like of connecting with your body? 2. Was it difficult? 3. Was it easy? 4. What feelings did you have as you did this activity? You can also do this activity with your eyes open to help ground yourselves. The directions for this activity are in your workbook. Try to practice this exercise periodically, so it becomes easier for you to focus on the four basic sensations: temperature, pressure, texture, and moisture.
10 min. **Activity 2: Texture and Sensation**	*Have the women close their eyes. If any women need to keep their eyes open, ask them to look away from the bags you're going to give them. Give each woman a small brown paper lunch bag with a variety of objects in it that feel different from one another. With her eyes closed, have each woman open her bag and feel the objects inside. The idea is to be able to feel a variety of physical sensations (and perhaps detect a variety of smells).* *Have the women discuss the activity and describe what they felt.*	Both abuse and addiction can numb our bodies and our senses. This activity is about learning to feel different sensations. Without looking in your bag, spend a few minutes feeling (or even smelling) each item in your bag. 1. What was this experience like? 2. Could you sense all the different shapes and textures? What were they?

TIME & TOPIC	FACILITATOR NOTES	DISCUSSION WITH WOMEN
5–10 min. **Reflection**	*Allow participants to spend a minute or two writing some brief notes in the Reflection section of their workbook on page 53. Then ask the women to share their thoughts after they are done writing.*	Now let's reflect on what happened in our group today. What was the most meaningful or important part of today's session for you?
5 min. **Between-Sessions Activity**		As you know, trauma is very common in women's lives, and many women have experienced multiple traumatic events. Please turn to page 54 in the workbook. For your Between-Sessions Activity, you'll have an opportunity to look back at your history of trauma at different points in your life. You may want to practice one or more grounding techniques before and after you do this.

History of Trauma

	CHILD	ADOLESCENT	ADULT
A. Event(s)			
B. Life before the event(s)			
C. Life after the event(s)			
D. Overall impact of the event(s)			

TIME & TOPIC	FACILITATOR NOTES	DISCUSSION WITH WOMEN
		To complete your chart, pick three traumatic experiences: one from childhood, one from adolescence, and one from adulthood, if possible. (You can pick more than one if you want.) If not, just pick three events from any period in your life. In filling out your chart, remember, trauma can be many things, including physical, emotional, and sexual abuse. In the boxes, list each event, if you feel comfortable doing that. Then list how your life was before the event, how your life was after the event, and the overall impact of these traumas on your life. If you're questioning whether an event was traumatic, review the questions below that we discussed earlier. These are also listed on page 37 in your workbook, so you can follow along as I read them: 1. Was there full consent? 2. Was there an element of betrayal or loss of trust? 3. Have you ever feared for your physical safety in your relationship? 4. Have you felt afraid in other ways? 5. Have you ever been forced to do things against your will? 6. Have you ever been hit or threatened? 7. Have you ever been kicked or choked? 8. Have you ever sustained bodily injuries such as bruises, cuts, or broken bones? 9. Have your children been hit or threatened? 10. Was there violence, pain, restriction, force, or bodily harm? 11. Have you been verbally put down? 12. Have you been harassed, stalked, or monitored? 13. Did it feel like abuse to you?

TIME & TOPIC	FACILITATOR NOTES	DISCUSSION WITH WOMEN
		Although you won't be asked to share any specific events within the group, there's power in naming. We may think we can control our grief, our terror, or our shame by staying silent, but naming offers the possibility of a different kind of control. So if you don't want to share with the group, please consider talking to someone individually and naming the traumatic events in your past and present to yourself. If you don't want to write or do part A, just leave it out. Then focus on parts B, C, and D of the chart. That will be just fine. It's important to remember that any memories you visit are in the past. Any feelings you have are part of the process of healing, and right now you're safe. Charting the trauma you've faced in your life allows you to see the strength, resilience, and survival skills that have brought you to where you are today.

There is a list of calming strategies on page 46 of the workbook. Add any we discussed in the session that are not on that list. Then mark the ones you think will work best for you.

Please bring a couple of magazines with you to the next session. *(This will not be possible in residential or custodial settings.)* Old magazines are fine, as we're going to be taking things out of them. |

TIME & TOPIC	FACILITATOR NOTES	DISCUSSION WITH WOMEN
1 min. **Closing**		When you do the Between-Sessions Activities, be sure to use your grounding and calming techniques as you need them. I hope this session has given you more insight as to what constitutes trauma and the effects of trauma, such as the process of trauma and the responses associated with trauma. I'm impressed with your ability to explore these issues, and I look forward to seeing each of you at our next session, which will be *[give the date and time].*

Session Notes

ADAPTING THE SESSION FOR USE WITH GIRLS

All the content in this session needs some adaptation so it is relevant for this younger age group. In describing the Process of Trauma chart, you may want to adapt your wording to make it more relevant to the lives of girls. Also simplify the definitions and examples of the three different types of abuse and make these descriptions more relevant to the lives of the girls. When discussing the biological reactions to trauma, break these down and then ask questions such as, "What does that look like for you?" and "What have you experienced in the past?" When discussing the responses to trauma that take more time to develop, ask them if they've ever experienced any of them. How did this affect their relationships with boys and other girls?

In presenting the Between-Sessions Activity to girls, the history chart is adapted by removing the adult space, as shown. You can have this printed on 8 1/2 x 11-inch paper and distribute it to the girls to place in their workbooks. (This handout is in appendix 4.) This also will give them more space to write. Tell the girls they may also draw pictures, if they like.

History of Trauma		
	CHILD	ADOLESCENT
A. Event(s)		
B. Life before the event(s)		
C. Life after the event(s)		
D. Overall impact of the event(s)		

continued

ADAPTING THE SESSION FOR USE WITH GIRLS

The instructions can be amended as follows:

To complete your chart, pick two traumatic experiences: one from your child-hood and one from adolescence, if possible. If not, just pick any two from any period in your life. In filling out your chart, remember, trauma can be many things, including physical, emotional, and sexual abuse. In the boxes, list each event, how your life was before the event, how your life was after the event, and the overall impact of these traumas on your life. If it's too upset-ting to you to list the event, skip that and just work on the other sections. You can fill in what you remember from when you were younger or what you are currently experiencing at home or in this program. If you're questioning whether an event was traumatic, look back at page 37 in the workbook, to the questions to ask yourself that we discussed earlier:

1. Was there full consent?

2. Was there an element of betrayal or loss of trust?

3. Have you ever feared for your physical safety in your relationship?

4. Have you felt afraid in other ways?

5. Have you ever been forced to do things against your will?

6. Have you ever been hit or threatened?

7. Have you ever been kicked or choked?

8. Have you ever sustained bodily injuries, such as bruises, cuts, or broken bones?

9. Have your children been hit or threatened?

10. Was there violence, pain, restriction, force, or bodily harm?

11. Have you been verbally put down?

12. Have you been harassed, stalked, or monitored?

13. Did it feel like abuse to you?

continued

ADAPTING THE SESSION FOR USE WITH GIRLS

You may also want to explore the concept of consent with girls. Teens often take responsibility for what happens around them. For example, girls may say they gave consent when they said yes because it wasn't safe to say no.

You may also want to remind the girls of the warning signs of abuse from session 3 and the types of abuse girls do to one another or experience in their relationships (also from session 3).

The Impact of Trauma on Women's Lives

How Trauma Affects Our Lives

▓ Time

Two hours

▓ Goals of the Session

1. To increase understanding of the effects of trauma on physical health
2. To increase understanding of the effects of trauma on mental health

▓ Participant Objectives

At the end of this session, participants will be able to:

1. Describe how traumatic events affect women's lives
2. Define what a trigger is
3. Explain how trauma has affected their lives.

▓ Materials Needed

- Relaxing music and equipment to play music
- Each participant's and the facilitator's workbook
- A pencil or pen for the facilitator and each woman
- A newsprint flip-chart pad, an easel, and felt-tip pens
- Magazines for the collage activity
- A piece of poster board for each woman
- Colored felt-tip pens or crayons for each woman
- Enough glue sticks and scissors for two or three (maximum) women to share each set
- Masking tape
- Facial tissues

continued

Duplicating this page is illegal. Do not copy this material without written permission from the publisher.

215

HOW TRAUMA AFFECTS OUR LIVES

■ **Session Overview**

- Quiet Time
- Check-In
- Review of Between-Sessions Activity
- Goals of the Session
- Lecture: Trauma and Its Aftermath
- Lecture: Triggers
- Activity: Triggers and the Body
- Activity: Adverse Childhood Experiences Questionnaire
- Lecture: The Adverse Childhood Experiences Study
- Lecture: The Effects of Substance Use on the Brain
- Activity: Collage of the Effect of Violence, Abuse, and Trauma on Your Life
- Reflection
- Between-Sessions Activity
- Activity: Yoga Pose
- *Optional Activity: Palms Down, Palms Up*
- Closing

continued

HOW TRAUMA AFFECTS OUR LIVES

Background Information for the Facilitator

The Impact of Trauma Module

If any women become upset while discussing this topic, you can offer to talk to them individually after the session or ask if they want to speak to another counselor. Explain that there are ways that women can heal from trauma by acknowledging it, talking and writing about it, and developing coping skills for symptom management, such as the grounding and self-soothing techniques they are learning.

Preparing for the Collage Activity

Most women find the collage activity to be fun and playful, and some are able to express things they cannot put into words. However, some women may feel unskilled at crafts and may complain about being asked to make a collage. Explain to them that different people express themselves in different ways and that this is a chance for the more visual people to use their most comfortable form of expression. Watch and listen as the women create their collages. What does each woman's collage tell you about her? Where does she reflect shame, fear, anger, and so on? Avoid preconceptions about the "right" way to do a collage. Some women may use no words—only colors and shapes. A rape victim, for instance, probably won't want to spell out the words the rapist used when assaulting her. Note that even though the directions are to create a collage about the impact of trauma on one's life, it's not unusual for some women to use their collages as ways to share about the traumatic events in their lives.

Provide at least one magazine for each woman in the group. In community settings, the women may be able to bring in magazines (as requested as part of the Between-Sessions Activity in session 4), but they may not all remember or be able to do so, so plan for that. In residential and correctional settings, you probably will have to supply all the magazines yourself. It's very important that the group members are able to find women from their ethnic backgrounds in the magazine pictures. For example, you may want to include *Essence* and

continued

Duplicating this page is illegal. Do not copy this material without written permission from the publisher.

217

HOW TRAUMA AFFECTS OUR LIVES

O, the Oprah Magazine when working with African American women and *Latina* and *Siempre Mujer* magazines when working with Latinas. You can also ask the women what magazines they like and plan to get those ahead of time for collage work. These don't have to be current magazines; anything up to five years old should work.

If possible, have enough felt-tip pens or crayons, glue sticks, and scissors so all the women can work on their individual collages without having to wait for materials to use. In a correctional setting, where scissors are prohibited, the women can tear the pictures and phrases out of their magazines rather than cutting them out.

Preparing for the Between-Sessions Activity

Optional: You'll want to remind participants to choose a childhood photo of themselves when they were between the ages of three and ten to bring to the next session. You should plan to bring a photo as well.

Yoga Pose

We highly recommend teaching the Breath of Joy yoga pose as the concluding activity, rather than the Palms Down, Palms Up activity. You may want to review the brief discussion on page 78 of chapter 2 about the mind-body connection and the value of doing yoga poses. There are four poses presented in the program (in this session and in sessions 6, 10, and 11). Appendix 2 contains instructions and illustrations for all the yoga poses. These yoga poses were selected because they are easy to teach and do. Also, the women can do the poses on their own, even in small living spaces.

The Session

TIME & TOPIC	FACILITATOR NOTES	DISCUSSION WITH WOMEN
2 min. **Quiet Time**	*Begin playing the soft music.* *After one and a half to two minutes, ask the women to take a deep breath and focus on the group.*	Welcome to session 5 of *Beyond Trauma: A Healing Journey for Women.* Let's just settle in for a few minutes. You may want to sit silently in order to let yourself unwind and relax. You may want to focus on your breathing. Some of you may prefer to stand and slowly walk around the room. Some of you may want to do tapping on the top of your head, your forehead, your cheeks, and your shoulders. Or you may want to find a focal point in the room and just look at it for the next minute or so. Let's begin our quiet time.
5 min. **Check-In**	 *Allow participants to briefly answer these questions. If people want to pass, let them. If a woman expresses distress or strong feelings, you may want to talk with her individually after the session.*	Again, welcome to session 5. In our last session, we discussed the process of trauma and the importance of using calming techniques. In this session, we'll be learning more about the effects of trauma on our physical and mental health. First, let's check in. What have you been thinking about as a result of the last session? Have your thoughts about these things generated any particular feelings?

TIME & TOPIC	FACILITATOR NOTES	DISCUSSION WITH WOMEN
10–15 min. **Review of Between-Sessions Activity**	*Allow participants to briefly share.*	I'd like to hear about the calming strategies on your lists. Who will volunteer to share two or three strategies on her list first? These are on page 46 in your workbook. Now please turn to page 54 in the workbook. For one of your Between-Sessions Activities, you looked back at your history of trauma at different points in your life and picked three traumatic experiences: one from childhood, one from adolescence, and one from adulthood, if possible. Then you filled out your chart, listing each event, how your life was before the event, how your life was after the event, and the overall impact of these traumas on your life. It's important to remember that what you listed is in the past. Any feelings you had about doing this are part of the process of healing, and right now you're safe. There's no requirement to share any of your chart with the group, but would anyone like to share what you found when you thought about life before the trauma and then after the trauma? What do you think the overall effect has been on your life? We have about a minute or so for each of you to share, if you want to.
1 min. **Goals of the Session**		Our goals for this session are: 1. To increase understanding of the effects of trauma on physical health 2. To increase understanding of the effects of trauma on mental health

TIME & TOPIC	FACILITATOR NOTES	DISCUSSION WITH WOMEN
10–15 min. **Lecture: Trauma and Its Aftermath**		Experiencing trauma can affect many parts of a woman's life. Many women re-experience the traumatic incidents in their thoughts and dreams. These re-experienced traumas can be so intense that it feels as though the events are happening all over again. When this occurs, many women say they feel they're "losing control" of their lives. They may find it hard to concentrate and keep their minds on tasks or activities—even something as simple as watching television. This often can add to feeling out of control. A woman's self-image may change after a traumatic incident. She may find she neglects herself and feels worthless. She may feel labeled or tarnished in some way. This may be particularly true if there was public knowledge of the event and little support for her. Some women experience depression, feelings of isolation, and sadness. A woman may find she cries often for no apparent reason, she feels she cannot or should not have fun anymore, she has lost interest in many things, and she has no energy. Getting out of bed in the morning may feel like a chore. It's also not unusual for a woman's relationships to be disrupted. She may find, along with being depressed, that she withdraws from others, even though support from friends or family members is particularly important at this time. Perhaps the most common reaction of women who have experienced trauma is that fear and anxiety become part of everyday life. If the cause of the trauma is still

TIME & TOPIC	FACILITATOR NOTES	DISCUSSION WITH WOMEN
	Ask the women if any of this sounds familiar. Ask if they, their friends, or their family members have had any of these experiences. Discuss them. *Have women read along with you on pages 59 and 60 in their workbooks.*	present, nearby, or at large, a woman may feel she's still in danger. She may feel jittery, overcautious, or unable to function in certain situations. For example, she may be afraid to leave her home, be alone, go to locations near where the traumatic event took place, be in situations that remind her of the event, or see people who had anything to do with the event—whether they were positively or negatively involved. Women's lives often become limited and constricted from fear of harm. In addition, their relationships may be affected. **Effects of Trauma on Relationships** There are some typical relationship problems that often result from trauma. These include: • idealizing or overvaluing relationships • fear of commitment • self-imposed isolation • triangulating with others (not being able to be alone as a couple; always having a third person there—a child, parent, roommate, etc.) • humiliating interactions (such as being "put down" or made fun of by one's partner in public) • involvement in abusive or criticizing relationships • difficulty trusting oneself or others with intimacy • tolerating patterns of abuse or excessive neediness • emotional and physical caretaking of others at the expense of the self

TIME & TOPIC	FACILITATOR NOTES	DISCUSSION WITH WOMEN
	Again, ask if any of this relates to the women's experiences or the experiences of friends or family members. *Suggest that if any of the women would like to read more about relationships, there is a book written by Dr. Stephanie Covington entitled* Leaving the Enchanted Forest: The Path from Relationship Addiction to Intimacy *(Covington and Beckett 1988).* *Continue to present this information or have the women take turns reading the adjacent information aloud, which appears on page 60 in their workbooks.*	In addition, some women are compelled to go back into risky situations. One theory for this is that there's a desire to master the situation in order to create a different outcome. **Effects of Trauma on Sexuality** A woman's sexuality also may be affected by trauma. This may be true whether or not the trauma involved sexual abuse. Some women lose interest in sex, while others engage in more sex than usual. Traumatic events, particularly sexual abuse, also can affect a woman's sexual relationships in the following ways: • fear of or avoidance of sex • approaching sex as an obligation • negative feelings about being touched • difficulty with arousal and sensation • vaginal pain • emotional distance during sex (such as spacing out) • disturbing sexual thoughts and images • compulsive or inappropriate sexual behavior • difficulty forming and maintaining intimate relationships

TIME & TOPIC	FACILITATOR NOTES	DISCUSSION WITH WOMEN
	Allow participants a few minutes to write about any relationship concerns in the space provided on page 60 of the workbook.	If you would like to read more about women and sexual healing, the author of our *Beyond Trauma* curriculum has written a book for women called *Awakening Your Sexuality: A Guide for Recovering Women* (Covington 2000a). All these things can interact with one another, which can cause the overall response to be even more intense. Remember that all these reactions to a traumatic event are normal. Learning more positive ways to cope with trauma is an important part of the healing journey.
2–3 min. **Lecture: Triggers**		We know some of our responses to trauma, such as the fight-or-flight response, are physical and automatic. The brain sends a signal to the body to be on alert: There's a flow of adrenaline, the heart rate and blood pressure increase, muscles tense, and the eyes dilate. Breathing may be affected, and the person may experience flushing and tunnel vision. During a traumatic event, a person may be so overwhelmed that she can't understand or process what's happening. The unprocessed, emotionally charged bits of trauma can be stored in her memory and in her body. Did you know that there's such a thing as physical memory? That's how you learn to do a repetitive task, such as typing or riding a bicycle. There can be physical memories of good things and bad things. Feelings, sights, smells, and sounds associated with an abusive incident may be remembered and remain very real to a woman weeks,

TIME & TOPIC	FACILITATOR NOTES	DISCUSSION WITH WOMEN
		months, or even years later. They may act as triggers that put her back into the traumatic experience. A trigger is an external or internal stimulus that sets off a physical or emotional reaction in a person. The stimulus can be a sound, another person, a place, a smell, a behavior—almost anything that consciously or subconsciously reminds the woman of the past trauma. If a woman is triggered by a stimulus, her body reacts as though it's reliving the traumatic events of the past. Triggers also are referred to as *threat clues*. This may help you understand why we've talked about the need for self-soothing and grounding techniques. Now we're going to do some more work with triggers.
10–15 min. **Activity: Triggers and the Body**	*Have the group members brainstorm answers to the adjacent questions. Write their answers on the flip-chart pad.* *If the women do not mention them, you may add these items (e.g., "How about . . . ?"). Have women read along from this list in their workbooks on page 62. Have women put check marks next to the items that affect them.* • *lack of privacy* • *not being listened to* • *being teased or picked on*	What makes you feel scared, upset, or angry that could cause you to go into a crisis reaction? When do you feel overwhelmed? What increases your sense of being overwhelmed?

TIME & TOPIC	FACILITATOR NOTES	DISCUSSION WITH WOMEN
	• *feeling criticized* • *feeling humiliated* • *feeling hurt* • *feeling lonely* • *feeling pressured* • *feeling confused* • *darkness* • *loud noises* • *people yelling* • *arguments* • *being isolated* • *being touched* • *experiencing unfair treatment* • *not having control* • *having others interfere in plans or goals* • *receiving "mixed" messages* • *being stared at* • *contact with family members* • *being around people who are drunk or high on drugs* • *being around someone who is expressing explosive anger* *Ask the women to share their answers and record them on the flip-chart pad.*	There usually are early warning signs of triggers. These are physical or emotional signals of distress. Some signals are observable, and some aren't. What are some of the indications that someone is being triggered? Or, if you've been triggered, what did you notice just before losing control or having some other response?

TIME & TOPIC	FACILITATOR NOTES	DISCUSSION WITH WOMEN
	You may add the following to the list if the women do not mention them (National Association of State Mental Health Program Directors 2008). Have the women read the list along with you on pages 63 and 64 in their workbooks and place check marks or make notes next to the warning signs that have happened to them. • *restlessness* • *agitation* • *pacing* • *shortness of breath* • *increase in body temperature* • *hard breathing* • *tight muscles* • *feeling of being "on edge"* • *sensation of tightness in the chest* • *sensation of "knot" in the stomach* • *heart pounding* • *sweating* • *teeth clenching* • *hand wringing* • *shaking* • *crying* • *giggling* • *rocking* • *bouncing legs* • *swearing* • *singing inappropriately* • *eating more* • *smoking* • *drinking or using drugs*	

TIME & TOPIC	FACILITATOR NOTES	DISCUSSION WITH WOMEN
	Allow three to four minutes for the women to write their list in their workbooks.	On page 64 in the workbook, there are places for you to write in your own triggers and some warning signs that you may not have been aware of.
5–7 min. **Activity: Adverse Childhood Experiences Questionnaire**		As we've learned, there are many kinds of traumatic events, and there are many different responses to trauma. There are mental and emotional responses, which occur in the inner self, and there are external responses, which show up in behavior and in physical reactions in the body. One of the most important recent developments in health care is the recognition of the role that serious traumatic experiences play in the development of physical and mental health problems. Please turn to pages 66–67 in the workbook. Take a few minutes to answer yes or no to the questions, in terms of your own life

---

Adverse Childhood Experiences (ACE) Questionnaire

While you were growing up, during your first eighteen years of life:

YES

1. Did a parent or other adult in the household **often**
   * Swear at you, insult you, put you down, or humiliate you?
   or
   * Act in a way that made you afraid that you might be physically hurt?
   IF YES, ENTER 1 ____

2. Did a parent or other adult in the household **often**
   * Push, grab, or slap you or throw something at you?
   or
   * **Ever** hit you so hard that you had marks or were injured?
   IF YES, ENTER 1 ____

3. Did an adult or person at least five years older than you **ever**
   * Touch or fondle you or have you touch his or her body in a sexual way?
   or
   * Try to or actually have oral, anal, or vaginal sex with you?
   IF YES, ENTER 1 ____

4. Did you **often** feel that
   * No one in your family loved you or thought you were important or special?
   or
   * Your family members didn't look out for one another, feel close to one another, or support one another?
   IF YES, ENTER 1 ____

5. Did you **often** feel that
   * You didn't have enough to eat, had to wear dirty clothes, and had no one to protect you?
   or
   * Your parents were too drunk or high to take care of you or take you to the doctor if you needed it?
   IF YES, ENTER 1 ____

Continued on next page

Adapted from *"One Page" ACE Questionnaire Handout* by V. J. Felitti. 2000. Self-published. Personal communication with S. Covington on December 7, 2015.

Adverse Childhood Experiences (ACE) Questionnaire

PAGE 2

YES

6. Were your parents **ever** separated or divorced?
   IF YES, ENTER 1 ____

7. Was your mother or stepmother:
   * **Often** pushed, grabbed, or slapped or had something thrown at her?
   or
   * **Sometimes or often** kicked, bitten, hit with a fist, or hit with something hard
   or
   * **Ever** repeatedly hit over at least a few minutes or threatened with a gun or knife?
   IF YES, ENTER 1 ____

8. Did you live with anyone who was a problem drinker or alcoholic or who used street drugs?
   IF YES, ENTER 1 ____

9. Was a household member depressed or mentally ill or did a household member attempt suicide?
   IF YES, ENTER 1 ____

10. Did a household member go to prison?
    IF YES, ENTER 1 ____

Now add up your "Yes" answers: _____
This is your ACE Score.

Your score will range from zero to ten.

TIME & TOPIC	FACILITATOR NOTES	DISCUSSION WITH WOMEN
	Ask the women to total their yes answers. *The women don't need to share their scores, but it's fine if they do. You may find that it becomes a "contest" regarding who has the higher or "worse" score.*	history. If your answer to a question is yes, enter a 1. If your answer is no, don't enter anything. Please note that the term *household member* in some of the questions means someone else in the household when you were growing up. I'll read the questions aloud and give you time to answer after each one. Each of you now has a score from zero to ten. I won't ask you for your specific scores, but think of them when we talk about this questionnaire.
10–15 min. **Lecture:** **The Adverse Childhood Experiences Study**		A study of adverse—meaning difficult—childhood experiences, called the ACE study, shows that the types of experiences on the questionnaire still have profound effects on people forty and fifty years later. Experiencing these things in childhood puts people at greater risk of having certain physical diseases and mental illnesses, even later in life. People who answer yes to four or more of the items are at greatest risk for having ongoing health problems, such as heart disease, diabetes, lung problems, autoimmune diseases, and others (Felitti and Anda 2010). The ACE study also indicates that a person with a score of four or more yes answers is at greater risk for addiction. The connection between interpersonal violence and substance use is complex, especially for women. Survivors of abuse can become dependent on alcohol and other drugs as a way of managing the effects of trauma and reducing the stress of living in a violent environment. Men who abuse substances

TIME & TOPIC	FACILITATOR NOTES	DISCUSSION WITH WOMEN
		are at risk of perpetrating violence against women and children. Women who use substances are more vulnerable to violence—as either perpetrators or victims—because of their relationships with others who abuse substances, their impaired judgment while drinking or using, and their being in risky and violence-prone situations. Many women who aren't overtly angry when sober find themselves raging when drunk. In addition, many women are under the influence of alcohol or other drugs when they commit crimes. There is a cycle of victimization, use of alcohol or other drugs, shut-down feelings, limited ability to deal with stress, more use of alcohol or other drugs, and an increased vulnerability to further victimization, as well as to perpetrating abuse. We also know that women in addiction treatment programs and in mental health settings report high rates of past emotional, physical, and sexual abuse. What are your reactions to this information?
	Participants may want to make some notes in their workbooks as they are having this group discussion.	Often, adults minimize what happened to them in childhood. However, it's important to realize that childhood events can affect us in our adult lives. The information in this session is being shared to encourage you to think about your past experiences and to understand the impact of the past on the present and the future. We can use our ACE scores to evaluate the potential effects trauma has had on us in terms of our risk for having physical and mental health problems. As we saw on the Process of Trauma chart, mental health issues, substance abuse, and physical health problems can be

TIME & TOPIC	FACILITATOR NOTES	DISCUSSION WITH WOMEN
		related to past trauma. However, there are things we can do now to relieve our stress, to take care of ourselves, and to improve our lives. As mentioned in session 4, self-care is very important if trauma is part of our life story; it is one of the most important things each of us can do. This means eating healthy foods, exercising, getting enough sleep, having friends who are supportive and positive, and using your calming techniques to de-stress yourself as much as possible. These things can help you reduce your risk of having physical and mental health problems.
	There is also a place on page 68 in the workbooks for the participants to write their answers.	Let's go around the group, with each person sharing one thing she is doing now for self-care.
6 min. **Lecture: The Effects of Substance Use on the Brain**		We've talked about the effects of trauma on the brain. We also know that substance use affects the brain. Alcohol and other drugs affect nerve cells in the brain that produce and regulate pleasure. Your brain naturally motivates you to engage in survival behaviors by giving you pleasurable sensations after life-sustaining activities such as eating, sleeping, and pleasurable sexual activity. It also gets your attention by giving you painful, uncomfortable feelings when you don't engage in life-sustaining activities. For example, think of what it feels like when you're really hungry, tired, angry, or thirsty. Feelings of pain and discomfort are signals from your brain that motivate you to do the things you've learned will make the pain go away. Alcohol and other drugs hijack these brain functions to reward repeated use of

Duplicating this page is illegal. Do not copy this material without written permission from the publisher.

231

TIME & TOPIC	FACILITATOR NOTES	DISCUSSION WITH WOMEN
		substances and to cause discomfort when their use is interrupted. This makes it difficult to experience pleasure from natural behaviors and relationships, and the brain can experience pleasure only when the substance is present. Ultimately, this can lead to a person becoming addicted to alcohol or other drugs. This is also why addiction can cause people to make irrational, destructive decisions. Everyone who chooses to use a mood-altering substance runs some risk of developing an addiction, and some people are much more vulnerable than others.
	Take turns reading the following risk factors. *Thank the volunteer readers when they are finished.*	Fifty percent of the risk of becoming addicted is genetic, which means that if addiction runs in your family, your risk of becoming addicted is significantly greater if you choose to use. That's a risk we can't change. The other 50 percent of risk comes from environmental factors. Please turn to page 69 in the workbook. I'd like some volunteers to read the risk factors. Who will start?

RISK FACTORS FOR ADDICTION

- ☐ traumatic or highly stressful childhood experiences

- ☐ experiencing abuse and violence

- ☐ early substance use, meaning the younger you are when you start using alcohol or other drugs, the greater the risk of addiction

- ☐ spending a lot of time around people who use alcohol or other drugs

- ☐ poor coping skills

- ☐ high levels of stress

- ☐ poor nutrition

- ☐ chronic illness—this includes mental illness, such as depression, bipolar disorder, ADD or ADHD, PTSD, and eating disorders

- ☐ grief and loss

- ☐ inability to deal with difficult or painful feelings

- ☐ a genetic predisposition to addiction

TIME & TOPIC	FACILITATOR NOTES	DISCUSSION WITH WOMEN
35–40 min. **Activity: Collage of the Effect of Violence, Abuse, and Trauma on Your Life**	*Distribute a piece of poster board to each woman. Provide the magazines, felt-tip pens or crayons, glue sticks, and scissors. Tell the women that they'll be creating collages by cutting out pictures and words that describe the impact of violence, abuse, and/or trauma in their lives and gluing the pictures or words onto their poster boards. Tell them that they can use the felt-tip pens or crayons to add drawings or words to their collages. Ask if there are any questions about how to make a collage, and assure them that there is no "right" way to do it.* *Allow twenty or twenty-five minutes for the women to work on their collages. Tell them when they have five minutes left. After five minutes, call time.* *Ask the women to join the group and share their collages. Remember to model nonjudgment, acceptance, and encouragement. The experience and what her collage means to a woman is what matters, not its artistic merit.* *If there is time, suggest that the women take a few minutes to write about their collage and what it means to them in their workbooks on page 70. Or have them do this as part of their Between-Sessions Activity.*	

TIME & TOPIC	FACILITATOR NOTES	DISCUSSION WITH WOMEN
5 min. **Reflection**	*Ask participants to share their answers to the questions in the Reflection section on page 71 in their workbooks. Allow people to pass if they want to. Then give participants a few minutes to write their answers in their workbooks or have them do this during their Between-Sessions Activity.*	What was meaningful to you in this session? What did you learn?
5 min. **Between-Sessions Activity**	*Have the women read along on page 72 in their workbooks as you describe the activities they should do before the next session.*	If any of you would like to work more on your collages, you can add to them this week. Please review the History of Trauma chart you completed as the last session's Between-Sessions Activity. If there's anything you'd like to add to it now since we have explored new information about trauma, please do that. Also, please go to pages 63 and 64 of the workbook, where you listed the warning signs of being triggered, and place a check mark next to each of your personal warning signs, to remind yourself of those, if you haven't done this already. When we are feeling stress, it's important to have ways to alleviate it. I am going to suggest that you take a "vacation" every day. This is a thirty-second daily vacation. Each day before our next session, I would like you to do at least one, and preferably all, of the following: 1. Practice deep breathing for thirty seconds 2. Look at something beautiful for thirty seconds

TIME & TOPIC	FACILITATOR NOTES	DISCUSSION WITH WOMEN
		3. Smile at another human being. Also, please look at the list of risk factors for addiction on page 69 in your workbook and make a check mark next to those that relate to you and your life.
	This may not be possible in residential treatment or custodial settings.	Finally, if you can, please bring a photograph of yourself between the ages of three and ten to our next group meeting.
8–10 min. **Activity:** **Yoga Pose**		Our bodies respond to the ways in which we think, feel, and act. This is called the *mind-body connection.* If feelings of stress, sadness, or anxiety are causing physical problems, keeping the feelings inside can make a person feel even worse. There are certain yoga poses that can help with the release of emotions stored in the body. *Yoga* is the Sanskrit word for "connection." Yoga poses help you to be more consciously aware of your body and your breathing. This is particularly important if you have a history of abuse and trauma. You can do yoga poses by yourself, even in a small space. The Breath of Joy yoga pose connects the use of breath with body movements to aid a physical and emotional release of tension. This is beneficial for letting go (or at least loosening the grip) of long-held anger or grief that's been stored in the body or in habitual thought patterns that aren't supportive of growth. The Breath of Joy consists of three quick inhalations through the nose and one audible exhalation through the mouth. The breaths are synchronized with arm movements to engage the whole body.

THE BREATH OF JOY YOGA POSE

1. Begin in a standing position with your feet about hip-width apart. Take a short breath in through the nose while bringing your arms straight out in front of your chest.

2. Take another quick breath in through the nose while opening your arms wide in a "T" shape.

3. Take one last breath in while reaching your arms straight overhead.

4. With an audible "ahh" sound, exhale through your mouth while bringing your arms in a sweeping motion down to the side of your body.

5. Let's repeat this.

Read the instructions aloud again while you and the women do the movements.

6. Once the pattern of synchronizing your breath with movement is comfortable, you can do this pose a little quicker with one breath in three parts. You can also create a fuller body expression by bending your knees when dropping your chest into a forward bend during the exhalation and letting your arms swing down and past the hips.

   Demonstrate this movement.

7. Repeat the movements. Then rise to a standing position.

8. Inhale through the nose with your arms forward.

9. Inhale a bit more while spreading your arms out into the "T" position.

10. Inhale to your fullest lung capacity while bringing your arms overhead.

11. Finally, bend forward with your knees bent, exhaling through the mouth as your arms swing down and past your hips.

Usually, you will repeat this five to ten times in a rhythmic flow.

For those who have limited mobility, a modification is to come down only halfway on the exhale.

TIME & TOPIC	FACILITATOR NOTES	DISCUSSION WITH WOMEN
1–2 min. **Optional Activity: Palms Down, Palms Up**	*You may choose to do the Palms Down, Palms Up activity again, rather than the yoga pose.* *Read the following slowly:*	Now let's do the Palms Down, Palms Up activity. 1. Sit comfortably with your back straight. Close your eyes or lower your eyelids and focus on your breathing. Take a slow, deep breath while counting to four. Then exhale slowly, counting to four. 2. Do this four more times until your breathing is slow and relaxed. 3. Keep breathing slowly and evenly. Hold your hands gently in front of you with your palms up and imagine them holding all the negative or upsetting thoughts and feelings you've had today. 4. Now turn your palms down. Imagine yourself emptying your hands of all the negative or upsetting things you've been carrying today. Let go of them. 5. Keep breathing slowly. Now, turn your palms up. Your palms are up and open to receive positive energy, thoughts, and feelings. Your palms are open to receive support and help. 6. Now slowly open your eyes. You can do this anytime you need to let go of something negative and receive the positive.
1 min. **Closing**		We've covered a lot of material during this session, and some of it may have brought up a lot of memories and feelings. This is why it's so important to learn self-soothing and grounding techniques. Thank you for your willingness to be together in this group, and I'll see you at our next session on *[give the date and time]*.

ADAPTING THE SESSION FOR USE WITH GIRLS

Remember that the girls in your group may be having difficulty with the quiet time that opens each session. See the hints at the end of session 2 (page 146) for help with this.

This session is entitled "How Trauma Affects Our Lives." Girls may not like this wording. Sometimes they find the word *trauma* as labeling and prefer the term *painful experience*.

Make the discussion about sexuality broader, not necessarily about their personal experiences with sex or fear of intimacy. You might discuss what others their age are doing and how they feel about that.

In presenting the lecture about the ACE study, be aware that younger girls may become fearful of what is to come, given their histories of trauma. So you need to emphasize the importance of knowing that, if and when certain things happen, it's a result of their trauma, and that they aren't alone with their experiences. It's also important to stress that by working through this program they are taking proactive steps to take care of their physical and mental health to prevent illnesses in the future.

In presenting the study questions, give each girl two extra copies of the study questionnaire (the original is in the workbook). Ask each girl to fill out three response forms, the first time for herself (the copy in the workbook), the second time for her mother (or foster mother, grandmother, or another woman in her life who fills the role of mother), and the third time for a friend or sister. Emphasize that the information the girls are learning can be helpful to them and to others they know. This information will also be important if they become mothers.

Let the girls know that if they have high ACE scores, they can protect themselves from future health problems by doing self-care. Emphasize the value of getting enough sleep (a minimum of nine or nine and a half hours for teenagers), eating healthy foods, drinking less soda and eating less

continued

ADAPTING THE SESSION FOR USE WITH GIRLS

junk food, getting enough exercise, laughing and playing, doing self-sooth-ing and grounding activities, and so on. Tell them that they'll be learning more about self-care in future sessions.

Stress that most adolescents are very sleep deprived and that sleep deprivation will affect many aspects of their functioning, as follows:

- *Mood.* Sleep deprivation will cause a teenager to be moody and irri-table. In addition, she'll have a difficult time regulating her mood. For example, she'll become frustrated or upset more easily.

- *Behavior.* Teenagers who are sleep deprived are more likely to engage in risk-taking behaviors, such as drinking alcohol, driving fast, and engaging in other dangerous activities.

- *Cognitive ability.* Inadequate sleep will result in problems with atten-tion, memory, decision making, reaction time, and creativity—all of which are important in school.

- *Academic performance.* Studies show that teenagers who get less sleep are more apt to get poor grades in school, fall asleep in school, and have tardiness and/or absences.

- *Drowsy driving.* Teenagers are at the highest risk for falling asleep at the wheel. Drowsy driving is most likely to occur in the middle of the night (2:00 to 4:00 a.m.) and in midafternoon (3:00 to 4:00 p.m.).

- *Complexion.* Lack of sleep increases a teenager's chances of having pimples and acne.

(The above is a handout in appendix 4.)

If there are girls who don't have high ACE scores, there are other questions you can ask them, particularly if they're in residential or custodial programs for girls. For example: "If none of you have had any painful

continued

ADAPTING THE SESSION FOR USE WITH GIRLS

experiences that you can remember, think about how it felt to come into this program. To possibly have to wear different clothes. To share a room with someone you don't know. To have people you don't know telling you what to do, what time to go to bed, and what and when to eat. When you think of these things, how do you feel?"

It's also important to discuss the genetic tendency toward addiction with the girls. Ask who in their families have addiction problems and what they are addicted to. Then review the risk factors for addiction again and remind the girls that 50 percent of this risk is genetic. The other 50 percent is where they have some choice, such as the friends they have and the places they go, finding activities with friends who are drug-free, learning to manage uncomfortable feelings without using substances, learning how to say no, and so on. You may also want to talk about media icons who report not drinking or doing drugs. Jennifer Lopez is one example. Provide some examples of famous people who abstain.

When debriefing the Between-Sessions Activity in which the girls completed the chart, remember to ask about memories from when they were younger as well as what might be happening now at home or in the program. In the lecture about trauma and its aftermath, ask if any of these things are happening now. Does the sharing of this information make them feel concerned? Assure them that they are safe in sharing information. Tell them to share only what they feel safe sharing. If these experiences happened at home and they are returning there, how do they feel about that?

It's important to emphasize to the girls that they may have stressful lives. Sometimes teenagers think only adults experience stress. Be sure to encourage them to do the thirty-second vacations.

MODULE B: SESSION 6

Abuse and the Family

▨ Time

Two hours

▨ Goals of the Session

1. To understand some typical family dynamics
2. To recognize the effects of abuse in families

▨ Participant Objectives

By the end of the session, participants will be able to:

1. Describe the types of abuse in families
2. Explain how family dynamics influence children
3. Identify the little girl/child within

▨ Materials Needed

- Relaxing music and equipment to play music
- Each participant's and the facilitator's workbook
- A pencil or pen for the facilitator and each woman
- *Optional: A piece of writing paper and a marker*
- A newsprint flip-chart pad, an easel, and felt-tip pens
- Masking tape
- *Optional: Women bringing photograph of themselves between the ages of three and ten*
- *Optional: A DVD player and monitor and Segment 7: Family Sculpture from the* Beyond Trauma *Participant Video*
- Facial tissues
- A sturdy chair

continued

Duplicating this page is illegal. Do not copy this material without written permission from the publisher.

243

ABUSE AND THE FAMILY

■ **Session Overview**

- Quiet Time
- Check-In
- Review of Between-Sessions Activity
- Goals of the Session
- *Optional:* Beyond Trauma *Participant Video (Segment 7: Family Sculpture)*
- Activity: Family Sculpture
- Discussion: Family Sculpture
- Activity: Calming and Grounding
- Lecture: Abuse in Families
- Activity: Yoga Pose
- Activity: Getting to Know My Inner Child
- Reflection
- Between-Sessions Activity
- Closing

continued

ABUSE AND THE FAMILY

Background Information for the Facilitator

Preparing for the Family Sculpture Activity

You have the option of showing segment 7 of the *Beyond Trauma* Participant Video, which contains the Family Sculpture activity, or of leading the group through the activity yourself. It's suggested that you watch the section containing the activity on the video before deciding. This will help you choose the best option and will also give you an idea of how to conduct the activity. Many people use the video as a "refresher" as they become more familiar with this process.

Keep in mind that some of the women in the group come from families in which their needs were not met. They took on roles in an effort to survive in emotionally confusing environments and to get their basic needs met. Roles in dysfunctional families typically are rigid. Family members try to manage their feelings of confusion and low self-esteem by hiding behind clearly defined and predictable roles. In abusive homes, children may try to become invisible in order to avoid punishment; the mask of an approved role is an attempt to create a protective cover. Unfortunately, "assigned" roles limit the free range of human expression. They diminish a person's ability to feel or listen to internal cues, as roles are responses to external cues. The primary function of a family structure is to meet growing children's needs. One of the characteristics that set troubled families apart from healthy ones is their reversal of this mission. They expect the children to meet the needs of the adults (such as taking on roles and tasks inappropriate for their ages), to serve the family, to live in denial, and to hide their true feelings.

For this activity, you'll need a chair that is safe and sturdy, for volunteers to stand on.

Duplicating this page is illegal. Do not copy this material without written permission from the publisher.

245

The Session

TIME & TOPIC	FACILITATOR NOTES	DISCUSSION WITH WOMEN
2 min. **Quiet Time**	*Begin playing the soft music.* *After one and a half to two minutes, ask the women to take a deep breath and focus on the group.*	Welcome to session 6 of *Beyond Trauma: A Healing Journey for Women.* Let's just settle in for a few minutes. You may want to sit silently in order to let yourself unwind and relax. You may want to focus on your breathing. Some of you may prefer to stand and slowly walk around the room. Some of you may want to do tapping on the top of your head, your forehead, your cheeks, and your shoulders. Or you may want to find a focal point in the room and just look at it for the next minute or so. Let's begin our quiet time.
5–10 min. **Check-In**	*Allow participants to briefly share.*	It's good to see you all again. Let's check in to see how everybody is doing. In our last session we discussed the ACE study. When people fill out the ACE questionnaire, it often generates some feelings and more questions. Does anyone want to share what came up for her this week as a result of the ACE study?

TIME & TOPIC	FACILITATOR NOTES	DISCUSSION WITH WOMEN
10 min. **Review of Between-Sessions Activity**	*Allow participants to briefly share their enhanced collages.* *Allow participants to briefly share their answers to these questions, if they are comfortable doing so.*	If anyone added to her collage, please describe what you added. I also asked you to place a check mark next to each of your personal warning signs for being triggered, if you didn't do this in our last session. What are some of the things you learned about yourself or became more aware of as a result of this? Will some of you share your experiences doing the daily thirty-second mini-vacation? What did you learn when you reviewed the information on the risk for addiction?
1 min. **Goals of the Session**		The goals for session 6 are: 1. To understand some typical family dynamics 2. To recognize the effects of abuse in families
20 min. Optional: ***Beyond Trauma* Participant Video** Segment 7	**Segment 7: Family Sculpture** *Rather than leading the group through the next Family Sculpture activity yourself, you may choose to show segment 7 of the video. When you have completed the activity, you will lead the group members in discussing it.*	Let's watch a video segment about families.
25–30 min. **Activity: Family Sculpture**		In this session, we are looking at families, whether they are birth families, blended families, adoptive families, or foster families. We will explore how they function, our roles in our families, and how our families have shaped who we are. Let's take a look at one family through a process known as creating a "family sculpture."

TIME & TOPIC	FACILITATOR NOTES	DISCUSSION WITH WOMEN
		The role or roles a child is given in his or her family is one of the major forces that shapes who the child becomes. Roles in the family help children begin to define their personal boundaries. If children's boundaries are violated in the family, such as from abuse, it can be difficult for a child to develop a strong sense of self.
		Relationships help form who we are. Our early relationships in our families helped establish patterns of how we view ourselves and relate to the world and others. It's easier to understand family relationships when you can see them, so I'm going to create a "family sculpture" using volunteers from our group. I'll place some of you in positions in the sculpture and build a sample family. You'll have a chance to talk about how your family was similar or different. This is how we begin to understand our past so we can begin our healing journey to build a positive future.
		You may find you experience strong feelings when we do this activity. Please respect any emotions you or other group members may show.
		Very few of us had an ideal family. Your family may not have had a father, a mother, and a couple of children. For this activity, I'm going to sculpt a family with two parents and four children, but that's just for illustration. I need six volunteers to come forward and participate in my sculpture, which will represent a family with an addiction problem. We're going to start with the father as the addicted person. We know many families don't have fathers, and that the mother may have the addiction, but this

Duplicating this page is illegal. Do not copy this material without written permission from the publisher.

249

TIME & TOPIC	FACILITATOR NOTES	DISCUSSION WITH WOMEN
		is a simple way to start thinking about a family. Who's willing to play the role of the father?
	Ask the volunteer to stand next to you.	
		This man might be the real father of the kids in this family or a stepfather or the mother's boyfriend. We'll call him the "father" for simplicity.
	Help the father stand on a chair facing the group. Be sure the chair is safe and sturdy.	The father in this family is standing on a chair to symbolize three things. The first is power. This father puts himself above the others in the family, and other family members may put him there as well. The second is lack of attention. The chair represents something that takes the father's attention away from the needs of the family. It might be alcohol or other drugs, it might be his work, it might be television or fishing or hanging out with his buddies, it might be that he is incarcerated, or it might be an affair. It could be any addiction or preoccupation that pulls his attention away from the needs of others. The third thing is disconnection. Standing on a chair symbolizes disconnection—mental, emotional, and/or physical—which happens with addictions and preoccupations.
	Say to the father:	Let's say your preoccupation is alcohol or other drugs. What's your favorite drink or drug?

TIME & TOPIC	FACILITATOR NOTES	DISCUSSION WITH WOMEN
	Allow the father to make up an answer, such as "bourbon" or "meth." On a piece of paper, draw an outline of a bottle or an image to represent the drug and tape it to the wall behind the group, so the father is facing it. Or pick an object directly across the room for the father to stare at, such as a light fixture or sign, to represent "his" preoccupation.	
	Say to the father:	Look at the _____ [name of preoccupation] and stay focused on it. This is your obsession. It's always on your mind.
	Ask for a volunteer to play the mother. Have her stand on the floor next to the father's chair.	
	Say to the mother: *The usual response is no.*	Do you feel close and connected to your partner?
	Say to the women in the group:	We want to feel connected in relationships. But because this woman's partner is preoccupied with something, or because the power between them is unequal, she feels disconnected.
	Say to the mother:	Look out at the group and imagine your family and friends. What do you want your family and friends to know about your partner's _____ [alcoholism or other drug use]?

TIME & TOPIC	FACILITATOR NOTES	DISCUSSION WITH WOMEN
	The mother usually will answer, "Nothing," because she feels shame or the need for secrecy to protect their reputations. If she wants to tell others about the alcohol or other drug problem, ask her to proceed with what she would say to her friends, parents, or colleagues. This usually leaves her silent. She doesn't know what to say.	
	Ask the mother to step in front of the chair. Say to the mother:	You are now standing in front of your partner's chair to cover up his addiction or dysfunction. Now, what do you want your family and friends to know about your relationship?
	The usual response is "Everything is fine."	
	Say to the mother:	I want you to smile so people will think everything is fine in your relationship. Keep smiling. Never stop smiling.
	Stand behind the chair. Warn the father and then start shaking the chair a little. Be careful not to cause the father to fall.	
	Say to the group:	Notice how the father starts to lean on the mother in order to feel more stable. He maintains his stability by holding on to the mother's shoulders.
	Say to the father:	How does that feel, holding your partner's shoulders?
	The usual response is "I feel better" or "I feel more stable" or "Safer."	

TIME & TOPIC	FACILITATOR NOTES	DISCUSSION WITH WOMEN
	Say to the mother: *The usual response is yes.* *Ask the mother to step forward three or four steps. She probably will stop and step back in order to keep the father from falling, because he's leaning on her shoulders and might fall. The father will have to stretch or reach out in order to stay connected to the mother.*	Do you feel more connected to your partner now than you did when you were standing next to him?
	Say to the mother: *The usual response is that the mother thinks of his concerns, safety, and well-being, not of herself. She thinks she needs to step back closer to keep him from falling.*	What if you were considering ending the relationship or branching out into the world more? How does it feel when you step away while your partner is leaning on you?
	Say to the father: *The father's usual answer is "It's better when she is close."*	Which feels better: having her step away or having her stay close to you?
	Say to the group: *Ask the mother and father to remain in their positions.*	It's normal to seek comfort and stability. Sometimes maintaining the status quo in a family is perceived as easier. As women, we reorganize our lives to stay connected, even if it's uncomfortable for us. If a partner is drinking or using drugs or abusing us, we may drink or use drugs or accept the abuse in order to maintain the relationship. We may stay connected by sharing other activities, such as going to a bar and drinking or watching television and using drugs together.

TIME & TOPIC	FACILITATOR NOTES	DISCUSSION WITH WOMEN
	Ask the group:	Who would like to play the role of the oldest child in this family?
	Direct the oldest child to stand to the right of the mother and father.	
		The family is supposed to meet the children's needs. In unhealthy families, the children often exist to meet the adults' needs. All children want to feel safe and loved in their families. In a family like this one, the children take on roles to survive, keep the peace, and be accepted.
		The oldest, or firstborn, child is often the Hero. She has all the privileges of an only child for a while until other siblings come along. When a brother or sister is born, she may feel threatened at first but then looks for ways to win back her parents' attention and approval. She may try to follow all the rules perfectly. The more unstable the home life becomes, the more she'll overachieve and be super-responsible to try to keep the family together. The Hero often gets good grades and excels in activities. Her behavior is a way for her to control her life.
	Say to the Hero:	Imagine you come home from school every day, having done well in everything. Tell your mother all about how well you're doing. Share about your good grades, participation in activities and sports, awards, and so on. How do you feel about your mother?
	The response usually is that she feels good about her mother.	
	Ask the Hero to link arms with the mother. Say to the Hero:	How do you feel about your father up there?
	The response usually is that her father seems uninvolved and disconnected.	

TIME & TOPIC	FACILITATOR NOTES	DISCUSSION WITH WOMEN
	Say to the Hero:	How do you feel about that?
	The Hero may say she feels angry toward the father.	
	Ask the Hero to point her finger at the father to show that she feels angry. Say to the Hero child:	What do you want the kids at school to know about your family?
	The response usually is that she wants outsiders to think everything at home is "just fine" or even perfect.	
	Say to the Hero:	Okay, if everything is fine, then smile. Keep smiling so everyone will know your family is fine.
	Say to the volunteer group:	Who will volunteer to be the second-born child?
	Direct the second-born child to stand to the left of and apart from the family, but still facing the group. Say to the second-born child:	Can you compete with the Hero in your family? No. If you're going to get any attention, you'll probably need to make connection in your own way. You probably will connect more with the kids at school than at home.
	Say to the group:	The second child might be called the Scapegoat. This child gets attention at home only from acting out. Sometimes the child deliberately causes trouble just to escape boredom. She relieves stress in the family by taking attention away from the issues between the mother and father that they aren't addressing. So, everyone pretends the real family problem is the Scapegoat. Because of this acting out, the Scapegoat may be at risk for physical abuse by parents,

TIME & TOPIC	FACILITATOR NOTES	DISCUSSION WITH WOMEN
		school officials, or other authority figures. She's more likely to skip school, become pregnant, shoplift, and use alcohol or other drugs. At home, she may withdraw or act disengaged. The Scapegoat is often the first child or the only child in the family to be involved in the juvenile justice system.
	Direct the Scapegoat to cross her arms to show an attitude that says, "You can't tell me what to do."	
	Say to the volunteer group:	Who will volunteer to play child number three, the Lost Child?
	Direct the Lost Child to stand apart from and behind the family, with her back to the group. Say to the Lost Child:	Can you connect with the family? No, not with your parents, not with your perfect Hero sibling, and not with your wild, socially challenged Scapegoat sibling. You're on your own, floating and feeling lost.
	Say to the group:	This child turns her back on the family altogether. She stays home and does quiet activities or hangs out alone, losing herself in her computer, iPad, smartphone, video games, or television. Spending a lot of time texting, instant messaging, running apps, posting to Facebook, tweeting, using Snapchat, video chatting, blogging, gaming, and so on, allows her to substitute this for real interpersonal contact. She lives in a world of imagination and/or cyberspace. In a healthy family, a third child might learn to compete and excel in something uniquely her own. But in a high-stress family like this one, the Lost Child often is at high risk for sexual abuse because she's vulnerable and isolated.

TIME & TOPIC	FACILITATOR NOTES	DISCUSSION WITH WOMEN
	Say to the family group:	Who would like to volunteer to play child number four, the Mascot?
	Direct the Mascot to bounce around the family members, pulling on the mother and father and then jumping away. Tell the Mascot to keep moving.	
	Say to the whole group:	This is the fourth child, the Mascot. In healthy families, the youngest child is often the most relaxed and cheerful. Parents may have eased up on their child-rearing methods by this time. This child has plenty of opportunities to play with brothers and sisters. But in a troubled home, each additional child adds more stress to the family. With more kids, each child has more difficulty getting the parents' attention, especially since the addicted parent takes a lot of energy from the family. So the role of the fourth child is that of family Mascot. She'll do anything to attract attention through humor, charm, or hyperactivity. This, too, takes the focus off the tension between the mother and father, relieving family stress. The hyperactive Mascot, as well as the Scapegoat, may be at high risk for physical abuse.
		Each child has a role that contributes something to the family's survival. The Hero gives the family self-esteem. The Scapegoat acts out the family's pain. The Lost Child takes care of herself, asks for nothing, and is almost invisible. The Mascot is a pressure valve that relieves the family's stress. The key points are that this is a high-stress, high-tension family. The whole family is affected by the addicted person.

257

TIME & TOPIC	FACILITATOR NOTES	DISCUSSION WITH WOMEN
	Ask the father to carefully step off the chair. Ask the mother to carefully step onto the chair and to stare off into the distance. Ask the father to stand in front of the mother. Direct the mother to lean on the father.	
	Say to the group:	This is just one example of a troubled family. The scenario easily could be that the mother has the addiction.
	Ask the father to wander away from the mother a few steps, to show that he's distracted from the family by something.	
	Say to the group:	What often happens when the mother has an addiction or a mental health problem or something that makes her unavailable is that the father will find something outside the family to distract him, such as an affair or working long hours. He'll not necessarily divorce her, but he'll cease to be an emotionally present partner, someone the mother can lean on. Or it may be a single-parent family in which the mother is a substance user.
		If either happens, the family will need the Hero to step into the parental role and be the person the addicted mother can lean on. Typically, when fathers are substance abusers, mothers become overly involved in their kids' lives. However, when mothers are substance abusers, fathers usually don't become overly involved and may let one of the older kids take on the parenting role. Or, there may not be a father in the family.

TIME & TOPIC	FACILITATOR NOTES	DISCUSSION WITH WOMEN
	Ask the Hero to step in front of the chair so the mother can lean on her. Ask the mother to lean on the Hero. *Ask the parents to get back into their original positions.* *Say to the group:*	So, the Hero, who now plays the role of a parent, can be at a high risk for emotional abuse. Sometimes if the father abuses substances, the mother will have her emotional needs met through her oldest child in an incestuous way, even if the incest is not physical. Sometimes fathers will do this with Hero daughters. An incestuous relationship between mother and daughter is also possible, but it's more unusual. The Scapegoat and Mascot are at risk of physical abuse. The Hero and Lost Child are at risk of sexual abuse. The mother is at risk of domestic violence. All family members are at risk of emotional abuse. Each role a child plays in a troubled family comes with its own vulnerability to abuse. It's not safe to have or share feelings. Why are we looking at these family dynamics? These roles were important to our survival as children. Yet most of us carry these roles into adulthood, even though they've outlived their usefulness and may have little connection to who we are now. These roles can be another form of constriction, in addition to the constrictions of gender expectations, abuse or other trauma, and addiction.
	Thank the volunteers and instruct them to remove their "hats" from the roles they have played. Tell them they're now themselves and can go back to their chairs in the group.	

TIME & TOPIC	FACILITATOR NOTES	DISCUSSION WITH WOMEN
	Say to the group:	Let's give our volunteer family members a round of applause for their good work. Here is some more information about dynamics in families: • An only child in a troubled family often moves among the childhood roles we've seen and carries the weight of the family's problems. Only children tend to become isolated because they have no siblings with whom to bond. • If there's only one parent in the home and that parent abuses substances, usually the oldest child—or the oldest daughter—takes over the parental role and responsibilities. • If there's a large gap in age between siblings, any child may become the Hero. Sometimes the sexes of the children affect who takes what role. Daughters are never the Heroes in some families. Sometimes it's not easy to look at our families and our pasts, but it can help us take charge of and change our futures.
15–20 min. **Discussion: Family Sculpture**	*Have the women form duos.* *After about two minutes, tell the women to switch, with the one who was listening now doing the sharing.* *Call time after another two minutes. Then spend ten to fifteen minutes sharing in the large group.*	Now discuss with your partners your reactions and insights as a result of this Family Sculpture activity. Choose which one of you will share first. You'll each have about two minutes to share.

TIME & TOPIC	FACILITATOR NOTES	DISCUSSION WITH WOMEN
	Some women will feel sadness and shame about their own parenting after seeing how an addicted or unavailable parent affects a family sculpture. Empower the women by saying that, as they become more conscious of their thoughts, feelings, and behaviors, they'll be better able to choose to raise their children in healthy ways. Explain that it's important for women to focus right now on what they learned about parenting from their own parents, and then they'll realize what they want to do the same or differently with their own children. *Give participants a few minutes to reflect on what they learned from this activity by answering the questions on page 77 in their workbooks.*	
5 min. **Activity: Calming and Grounding**		This is a lot to hear, so let's take a moment and do some self-soothing. Let's stand up and stretch. Now let's check in with ourselves. Notice your bodies. What do you feel? Is there tightness anywhere? Do you feel warm or cold? What else? Now let's do some deep breathing before we move on.

TIME & TOPIC	FACILITATOR NOTES	DISCUSSION WITH WOMEN
5–10 min. **Lecture: Abuse in Families**		Now let's look at how trauma may affect a woman's ability to parent her own children. Some mothers want to protect their children from harm with such energy that the children feel smothered. They aren't allowed to have friends over or go to friends' houses or go to the park or to movies. The mother may convey inappropriate warnings to her children when there's only typical societal danger. At the other end of the extreme is the parent who pretty much ignores her children and is considered neglectful. Sometimes this is because the children have become triggers for the mother. This risk is particularly high when a child becomes the age the mother was when she was abused. It's easier for many children to blame themselves than to risk their relationship with their caregiver by expressing anger or by running away. As a result, abused children often grow up believing they are bad and unlovable. This is how they explain to themselves why they were treated so badly. They survive by denying, ignoring, or forgetting the abuse and suppressing their anger and rage. If you were abused as a child, there's probably a childlike part of yourself, frozen inside of you, that still feels unlovable and has a feeling of loss. Let's talk a little more about sexual abuse in families. We can draw a continuum of sexual abuse in families.
	Draw a horizontal line on the flip-chart pad. On the far left end, write "Psychological Abuse"; in the middle of the line, write "Covert Abuse"; and at the far right end, write "Overt Abuse."	**Sexual Abuse in Families** ⟶ Psychological Abuse Covert Abuse Overt Abuse

TIME & TOPIC	FACILITATOR NOTES	DISCUSSION WITH WOMEN
	Participants can also follow along by looking at the diagram on page 78 in their workbooks.	
		Psychological sexual abuse is more subtle than overt sexual abuse and, therefore, often is the hardest to recognize. It could be a parent looking to a child for emotional comfort that has a sexualized component to it.
		Can you think of some examples of psychological sexual abuse?
	List the women's responses. Some examples are sexual jokes, verbal harassment, violating personal boundaries, being affectionate with a child in a seductive or flirtatious or other eroticized way, telling a child inappropriate sexual information, and telling a child inappropriate sexual information about the parent's relationship or the other parent.	
		Many women don't know they've been abused because they assume their families are normal. What are some examples of covert or more hidden or subtle abuse?
	List the women's responses. Examples include "inadvertent" inappropriate touching, household voyeurism (for example, a "peeping tom" in the family), ridiculing or overly praising a child's developing body (for example, a young girl's developing breasts or a boy's developing genitalia), sexual hugs, and pornographic reading or video watching with a child.	

TIME & TOPIC	FACILITATOR NOTES	DISCUSSION WITH WOMEN
	List the women's responses. Examples include exhibitionism, French kissing, fondling, oral sex, and sexual penetration. (Examples adapted from *Helping Women Recover.* Copyright © 1999, 2008 by Stephanie S. Covington. This material is used by permission of John Wiley & Sons, Inc.)	What are some examples of more open or overt abuse? In session 3, we talked about the various forms of abuse. These included psychological abuse, emotional abuse, coercion, not feeling safe, and so on. All the things we have listed here are forms of abuse, even though many people think only of the overt, physical types of sexual abuse.
5–10 min. **Activity:** **Yoga Pose**	*The second yoga pose in this curriculum is the Seated Pigeon pose. (Appendix 2 contains instructions and illustrations for all the yoga poses.)*	Now let's do another yoga pose. Yoga poses can help you be more consciously aware of your body and your breathing. This is particularly important if you have a history of abuse and trauma. You can do yoga poses by yourself, even in a small space. The yoga pose I am teaching you today is also in your workbook on page 80, so you could follow those directions and do this pose outside of group. The Seated Pigeon pose provides a deep stretch through the side of the hip and the tissues that connect the outer hip and the outer side of the knee. This band of tissues often is tight, which can cause lower-back pain, knee problems, and aggravation of the sciatic nerve—sometimes felt as shooting pain through the outer hip, leg, or groin.

Giving these tissues a modest stretch with this pose can bring relief from aches and also increase physical comfort when sitting or walking. Practicing this pose can also provide an emotional release of stress or trauma around the hips. It can aid in the release of anger or depression. Some people experience a physical feeling of release or relief, and others exhibit an emotional response, such as tears.

THE SEATED PIGEON POSE

1. Sit straight in your chair, with both feet on the ground. Place your left foot on your right knee, so your legs resemble a number four when you're looking down at the shape.

2. Some people feel a tug immediately on the side of the left hip or buttock. It may radiate down the side of the leg toward the knee. If it isn't felt in these areas, simply lean forward. As the torso moves forward toward the legs, the tension to the outer hip is increased. You can hold on to the seat of your chair for support or lean your forearms on your knees. Hold this pose for one to three minutes for best results.

3. Now repeat the pose with your leg positions reversed. Remember to breathe while you're doing these movements.

Have the women hold the reversed position for a few minutes.

Now relax and get comfortable in your seats.

TIME & TOPIC	FACILITATOR NOTES	DISCUSSION WITH WOMEN
15–20 min. **Activity: Getting to Know My Inner Child**		If you brought a childhood photo of yourself, please place it in front of you. Please look at this photo of yourself carefully. In discussing families and our childhoods, it's important to realize each of us still has an inner child, no matter how old we are or what our life was like growing up. Our inner child, that little girl inside each of us, is our unique core self that is the essence of the true self. The inner child is the part that is most natural, creative, playful, and innocent. It also can be where we hold on to childhood trauma and scars. It's when we let go of the external expectations and go within to reclaim our neglected inner child that we can deal most effectively with the outer world. We're going to do a guided-imagery activity called Getting to Know My Inner Child. You can close your eyes or lower your eyelids. Think about your childhood and pick an age between three and ten years old. You may want to pick the age you are in the photograph you brought or a different age.
	Slowly ask the adjacent questions, pausing between each one and leaving time for the women to think about their responses.	Think about what you looked like at that age. How was your hair done? What kind of clothes did you wear? What kind of clothes did you want to wear? Where did you live? Visualize that place. Maybe it was a house or apartment, a car, a shelter, or the street. What were the rooms like? If you had a room, what was your room like? What were the colors of the floor or the walls?

TIME & TOPIC	FACILITATOR NOTES	DISCUSSION WITH WOMEN
		Did you have a nickname?
		Did you have any pets? What were they?
		What were your favorite foods?
		Who lived in this place with you at this age? Were you special to anyone at that time? How were your needs taken care of?
		How were you disciplined?
		Who were your best friends? What did you like to do with your best friends?
		What made you laugh?
		What scared you?
		What did you want to do when you grew up?
		Gently say good-bye to your inner child.
		Slowly open your eyes.
		Please turn to page 81 in the workbook and make some notes about what you remembered.
	Allow three to five minutes for the women to write in their workbooks.	
	Allow participants to briefly share.	Does anyone want to share anything about the inner child she found in the visualization?
		Sometimes it's helpful to "reparent" your inner child. The most powerful and effective way to step safely out of rigid childhood roles and heal the wounds of the past is to begin to reparent yourself. No parent is perfect. But you can be a "good enough" parent and provide goodwill, support, understanding, warmth, and gentle caring to your inner child.

TIME & TOPIC	FACILITATOR NOTES	DISCUSSION WITH WOMEN
		To do this, you need to understand and be attuned to your inner child's feelings and needs, and to commit to the reparenting as you would an adoption. Being attentive to your inner child can be a first step toward love and healing. To do this you'll show empathy, be understanding, and be gentle—validating your inner child's feelings and addressing them openly. After all, that's what a kind parent would do. Listen carefully to what your inner child says, then calmly reassure and soothe her.

Some of you may feel comfortable reaching out to a close friend or partner, with whom you can be open and vulnerable, to allow this inner child to be held, loved, and nurtured by a trusted, intimate other. |
| | *When asking the following questions, pause between each one.* | Close your eyes again and picture your inner child one more time.

Do you have a sense of your child's age? What is it?

What are her feelings?

What is her state of mind?

Ask her what she needs now. Ask her what is the most important thing she needs from you now. Ask her what she wants. Think about the things a girl that age might typically need and want. |
| | *Allow three to five minutes for the women to fill in their answers in their workbooks.* | Slowly open your eyes. Look at page 82 of your workbook and list the additional clues you have uncovered about your inner child. Remember, you can't treat a three-year-old the same as you would an eight-year-old. |

TIME & TOPIC	FACILITATOR NOTES	DISCUSSION WITH WOMEN
		Even though it may be hard to look into yourself and face your inner child, reparenting your inner child is a critical part of self-healing that will allow you to know and love yourself and have healthy, intimate relationships in the future. Whenever you neglect your inner child, it interferes not only with your love relationships, but also with relationships in your wider support system, such as friendships. If you haven't met the needs of your inner child, it can be difficult to meet your adult needs and the needs of those around you. Like any child, your inner child will continue to protest loudly until her needs are met. It's important to take the time to give your inner child the attention and support she didn't receive in childhood.
5–10 min. **Reflection**	*Allow several people to share. If there is time, allow participants to also write their answers in the Reflection section on page 83 in their workbooks.*	What is particularly important for you in this session?
5 min. **Between-Sessions Activity**		For your Between-Sessions Activity, look on pages 83–84 in the workbook. These activities are based on the visualization that you just did about your inner child. For the first activity, think about your inner child and describe it based on your visualization, continuing to add to the work you did in this session. In the space provided in the workbook, list all the clues and descriptions you have about your inner child.

		The second activity is a reparenting activity. Draw or describe how you would reparent your inner child. Create a reparenting plan that suits your inner child's age and needs. Then try to meet one of your inner child's needs this coming week.
1 min. **Closing**		This session can be a very emotional one for many women. It can also be filled with new information about families and maybe new ways of looking at your own family and childhood. Now it's important to think about ways to take care of yourselves. Please practice some of the self-soothing activities we have been learning. Thank you all for your courage in participating today.

Session Notes

ADAPTING THE SESSION FOR USE WITH GIRLS

During the check-in, you can emphasize the genetic predisposition for addiction. For example, you can ask, "What thoughts have you had this week about addiction in your family?" If the girls are receptive, you can ask, "Who in your family has an addiction?"

Use this session's Family Sculpture activity with girls. It's usually very impactful. Be aware, however, that many girls are still living in the homes where these family dynamics are happening. They may also be in homes where the abuse is ongoing. Review the mandated reporting requirements in your state.

You may want to discuss what their current families look like. Who are the people they consider to be their families? Many of them consider neighbors, peers, and others to be their families. After they've described the members of their families, you can create the family sculpture with those specific family members and have the girls tell the members of the family what their roles are. In the discussion after the family sculpture, have them discuss "What was missing from the family?" and "If you could sculpt a better family, what would it look like?"

It's important to remember that many girls feel a lot of loyalty toward their families and may feel vulnerable and be hesitant to "criticize" them by discussing dysfunction or abuse in their families. Some focus questions you can use are these:

- What kinds of things does your family do together?

- What do you like about your family?

- What are your favorite fun activities with your family?

- If you were the parent in your family, what would you change?

continued

ADAPTING THE SESSION FOR USE WITH GIRLS

You may want to limit the discussion of the sexual-abuse continuum. Although the girls may be in a facility or program with a trained facilitator of the *Beyond Trauma* curriculum, this topic may need to be presented only by those who have extensive clinical expertise. Rather than spend time on the continuum of sexual abuse, it's suggested that you have the girls create Family Maps. Make a copy of the Family Map (see appendix 4) for each girl before the session and distribute the copies during the session.

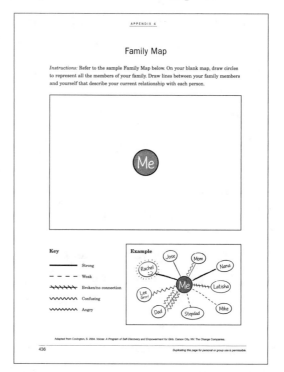

You can introduce the activity as follows:

> A family can be defined as a group of kindred or closely related individuals or as two or more people who share goals and values and have long-term commitments to one another. So families can take many forms. Your family may include parents, foster parents, sisters and brothers, grandparents, aunts and uncles, cousins, in-laws, neighbors, and other significant people in your life.

continued

ADAPTING THE SESSION FOR USE WITH GIRLS

Our relationships with family members have significant effects on our lives. Much of what we know about how to connect with others is learned from our families. Our families teach us how to love, how to communicate, how to treat people, and what to expect from relationships.

Then you can help the girls process the activity by asking questions such as the following:

- What observations do you have about the family map you drew?
- What feelings come up for you when you think about your family?
- What are your family's greatest strengths?
- What are your greatest strengths as a member of your family?
- What observations do you have about the family maps of other members of your group?

When doing the Getting to Know My Inner Child activity, you'll want to change the language to "when you were younger" rather than "inner child." Also be aware that some of the girls are currently fulfilling parental roles: they may be cooking, cleaning, and/or managing households; in charge of younger siblings; caring for parents; and so on.

In closing, remind the girls to use some of the self-soothing techniques. For girls who are fulfilling parental roles, it's especially important that they have some time to focus on and care for themselves.

MODULE C

Healing from Trauma

MODULE C: SESSION 7

The Connection between Trauma and Addiction
Spirals of Recovery and Healing

▓ Time

Two hours

▓ Goals of the Session

1. To understand the connection between trauma and addiction
2. To understand the similarities between the process of healing from trauma and the process of recovery from addiction

▓ Participant Objectives

At the end of this session, participants will be able to:

1. Explain why some women use substances after trauma
2. Describe the spirals of addiction and trauma
3. Define what emotional and physical safety are
4. Explain the importance of self-care

▓ Materials Needed

- Relaxing music and equipment to play music
- Each participant's and the facilitator's workbook
- A pencil or pen for the facilitator and each woman
- A newsprint flip-chart pad, an easel, and felt-tip pens
- Masking tape
- *Optional: A DVD player and monitor and Segment 8: The Spiral of Addiction and Recovery and the Spiral of Trauma and Healing from the* Beyond Trauma *Participant Video*
- Crayons or colored pencils for the women
- Facial tissues

continued

THE CONNECTION BETWEEN TRAUMA AND ADDICTION

■ **Session Overview**

- Quiet Time

- Check-In

- Review of Between-Sessions Activity

- Goals of the Session

- Discussion: Why Some Women Use Substances after Trauma

- *Optional:* Beyond Trauma *Participant Video (Segment 8: The Spiral of Addiction and Recovery and the Spiral of Trauma and Healing)*

- Lecture: The Spiral of Addiction and Recovery

- Lecture: The Spiral of Trauma and Healing

- Activity: Our Own Spirals

- Discussion: Personal Experiences with Substances

- Discussion: Safety

- Activity: Drawing Safety

- Discussion: What Is Self-Care?

- Activity: Self-Care Scale

- Reflection

- Between-Sessions Activity

- Closing

continued

THE CONNECTION BETWEEN TRAUMA AND ADDICTION

Background Information for the Facilitator

Preparing for the Lecture on the Spiral of Addiction and Recovery and the Spiral of Trauma and Healing

You have the option of delivering the lecture yourself or using the *Beyond Trauma* Participant Video (segment 8) to present it.

The Session

TIME & TOPIC	FACILITATOR NOTES	DISCUSSION WITH WOMEN
2 min. **Quiet Time**	*Begin playing the soft music.* *After one and a half to two minutes, ask the women to take a deep breath and focus on the group.*	Welcome to session 7 of *Beyond Trauma: A Healing Journey for Women.* Let's just settle in for a few minutes. You may want to sit silently in order to let yourself unwind and relax. You may want to focus on your breathing. Some of you may prefer to stand and slowly walk around the room. Some of you may want to do tapping on the top of your head, your forehead, and your cheeks. You may want to do the "butterfly hug," where you cross your arms, touch your shoulders, and alternate tapping on each shoulder. Or you may want to find a focal point in the room and just look at it for the next minute or so. Let's begin our quiet time.
5–10 min. **Check-In**	 *Allow each participant to briefly respond.*	We'll do our check-in a little differently today by using a weather report as a way to tell one another how we're doing and how we're feeling. If your emotions were weather, what would the weather be today? Bright sunshine? Rain? Mixed sun and clouds? Thunderstorms? Hurricanes?

TIME & TOPIC	FACILITATOR NOTES	DISCUSSION WITH WOMEN
10 min. **Review of Between-Sessions Activity**	*Allow participants to briefly share their plans.*	Will each of you please share something from your reparenting plan found in your workbooks? Another way to think about this is: How did you meet your inner child's needs since our last session? Let's find out what you decided to do for your inner child and how you decided this would be important to her. What were the clues that helped you pick whatever you did?
1 min. **Goals of the Session**		Welcome to session 7. Its title is "The Connection between Trauma and Addiction: Spirals of Recovery and Healing." The goals of this session are: 1. To understand the connection between trauma and addiction 2. To understand the similarities between the process of healing from trauma and the process of recovery from addiction
15 min. **Discussion: Why Some Women Use Substances after Trauma**	*You could present this information or have the women volunteer and take turns reading the information aloud from page 87 in the workbook.* *Write the women's responses on the flip-chart pad. If they don't mention all of the following, you may add these items to the list:* *• to temporarily dissociate (achieve an altered state)* *• to disconnect the traumatic event from one's consciousness*	Some women use alcohol and other drugs to numb the physical and emotional effects of trauma. What do you believe are some specific reasons why women who've experienced trauma may abuse alcohol and other drugs?

TIME & TOPIC	FACILITATOR NOTES	DISCUSSION WITH WOMEN
	• *to make connections with others* • *to comfort themselves* • *to manage or avoid feelings* • *to escape physical pain* • *to ease their sense of isolation* • *to feel comfortable with sexual intimacy* • *to create distance from or withdraw from others* • *to build courage* • *to increase hope or make the world seem better* • *to forget the past* • *to keep company with an alcoholic or addicted partner* • *to try to "forget" a partner is violent* • *to feel numb* • *to maintain the status quo* *Allow participants to add any other ideas shared in the group to their workbook on pages 87–88.*	So we can see that a woman's use of alcohol or other drugs can be complicated and often is motivated by many different feelings and situations.
10 min. Optional: ***Beyond Trauma*** **Participant Video** Segment 8	**Segment 8: The Spiral of Addiction and Recovery and the Spiral of Trauma and Healing** *Rather than deliver the next two lectures yourself, you may choose to show segment 8 of the video.*	

Duplicating this page is illegal. Do not copy this material without written permission from the publisher.

283

TIME & TOPIC	FACILITATOR NOTES	DISCUSSION WITH WOMEN
5 min. **Lecture: The Spiral of Addiction and Recovery**	*Draw a downward spiral on the flip-chart pad.*	For many women, there is a connection between addiction and trauma, and there's a similarity in how each can affect their lives. We can use a spiral to help demonstrate this. First we'll look at the process of addiction. Please turn to page 88 in the workbook. **Spiral of Addiction and Recovery** (Transformation) Adapted from *Helping Women Recover.* Copyright © 1999, 2008 by Stephanie S. Covington. This material is used by permission of John Wiley & Sons, Inc. There are two parts to the spiral. One part is a path that goes downward, representing a woman's life as addiction takes hold. The path isn't always a straight line but, rather, is revolving and circular as it goes along in a downward direction. At the bottom of the downward spiral, there's a turning point. This is where a woman steps onto a new path toward recovery. This new path moves upward and represents the woman's recovery from the addiction. The downward spiral of addiction revolves around the object of addiction, such as alcohol, marijuana, cocaine, heroin, meth, and other drugs. The object of the addiction is shown by the line that goes through the

TIME & TOPIC	FACILITATOR NOTES	DISCUSSION WITH WOMEN
		middle of the spiral and is ever-present in the woman's life. The process of addiction pulls the addicted person into tighter and tighter circles along this path, constricting her life, isolating her from others, and limiting healthy activities until she's completely focused on the substance. The object of her addiction becomes the organizing principle of her life. Using alcohol or other drugs, protecting her supply, hiding her addiction from others, and cultivating her love-hate relationship with her drug of choice begin to interfere in her world and constrict her life.
		For women, addiction is particularly hard, because society's double standard inflicts far more shame on a woman for having an addiction than it does on a man. What are some of the labels given to women who are alcoholics or substance abusers?
	Typical responses include slut, lush, ho, piece of trash, sleaze, bad mother, *and* unfit mother.	
		Although society may stigmatize a male substance abuser as a "bum," it rarely attacks his sexuality or his competence as a parent. A woman who enters treatment may come with a heavy burden of shame.
	Draw the upward spiral.	Women's recovery from addiction can be viewed as an upward spiral. A woman's choices, life options, and opportunities expand when she stops using alcohol or other drugs. Her world is broadened, and the drug doesn't have the same grip on her daily decisions. The upward spiral of recovery revolves around the drug in wider and wider circles as the addiction loosens its grip and the woman's world opens up to include healthy relationships, an expanded self-concept, and richer sexual and spiritual lives. It's a time for change, growth, opportunity, and expansion.

TIME & TOPIC	FACILITATOR NOTES	DISCUSSION WITH WOMEN
		One way of thinking about addiction is as "a chronic neglect of self in favor of something or someone else" (Covington 2008). So, how does an addicted woman shift from this chronic neglect of self to a healthy care of self? How does a woman get from the downward spiral of constriction to the upward, ever-widening spiral of expansion and growth? How does a woman grow, recover, and get her life on a healthy course? In the next section, we'll explore these questions further.
5 min. **Lecture: The Spiral of Trauma and Healing**	*Redraw the spiral, but label it as it appears on page 90 of the workbook.*	Now let's use the same concept of a spiral and apply it to trauma. Please look at page 90 in the workbook.

Spiral of Trauma and Healing

(Transformation)

Downward Spiral

Upward Spiral

Trauma
(Constriction)

Healing
(Expansion)

Adapted from the Spiral of Addiction and Recovery in *Helping Women Recover.* Copyright 1999, 2008 by Stephanie S. Covington.

TIME & TOPIC	FACILITATOR NOTES	DISCUSSION WITH WOMEN
		As we talked about in an earlier session, trauma can also constrict and limit a woman's life. The trauma in her life often becomes a central issue for her, as is represented by the line through the middle of the downward spiral. Again, there is a turning point at the bottom of the downward spiral. The upward spiral can represent the process of healing from trauma. As a woman becomes more aware of how trauma has affected her life, she experiences less constriction and limitation. With new behaviors and coping skills, there is greater opportunity for growth and expansion. Although the trauma is still a thread that runs through her life, it's no longer the central focus. In both upward spirals—Recovery and Healing—a profound internal shift takes place when you move to the upward spiral. Something transformational happens.
15 min. **Activity:** **Our Own** **Spirals**		Now let's do an activity to focus on our own spirals. On page 91 of the workbook, there's space for you to list all the things that constrict—meaning they limit or restrict—your life. If you have an addiction, how has that constricted your life? How has trauma constricted your life? There also is space to list all the things that allow for growth and expansion and recovery in your life. What are the things in your life that can help you grow and expand and recover? Take three to five minutes to write down your ideas.

TIME & TOPIC	FACILITATOR NOTES	DISCUSSION WITH WOMEN
	After three to five minutes (when the women seem to be finished with their lists), either use the spiral you just drew or draw another spiral on the flip-chart pad and ask the women to identify where they think they are on the spiral. Some may feel comfortable speaking aloud about where they are on the spiral, while others may not. Encourage the women to share while you write their responses on the flip-chart pad. For those who don't want to say it aloud, they can write it in their workbooks.	
		Now I'd like each of you to pick one constriction issue to work on. Think about your life and that constriction. What will it take to make that constriction change and begin to open up the spiral toward expansion and recovery? Write your ideas in the space on pages 92–93 of the workbook. You'll have more time to complete this after our session.
	Allow about three minutes for the women to write, then ask if any of the women would like to share their ideas.	
		How do you think a woman can shift from chronic neglect of the self—often sparked by a life trauma—to healthy care of the self, such as eating well, getting enough sleep, creating a safe environment, developing a support system, and practicing self-soothing and grounding techniques? How does a woman shift from constriction to expansion and growth? How does she grow and recover?
	Write the women's responses on the flip-chart pad.	

TIME & TOPIC	FACILITATOR NOTES	DISCUSSION WITH WOMEN
10–15 min. **Discussion: Personal Experiences with Substances**	*Have a group discussion of the adjacent questions. Women can write notes in their workbooks on pages 93–96 as the discussion proceeds, or they can write answers to these questions after the session.*	When you think about your life, how do you think substance use has affected your thinking, emotions, relationships, choices, and other behaviors? Perhaps one or more of you have never used alcohol or any mood-altering substances. If so, then please share about a woman you know who has used. What alcohol and other drugs have you used or abused in your life? What was going on in your life when you began to use? What feelings did the substances give you, or what feelings did they help you medicate or avoid? Think specifically about the feeling of anger. Has alcohol or other drugs increased your anger or lessened it? Do you express anger differently when you're using? Think about the genetic and environmental factors that increase the risk of addiction. How many of these risks are present in your life? What kinds of activities and relationships give you natural feelings of pleasure and satisfaction? What support do you have for abstinence and self-care? With abstinence, good nutrition, stress-management skills, and sometimes with prescribed medication, the brain can heal and return to normal functioning. But it's important to remember that the brain has now been changed and has a lifelong vulnerability to the addictive qualities of alcohol and other drugs.

TIME & TOPIC	FACILITATOR NOTES	DISCUSSION WITH WOMEN
5 min. **Discussion: Safety**	*List the women's responses on the flip-chart pad. Typical responses include locking doors, not going out at night alone, not accepting drinks from unknown people, not accepting rides from unknown people, carrying a cell phone, and going to a friend's house if home doesn't feel safe. Keep in mind there are no right or wrong answers. Each woman is unique in her feelings about safety.* *As you discuss the following questions, participants could write answers in the spaces provided on pages 96–97 in their workbooks.* *Typical responses include being around people who won't hurt me or play games with my mind, having a good friend to call if I need her, and being around people who support and love me.* *Typical responses include in my car when I am driving, hugging my kids, in my home, and in my bed with the doors locked and the porch light on.* *Typical responses include at my parents' house, around people who have been drinking or doing drugs, and around men.*	Let's take a look at what a woman needs to do to begin the process of healing from trauma. As we learned before, safety is the first priority in healing from trauma. This includes both physical and emotional safety. Safety is so important that we'll be referring to it throughout our sessions. What are some of the things a woman can do to increase her safety in the world? What is emotional safety? When and where do you feel emotionally safe? When and where do you feel emotionally unsafe?

TIME & TOPIC	FACILITATOR NOTES	DISCUSSION WITH WOMEN
	Typical responses include being far away from a person who can abuse me, being in a safe environment like a women's shelter, being with friends or with family members, and having a safe place to go.	What is physical safety? What do you do to keep yourself physically safe?
15 min. **Activity: Drawing Safety**	*Distribute equal varieties of crayons or colored pencils to the women or place them all on a table so the women can take what they like.* *Give the adjacent instructions slowly, in a calming way. (Remember, some women may not want to close their eyes.)*	1. Close your eyes or lower your eyelids. 2. Relax. Breathe deeply and slowly. 3. Begin to focus and think back to a time or place when you felt safe. If you can't think of a safe place, then think of a time or place where you were least afraid. Think about the sights, the sounds, and the smells. 4. What were the colors? 5. What were the sounds and smells? 6. What made you feel safe? 7. Relax and just enjoy where you are. 8. Slowly begin to open your eyes.
	Allow five to seven minutes for the women to draw in their workbooks.	Please begin to draw in your workbooks on page 97 what came to your mind: the images, feelings, and thoughts. Your drawing doesn't have to be artistic; the most important thing is to *draw what safety means to you.*
	Allow participants to briefly share their drawings. If people would like to pass, let them.	Now let's share our drawings with one another. As you show your drawing, please tell us about it.

TIME & TOPIC	FACILITATOR NOTES	DISCUSSION WITH WOMEN
2–3 min. **Discussion: What Is Self-Care?**		We have been discussing safety, particularly safety with others. A key part of safety that we often overlook is safety with ourselves. Often, women who have been abused don't know how to focus on their own needs. One way we develop safety with ourselves is through self-care. Self-care is a range of behaviors that includes everything from what we eat and personal hygiene to valuing ourselves and acknowledging our feelings. How we take care of ourselves is very important. When we're doing a good job of caring for ourselves, we're at less risk for self-destructive behaviors. Let's discuss what self-care can be for you. Please pick one element of self-care you need to develop or change for yourself at this time in your life.
	Allow participants to briefly share their item.	Now let's go around the group and have everybody share what her self-care item is.
10–15 min. **Activity: Self-Care Scale**		On pages 98 and 99 in the workbook, you'll find a Self-Care Scale that is designed to help you see areas in which you are already taking care of yourself. It also helps you see areas you might be neglecting and areas you might want to continue to work on in the future. It isn't a test. There are no right or wrong answers, nor is this a way to measure yourself against others. This is just for you. Take about five minutes to fill out the scale. You'll notice that it lists various tasks related to the self. Please respond to each of the scale items in terms of how you act now and what your life is like now.

TIME & TOPIC	FACILITATOR NOTES	DISCUSSION WITH WOMEN
	When everyone has completed the scale, ask the women for any comments or insights.	Put an X on the line to show where you think you are on the scale. Remember, this isn't a test. It's a tool you can use to see areas in which you are caring for yourself effectively and areas you may want to work on.

Self-Care Scale

	Not at all	Just a little	Pretty much	Very much
1. I keep up my physical appearance (hair, bathing, nails, clean clothes).				
2. I exercise regularly.				
3. I eat healthy meals.				
4. I get restful sleep.				
5. I go to work/school or complete tasks.				
6. I can adapt to change.				
7. I keep up my living space.				
8. I take constructive criticism well.				
9. I can accept praise.				
10. I laugh at funny things.				
11. I acknowledge my needs and feelings.				
12. I engage in new interests.				
13. I can relax without alcohol and other drugs.				
14. I value myself.				
15. I feel and express gratitude.				

TIME & TOPIC	FACILITATOR NOTES	DISCUSSION WITH WOMEN
1 min. **Reflection**		Think back to the activities we did in this session. In the future, you can use the weather report technique to check in with yourself, the Spiral of Addiction and Recovery and the Spiral of Trauma and Healing to pinpoint your place in the healing journey, and the Self-Care Scale to remind yourself of how you want to take care of yourself. They are all tools you can use whenever you need them.
1 min. **Between-Sessions Activity**		Your Between-Sessions Activity is to focus on self-care, identifying the obstacles to self-care and the areas of self-care you'd like to enhance in your life. See if there's one area of self-care that needs attention that you'd like to do some work on. Also, over the next few days, be aware of your environment and what makes you feel safe, comfortable, secure, and supported. Write your ideas in the space provided on pages 100–101 in your workbook.
1 min. **Closing**		Thank you for contributing to this session and for sharing your feelings and insights with all of us. I know this can take a lot of courage. I look forward to seeing you at our next session on *[day and time of next session]*.

ADAPTING THE SESSION FOR USE WITH GIRLS

Often, girls haven't had enough time with their use of alcohol and other drugs to experience the same constriction and consequences that women talk about when doing their spirals. You may have to provide more guidance during the spiral activity. If you're working with girls in a detention facility or probation setting, you can suggest they talk about the things that led them to their current situations as part of the downward spiral. Then discuss the people and events in their lives that will help them avoid further trouble in the future.

For many girls and young women, the risk of sexual abuse is tied to the use of alcohol and other drugs. The following are some examples:

- The abuser may have been drunk or high when the abuse happened.

- The girl may have been drunk or high, which increases a girl's risk of sexual abuse.

- Someone may have given her alcohol or other drugs in order to have sex with her (with or without her knowledge).

- She may be using alcohol or other drugs as a way to numb feelings and cope with abuse.

You can have the girls brainstorm reasons for this connection between the risk of sexual abuse and the use of alcohol and other drugs, and then discuss their responses. You can also emphasize that one way to increase a girl's safety is for her to not use alcohol or other drugs or to use them only in a very limited way.

You can also tell the girls there are rules boys and young men need to learn in order for there to be less rape. Note that these rules are often connected to the use of alcohol and other drugs. Also, tell the girls that, from

continued

ADAPTING THE SESSION FOR USE WITH GIRLS

a legal standpoint, a person should get verbal, affirmative consent before engaging in sex. This is a big issue on college campuses. Provide the girls with the following list found in appendix 4 and let them know that they may want to share this list with both boy and girl friends.

Simple Rules for Stopping Rape

No sex if . . .

- She has not given clear, verbal, affirmative consent.

- She has not given consent this time even if she has on previous occasions. Continue to ask for consent.

- She's drunk or high.

- She seems unsure if she wants to (you should never pressure anyone into it).

- She's passed out.

- It seems like there's any other reason she might regret it in the morning. (Even if it's not rape, do you really want to be someone's morning-after regret, when she can remember you as a total gentleman instead?)

If you have the ability to connect to the Internet in your group, you may want to show this excellent short video clip on consent and tea: www.youtube.com/watch?v=oQbei5JGiT8.

MODULE C: SESSION 8

Grounding and Self-Soothing

▪ Time

Two hours

▪ Goal of the Session

To be able to use grounding and self-soothing activities

▪ Participant Objectives

At the end of this session, participants will be able to:

1. Explain what feeling grounded means

2. Demonstrate grounding activities

3. Demonstrate self-soothing activities

▪ Materials Needed

- Relaxing music and equipment to play music

- Each participant's and the facilitator's workbook

- A pencil or pen for the facilitator and each woman

- A newsprint flip-chart pad, an easel, and felt-tip pens

- Masking tape

- *Optional: A DVD player and monitor and Segment 9: Feeling Grounded from the* Beyond Trauma *Participant Video*

- Facial tissues

continued

Duplicating this page is illegal. Do not copy this material without written permission from the publisher.

297

GROUNDING AND SELF-SOOTHING

■ **Session Overview**

- Quiet Time
- Check-In
- Review of Between-Sessions Activity
- Goal of the Session
- *Optional:* Beyond Trauma *Participant Video (Segment 9: Feeling Grounded)*
- Lecture: Feeling Grounded
- Activities: Physical Grounding
- Activities: Mental Grounding
- Discussion: Grounding Techniques
- Discussion: Self-Soothing Chart
- Activity: Relaxation
- Lecture: Developing Personal Boundaries
- Activity: Physical Boundaries
- Reflection
- Between-Sessions Activity
- Closing

continued

GROUNDING AND SELF-SOOTHING

Background Information for the Facilitator

Preparing for the Grounding and Relaxing Activities

During some of the grounding and relaxing activities, the participants will be asked to lie on the floor on their backs or walk without shoes. Therefore, it's important to make sure the floor will be cleaned prior to the session. If this isn't possible, ask the women to bring beach towels to lie on or provide some type of floor covering. If you can't be sure the floor surface is clean, don't conduct any floor activities or ask the women to remove their shoes.

The first physical grounding activity is called Emotional Freedom Techniques (EFT) or "tapping." This technique for working with trauma survivors is based on acupuncture, an ancient Chinese healing method. In acupuncture, the energy points in the body, called meridians, are touched with tiny needles to heal physical problems. This concept is used to work with psychological issues as well, by tapping on these energy points as a type of acupressure. This is part of an emerging field called energy psychology. The belief is that this can change the pathways in the brain and alter those pathways that are limiting a person.

You likely won't have time to do all the activities in the time allowed, so pick three or four of the physical activities you think will be best for your group. Be sure to let the women know all the activities are listed in their workbooks.

Duplicating this page is illegal. Do not copy this material without written permission from the publisher.

299

The Session

TIME & TOPIC	FACILITATOR NOTES	DISCUSSION WITH WOMEN
2 min. **Quiet Time**	*Begin playing the soft music.* *After one and a half to two minutes, ask the women to take a deep breath and focus on the group.*	Welcome to session 8 of *Beyond Trauma: A Healing Journey for Women.* Let's get settled for a few minutes. You may want to sit silently in order to let yourself unwind and relax. You may want to focus on your breathing. You may prefer to stand and slowly walk around the room. Some of you may want to do tapping on the top of your head, your forehead, your cheeks, and your shoulders. Or you may want to find a focal point in the room and just look at it for the next minute or so. Let's begin our quiet time.
5 min. **Check-In**	*Allow participants to share.*	Remember our emotional weather reports? What's your personal weather like today? Bright sunshine? Rain? Mixed sun and clouds? Thunderstorms? Hurricanes? Who would like to start the sharing?
5–10 min. **Review of Between-Sessions Activity**	*Have participants refer to the answers they wrote in their workbooks to begin this discussion.*	In our last session, we talked about the importance of self-care. I asked you to think about an area of self-care you'd like to enhance in your life. What area of self-care did you decide you would like to work on? What have you done for yourself this week that's self-care?

TIME & TOPIC	FACILITATOR NOTES	DISCUSSION WITH WOMEN
1 min. **Goal of the Session**		The goal of this session is for you to learn a variety of grounding and self-soothing activities you can use now and in the future.
10 min. Optional: ***Beyond Trauma* Participant Video** Segment 9	**Segment 9: Feeling Grounded** *Rather than deliver the next lecture yourself, you may choose to show segment 9 of the video.*	Let's watch a video segment that will help us understand what grounding and self-soothing are.
5 min. **Lecture: Feeling Grounded**	*As you present this information, you can suggest that the women can follow along in their workbooks if they would like, starting on page 103.*	This session is about things you can do to feel grounded and about self-soothing activities. In earlier sessions, we talked about grounding and self-soothing techniques as ways to detach or disconnect from inner emotional discomfort by focusing on the outer world. You have already learned several of these activities. Today we'll do more of them. When you experience trauma, you may lose any feelings of being grounded or centered. It's important to reestablish these feelings so you aren't easily knocked off balance by your emotions and your reactions to the trauma you've experienced. Grounding techniques can help you become aware of the here and now. They can help a person who is dissociating come back into current reality and feelings. When a woman is dissociating or having a flashback, she may feel as if she's watching a movie in her mind, as flashes of past memories appear. Grounding techniques can help her connect with the present and realize that what she's remembering is in the past; it isn't happening now.

TIME & TOPIC	FACILITATOR NOTES	DISCUSSION WITH WOMEN
	Allow participants to briefly respond.	What does it mean to you to feel centered or grounded? Now we're going to go through several grounding and self-soothing activities that help support deeper insight and resolution of trauma symptoms. These tools will help you feel more centered in your life. We'll do these slowly. If at any time you find an activity disturbing or if emotions build up inside of you, stop and let things settle, then try to continue with the activity. There will be time at the end of each activity to check in and see how each of these work for you. Each person responds to these activities differently, so I'd like you to find the ones that work best for you. Please turn to page 103 in the workbook for the first grounding activity. We'll be rating ourselves before and after each activity. This can help you see which activities work best for you.
20–28 min. total **Activities: Physical Grounding**	*Read the instructions to the following activities slowly, to allow the women time to respond to each instruction.*	First we will focus on physical grounding. **Physical Grounding Activity 1** *(5–8 minutes)* One technique for working with trauma survivors is based on acupuncture, an ancient Chinese healing method. People now use this technique to work with psychological issues by tapping on the body's energy points as a type of acupressure. The belief is that this can change the pathways in the brain and alter those pathways that are limiting a person. There is a karate chop point on the outside of the hands as well as eight tapping

TIME & TOPIC	FACILITATOR NOTES	DISCUSSION WITH WOMEN
		points: (1) on the inner edges of the eyebrows, closest to the bridge of the nose, (2) at the side of each eye, (3) under each eye, (4) under the nose, (5) on the chin, (6) on the collarbone, (7) under the arms, and (8) on the top of the head. Page 104 in the workbook shows these tapping points.

Tapping Points

eyebrow
side of eye
under eye
collarbone

top of head
under nose
chin

under arm

www.TheTappingSolution.com

karate chop

Reprinted with permission from *The Tapping Solution: A Revolutionary System for Stress-Free Living* by Nick Ortner. 2013. Hay House, Inc.: Carlsbad, CA. You can also watch Nick Ortner of the Tapping Solution demonstrating the process on video here: www.thetappingsolution.com/tappingvideo.

The instructions for this activity are adapted from the "Tapping Quick Reference Guide" in The Tapping Solution.

TIME & TOPIC	FACILITATOR NOTES	DISCUSSION WITH WOMEN
	1. Ask each of the women to rate how stressed she is feeling by giving her stress level a number between 0 and 10, with 0 being little or no stress and 10 being very stressed. Ask them their numbers and write the numbers on the flip-chart pad. 2. Ask the women where and how they are feeling their stress in their bodies. It may be pain in the neck or back, an upset stomach, a head-ache, tense shoulders, etc. Write these on the flip-chart pad. 3. Ask them how they know when they are stressed. How are they feeling emotionally? Examples of answers are anxious, fearful, agitated, cranky, and excited. Write their responses on the flip-chart pad. 4. Have each woman craft a statement, such as "Even though my stress level is a/an [a woman's number] and my [how the woman is feeling physically] and I am feeling [how she is feel-ing emotionally] . . ."	

Duplicating this page is illegal. Do not copy this material without written permission from the publisher.

305

TIME & TOPIC	FACILITATOR NOTES	DISCUSSION WITH WOMEN
	5. *Referring to page 104 in the workbook, describe the karate chop point and the other eight tapping points.*	
	6. *Ask the women to use the karate chop point (side) of one hand to do three gentle chops on the karate chop point of the other hand.*	
	7. *Then ask them to start tapping on the various tapping points as they say their statements aloud, very slowly (for example: "Even though my stress level is an 8, and my back hurts, and I am feeling cranky . . ."). As they say the statement, they will be tapping with both hands on the inner edges of the eyebrows, closest to the bridge of the nose; on the sides of their eyes; under their eyes; under their noses; on their chins; on their collarbones; and under their arms. Then have them say the following affirmation (or some other positive affirmation) aloud: ". . . I have the skills to get through this" as they tap on the tops of their heads.*	

TIME & TOPIC	FACILITATOR NOTES	DISCUSSION WITH WOMEN
	8. *Have them repeat this process two or three times.* 9. *Then ask each woman to pick a number to reflect her current stress. If the person with the highest number hasn't reduced her stress sufficiently, repeat the process. Also repeat the process if anyone says the stress has shifted to another place in her body.* 10. *If you need to repeat this because of step 9, you may want to change the directions as follows: "Even though I have a stress level of 6 and I wish it were lower . . ." or "Even though my stress has moved from my shoulder to my back. . . ."* *Different affirmations work for different people. Here are some options you can suggest:* • *I am going to take time to relax and slow things down.* • *I feel angry, and that probably means I've been hurt, I've been scared, or I have some other primary feeling and I can handle it.*	

TIME & TOPIC	FACILITATOR NOTES	DISCUSSION WITH WOMEN
	• *It's impossible to control other people and situations. The only thing I can control is myself and how I express my feelings.* • *It's nice to have other people's love and approval, but even without it, I can still accept and like myself.*	How do you feel now? Rate how you feel at this point and circle this number on page 106 of your workbook. **Physical Grounding Activity 2** *(3–4 minutes)* Please stand up. 1. Feel your feet on the ground. 2. Notice the springiness in your legs. 3. Feel the way your feet connect with the ground, almost like a magnet is holding you there or as if you are a tree with big, strong roots. 4. With your feet firmly planted, sway slowly from side to side from the ankles. 5. Now sway forward and backward. This will help you find your center of gravity. It usually is located in your lower torso. 6. As you continue to sway, place your hands on your lower belly and sense your center of gravity. Breathe into and from this place. 7. Now sit down in your chair. Sit back and relax. 8. Be sure your feet are firmly on the ground. Place your hands on your lower belly again and feel the energy coming into that area through your feet.

TIME & TOPIC	FACILITATOR NOTES	DISCUSSION WITH WOMEN
		How do you feel? Rate how you feel at this point and circle this number on page 106 of your workbook. **Physical Grounding Activity 3** *(2–3 minutes)* 1. Continue to sit with your feet on the floor and notice how that feels. 2. Notice your bottom sitting in the chair and how that feels. 3. Notice the temperature of the room and how that feels. 4. If there's an object near you, look at it. Perhaps feel it. Or take something out of your pocket or purse and look at it and feel it. 5. As you look, breathe slowly in and out. How do you feel? Rate yourself again on a scale of 1 to 5, with 1 feeling the best and 5 feeling the worst. Circle this number on page 107 in your workbook. **Physical Grounding Activity 4** *(3–4 minutes)* 1. Another important technique is deep breathing or belly breathing. Please lie on your backs (or sit in a chair). 2. It's healthy to learn to take very deep breaths, from all the way down in your abdomen, not just from your upper chest. Put one hand on your chest and one hand on your belly. 3. Take a couple of normal breaths. 4. You will probably find that you are feeling these breaths mostly in your chest.
	It's preferable if the women lie on their backs for this deep-breathing activity. If this isn't possible for some reason (for example, the floor is not clean or the venue prohibits it), the women may remain sitting in their chairs.	

TIME & TOPIC	FACILITATOR NOTES	DISCUSSION WITH WOMEN
		5. Try moving your breath deeper into your lower abdomen, so your hand on your belly moves up and down as you breathe. This is called deep breathing. Try it again. You'll find that you are breathing more slowly and more completely than usual. 6. Keep breathing deeply, but blow the air out of your mouth, rather than out of your nose. Let your abdomen fill with air each time. 7. Let's repeat this for [six to ten] breathing cycles. 8. Now please sit back in your chairs. Many people practice deep breathing as a way to counteract feelings of anger, stress, fear, panic, and so on. It also is healthier to breathe more deeply, rather than shallowly. Now rate how you feel again, with 1 for feeling the best and 5 for feeling the worst, and circle this number on page 107 in your workbook. **Physical Grounding Activity 5** *(3–4 minutes)* 1. Sit in a comfortable position with your feet on the floor. 2. Concentrate on your breathing: breathing in, pausing, and breathing out. 3. Feel your body expand from the center and release back toward the center. 4. Feel your body expanding from the front, the back, and the sides. 5. With each breath, breathe a little deeper, moving the air deeper down into your abdomen.

TIME & TOPIC	FACILITATOR NOTES	DISCUSSION WITH WOMEN
	Have the women continue to do this breathing for about three minutes.	6. As you breathe in, take in good things, such as self-love, hope, courage, and joy. As you breathe out, let go of things you don't want in your life, such as self-criticism, stress, and fear. How are you feeling now? Rate your feeling on a scale of 1 to 5 and circle this number on page 108 in your workbook. **Physical Grounding Activity 6** *(3–4 minutes)* Another way to feel grounded and centered is to walk without shoes, if the weather and ground permit. A park, some woods, the beach, your favorite street, a garden, or on the grass in your yard all are good places to try this. As you walk, breathe deeply and think about your feet as they connect with the ground. Look around and take in your surroundings. Be in the present and feel the connection with your world.
	If possible, take the women outside to practice this walking activity. Going outside to walk likely won't be possible in a correctional setting and some other settings. However, you can conduct the activity in the group room by having the women walk in a circle around the table and chairs. Many women in correctional settings like this kind of "walking meditation" and use it when walking to meals or recreation.	1. Now let's practice by taking off our shoes and walking around the [name the space]. 2. Breathe deeply and think about your feet as they connect with the ground. 3. Walk as slowly as you can. 4. Focus on the movement of each part of your body: your hips, your legs, your feet, your arms. 5. Be in the present and feel the connection with your world. 6. Slow down even more. Move just as slowly as you can. 7. Be aware of every tiny movement.

TIME & TOPIC	FACILITATOR NOTES	DISCUSSION WITH WOMEN
		This sometimes is called *walking meditation*. How did the walking activity feel to you? Please rate your feeling level again and circle it on page 108 in the workbook. **Physical Grounding Activity 7** *(2–3 minutes)* You can use a part of your body to help ground you physically. 1. Look at your hands. 2. Check in with your hands. Do they usually feel okay? 3. Now think of something that might disturb you. Hold that thought. 4. Begin to move your hands. Note their lightness and flexibility. 5. Notice how many ways you can move your hands. 6. See if you have shifted how you feel by shifting your focus to your hands. 7. Now try moving your arms up and down with each breath: your arms up with each inhalation and down with each exhalation. In doing this, you can identify any other body part, posture, or movement that isn't related to fear. The chest, stomach, and throat are usually not good choices. How did this activity work for you? Please rate how you feel again and circle the number on page 109 in your workbook.

TIME & TOPIC	FACILITATOR NOTES	DISCUSSION WITH WOMEN
		Physical Grounding Activity 8 *(3–4 minutes)* The next activity is based on an ancient Japanese healing system called *Jin Shin Jyutsu*. The idea is that we can help harmonize and balance our energy through the use of gentle touch. This activity involves two steps done in sequence. 1. Put one hand under your armpit and the other hand on the top of the opposite shoulder. 2. Hold yourself this way for about a minute. 3. Now put one hand on your forehead and the other on your chest. 4. Hold this for at least thirty seconds. 5. Move your hand on your chest to your belly and move the hand on your forehead to your chest. 6. Again, hold this position for at least thirty seconds. Please rate how you feel now and circle the number on page 109 in your workbook. Think about which of the physical grounding activities felt best or worked best for you. Make check marks next to those in your workbook. Does anyone want to share which of these activities worked best for her?
	For more information on this technique, see *Health in Your Hands: Jin Shin Jyutsu—Practicing the Art of Self-Healing* by Waltraud Riegger-Krause (New York: Upper West Side Publishing, 2014).	
	Allow participants to briefly share. If people don't want to share, that is okay.	

TIME & TOPIC	FACILITATOR NOTES	DISCUSSION WITH WOMEN
10–13 min. total **Activities: Mental Grounding**		Now we'll focus on mental grounding. **Mental Grounding Activity 1** *(4–5 minutes)* The first mental grounding activity is called *Containment*. It's designed to help us temporarily set aside some of our issues and concerns. This may be difficult to do. But obsessing about certain thoughts or experiences—especially negative ones—increases our stress. Doing this activity may seem silly at first, but, as you become more comfortable with it, you'll discover it's a quick and effective way to reduce your stress and anxiety. In your head, create a list of all the thoughts and feelings that are bothering you right now. Include any strong negative emotions, thoughts, and memories. For the first couple of times, you can write these down if it's easier for you. Who would like to write them down? You can do this on page 110 in your workbook. 1. Close your eyes or lower your eyelids. 2. Take a few deep breaths. 3. Now think of a container of some kind that can hold objects. It can be a box, a trash can, an empty room, or even a hole in the ground. 4. Imagine depositing each of your worries and concerns and bad memories into the container. Place all the distressing items into the container, knowing that it's just for a brief period of time. You can retrieve any of these items at any time.

TIME & TOPIC	FACILITATOR NOTES	DISCUSSION WITH WOMEN
		5. Take a few deep breaths and then open your eyes. Was everybody able to visualize depositing your negative thoughts and feelings into the container? Does anyone feel less anxious or less stressed out? Now rate your feelings again and circle this number on page 110 in your workbook. As you practice this, it'll get easier, and you'll notice that it really does help you feel calmer and more centered. Try it the next time you're feeling distracted and you have a task or activity that requires your full attention. **Mental Grounding Activity 2** *(3–4 minutes)* The next mental grounding technique is called *Focusing on the Here and Now.* 1. Try to relax. Take a deep breath. 2. Look at the room around you. Focus on the size of the room. 3. Focus on the color and texture of the walls. 4. The height of the ceiling. 5. The lights. 6. The windows *[if there are any].* 7. The doors. 8. The furniture. 9. The décor. 10. Think of today's date and what time it is. 11. Think of what city you are in.

TIME & TOPIC	FACILITATOR NOTES	DISCUSSION WITH WOMEN
		12. Now focus on yourself. Think of your name.
		13. Think of your age.
		How are you feeling now? Please rate your feeling level again and circle this number on page 111 in your workbook.
		Mental Grounding Activity 3 *(3–4 minutes)*
		The next activity is one way to take an emotional time-out. It'll take a few minutes and will become easier as you practice it.
		1. Inhale through your nose and hold it for a few seconds.
		2. Exhale through your mouth and hold it for a few seconds.
		3. Continue to do this slowly for seven more complete breaths.
		4. Now visualize how you'd like your physical body to feel.
		5. Imagine the kind of energy and well-being you want for yourself. Visualize how that feels. Try to experience what this would feel like for you.
		6. Say an affirmation to yourself three times. Say something that inspires you. Some women say things like "I am whole," "I am healing myself," or "I am a worthwhile human being." Pick an affirmation that means something to you.
		Now how do you feel in terms of your rating scale? Circle this number on page 111.
		Think about which of the mental grounding activities felt best or worked best for you.

TIME & TOPIC	FACILITATOR NOTES	DISCUSSION WITH WOMEN
	Allow participants to briefly share.	Make check marks next to those in your workbook. Does anyone want to share about which of these activities worked best for her?
3–5 min. **Discussion: Grounding Techniques**	 *Write the women's responses on the flip-chart pad.* *Write the women's responses on the flip-chart pad.*	When we're working through painful things, such as past trauma, it's important to have ways to comfort or soothe ourselves without using alcohol or other drugs. Those are temporary fixes that often may complicate our lives even more. So finding out how you can best ground yourself and soothe yourself is an important life skill. Some people help themselves feel grounded by holding an animal or lying down with an animal and listening to its heartbeat or the calmness in its breathing. Some find peace by looking up at the sky and watching the clouds go by or the stars. Others find it in walking through nature and connecting with the universe through their feet as well as their senses. Which type of grounding do you think works best for you? Your ratings before and after the activities we just did may give you a clue about this. You may want to make notes in your workbook on page 112 as we share. Let's look back at page 46 in the workbook, at the list of grounding and self-soothing activities we created in an earlier session. We've added to our possibilities with the activities we've done in this session. What are some new ways you can think of to help yourself feel grounded and centered?

TIME & TOPIC	FACILITATOR NOTES	DISCUSSION WITH WOMEN
10–12 min. **Discussion: Self-Soothing Chart**		In earlier sessions, we talked about "self-soothing." Just to clarify, grounding is a skill we learn to help us be in the present. In an earlier session, we learned about triggers and how often women can be triggered and flooded by feelings from the past. Grounding allows us to experience a safe place in the present. Self-soothing or calming activities are the things we learn to help us relax. There is no one way to self-soothe, because each person is unique. In fact, you probably have used various ways to self-soothe during these sessions. Let's explore more techniques and try to discover what works best for you. Please turn to page 113 in your workbook. You'll see a Self-Soothing Chart.

Self-Soothing Chart

	ALONE	WITH OTHERS
Daytime		
Nighttime		

Adapted from *Helping Women Recover*. Copyright © 1999, 2008 by Stephanie S. Covington. This material is used by permission of John Wiley & Sons, Inc.

TIME & TOPIC	FACILITATOR NOTES	DISCUSSION WITH WOMEN
	Allow participants to write their answers in their workbooks and then have them briefly share their answers. If people want to pass, let them.	Now we're going to think about the self-soothing activities that work best for you individually. Feel free to take notes and put them in the appropriate boxes as we discuss ways to self-soothe. We all need a variety of soothing strategies that are appropriate for different situations. Consequently, you'll find four boxes on the chart. For instance, one strategy might work when we're with others (such as at work or school) but not when we're at home alone, and vice versa. Some things will work during the night but not during the day. So, we need ways to soothe ourselves in all four circumstances: alone or with others during the night and alone or with others during the day.

Let's look at the box in the upper left-hand corner of the chart. What are some things you do to self-soothe (to calm and relax yourself) when you are alone in the daytime?

What are some things you do to self-soothe when alone in the nighttime? |
| | *Responses might include taking a long, hot shower; taking a walk and thinking; talking to a trusted friend; writing in a journal; sewing; reading; playing relaxing music while lying on the floor with your eyes closed; exercising; painting; writing down the words you want to say to someone; doing yoga; meditating; and deep breathing. Some women find that eating or buying something can be self-soothing. However, these methods* | |

TIME & TOPIC	FACILITATOR NOTES	DISCUSSION WITH WOMEN
	can be addictive in themselves. In criminal justice settings, you'll need to help the women find suitable self-soothing techniques, as many of the previous options aren't available to them. These might include reading, crocheting, mindful breathing, writing in a journal, and meditating.	
	Allow participants to write their answers in their workbooks and then briefly share their answers with the group. If people want to pass, let them.	What are some things you do to self-soothe during the day when you are with others? What are some things you do to relax or calm yourself when you are with others in the nighttime? The importance of self-soothing is to feel grounded and centered. Learning how to calm yourself and relax when you've been bombarded by intense emotions is a self-soothing skill we all need to develop. It can be very individual and a good way to take care of yourself. You'll be working more on this chart as part of your Between-Sessions Activity.
5 min. **Activity: Relaxation**		Relaxation is one of the best ways to self-soothe. One way to relax is to get off your feet. You may lie down on your back on the floor or sit, whichever you prefer. Now, close your eyes or just lower your eyelids

TIME & TOPIC	FACILITATOR NOTES	DISCUSSION WITH WOMEN
	Use a soft, melodic tone of voice. *Pause*	1. Take a deep breath in while you silently count to four: one, two, three, four. 2. Now begin breathing out slowly: one, two, three, four. 3. Try to breathe deeply from your abdomen, rather than higher in your chest. 4. Breathe in again and out again. 5. Let's repeat that slow breathing two more times. 6. Now, in your mind, picture your favorite safe place to be. Maybe you're walking in a beautiful park or garden. Maybe you're getting cozy in your favorite chair or in your bed. Maybe you're lying in the sun or boating on the water. 7. Picture that favorite place in your mind and imagine yourself there. 8. Keep breathing deeply and very slowly. 9. Starting with your head and working down your body like a scan, let your muscles relax. 10. Let your forehead relax. 11. Let your cheekbones relax. Let your jaw joints relax. 12. Let your neck and upper shoulders relax. 13. As you exhale, imagine all the tension going out with each breath. Let it go. 14. Let your hands and arms go limp. 15. Let your chest, stomach, and the whole middle part of your body relax. 16. Keep breathing in and out. 17. Let your hips, your buttocks, and your upper legs and lower legs relax.

TIME & TOPIC	FACILITATOR NOTES	DISCUSSION WITH WOMEN
		18. Let your feet and toes relax. 19. Let your whole body relax. Breathe in and out. 20. Keep imagining that safe place you selected. 21. Enjoy where you are. Enjoy the relaxation of your body. Be relaxed, almost floating and weightless, as you stay in that image. 22. Now slowly come back to the room and open your eyes. How do you feel right now? How do you feel different? As we've learned before, breathing deeply is a simple and easy way to feel less stress or anxiety. Letting your breath help you release the anxiety in your body is an important skill in self-care.
2–3 min. **Lecture: Developing Personal Boundaries**	*You can have the women turn to page 115 in their workbooks for a summary of the lecture.*	Another skill that helps a woman feel centered, grounded, and more in control of her life is developing personal boundaries. What do we mean when we talk about personal boundaries? I think most of us have had the experience of feeling that someone is standing too close to us or that his or her face is too close to us. We feel that this person is "in our face" and has crossed our physical boundary. Boundaries can be physical, but they can also be mental and emotional. For example, one boundary may be not staying around people who yell at you. Another boundary, or limit, might be refusing to be put in the middle of a disagreement between other family members.

TIME & TOPIC	FACILITATOR NOTES	DISCUSSION WITH WOMEN
		When a woman is abused, it's a boundary violation: her physical, sexual, and emotional boundaries are not respected and are crossed. When our boundaries have been violated and disrupted, we may have difficulty maintaining our boundaries with others in the future. For example, if a child has been sexually abused, there's a risk she'll have difficulty knowing what is sexually appropriate or inappropriate in her adolescent and adult life.

In order to create strong, caring relationships with others, it's important for each person not only to know when and how to set clear limits, but also how to accept and honor the boundaries and limits set by other people. Personal boundaries are based on our upbringing, our culture, and our experiences with others.

It can be empowering to set and control your own boundaries, but it isn't always easy to do. When we're caught unprepared, we may overreact or underreact.

Communicating clearly what your limits are with strangers, family members, and friends is an important first step. Other people can't guess your boundaries. Some people will try to test them or use their own comfort levels as the standard for yours. Therefore, it's important to tell people when you feel comfortable or uncomfortable.

It's best to determine your boundaries based on your own internal compass, not on your reaction to external things or people. One way to think about boundaries is like zippers. Imagine you have a zipper around you. When the zipper tab is on the outside, others can move it at will. If it's on the inside, you can control it. |

TIME & TOPIC	FACILITATOR NOTES	DISCUSSION WITH WOMEN
15–20 min. **Activity: Physical Boundaries**	*Have the women form duos and spread out around the room.* *Pause between each step while the women do as directed.*	I'd like the members of each duo to stand still and face each other, standing about six to eight feet apart. One of you, while maintaining eye contact, will silently motion to the other to move closer and then indicate "stop" with your hand when your partner is close enough for comfort. Those of you who are standing still, notice the feelings in your bodies as your partners move closer to you. What are you feeling? What are the sensations in your body? While the stationary woman is still facing straight ahead, her partner is to repeat the movement from all directions (walking toward her on the left side, right side, and back). The one standing still will be facing forward and will raise her hand when she feels the other person is close enough.
	For each movement, ask: *When the movement has been made from all four sides, have the women who were standing still make notes in their workbooks about their feelings and bodily sensations as their partners approached them.*	Each of you who is standing still, what are you feeling? What are the sensations in your body? Now switch roles and repeat the activity, from the front, both sides, and the back.

TIME & TOPIC	FACILITATOR NOTES	DISCUSSION WITH WOMEN
	Again, for each movement, ask:	Each of you who is standing still, what are you feeling? What are the sensations in your body?
	When the movement has been made from all four sides, have the women who were standing still this time make notes in their workbooks about their feelings and bodily sensations as their partners approached them.	
	Have all the group members come back to their chairs in the circle.	
		Each of you has just created a personal physical boundary—that bubble around you where you feel most safe and comfortable. What are the differences among the people in the room in terms of personal boundaries?
	One example might be that some women have three inches of personal space while some have four feet.	
	Allow participants to briefly share their answers. If people want to pass, let them.	What did you feel emotionally and physically as your partner approached you?
		Did what you feel depend on where your partner was: in front of you, beside you, or behind you?
		In general, how do you feel when someone gets too close to you?
		Are there differences if this person is someone you don't know or a friend?
		Are there differences if this person is a man or a woman?
		Are there cultural differences?

TIME & TOPIC	FACILITATOR NOTES	DISCUSSION WITH WOMEN
		This is an important activity for a number of reasons. Often, it's difficult for a trauma survivor to feel her body if she's freezing, shutting down, and disconnecting. This may be particularly true when she's around others. It's also often difficult to set a limit, to say no. Even people who haven't experienced trauma may have trouble identifying their physical, emotional, mental, and behavioral boundaries. And we all may have even more difficulty in communicating them to others. It's important for all of us to let those we associate with know what we will or will not do or accept from others. This helps them know how to "be" around us, how to best communicate with us, and what to expect from us. It also can help them learn to respect us. Some of the ways we build and reinforce our resilience is by having coping skills, such as learning grounding activities and self-soothing or calming techniques. Another way is by having firm and clear personal boundaries.
10 min. **Reflection**	*If there is time, allow participants to write their answer to this question in their workbooks on page 116. Then allow participants to briefly share their answers with the group. If people want to pass, let them.*	What is one thing you learned about yourself during this session?

TIME & TOPIC	FACILITATOR NOTES	DISCUSSION WITH WOMEN
5 min. **Between-Sessions Activity**		Between now and our next session, think about your personal boundaries. Remember situations where you felt comfortable and times when you felt uncomfortable in terms of your boundaries. You may want to make some notes in your workbooks about this. Second, I want you to try some grounding and self-soothing activities. Pay attention to how you feel before and after each one. Make notes on pages 116 and 117 in your workbooks. At our next session, we'll discuss what worked for you and what didn't work. Everyone is unique, and some activities will work better for you than others. You may also want to add things to your self-soothing chart.
1 min. **Closing**		I hope today's session was more relaxing for you than some of the past ones. I'm impressed and touched by your commitment to this work and by your resilience. We'll see one another again at our next session on *[date and time]*.

Session Notes

ADAPTING THE SESSION FOR USE WITH GIRLS

After practicing some of the grounding techniques, the girls may want to create a "calming collage." They can use words and pictures to represent what is calming and self-soothing for them. Or they may want to create a "calming catalogue." You can bring in small notebooks with unlined pages, and the girls can draw, write, or cut out pictures from magazines to create their personal catalogues of grounding and self-soothing techniques.

When doing the boundary activity, you can have each girl stand on a large sheet of butcher paper or newspaper sheets taped together. After doing the activity, each girl can draw a circle that represents the space she needs to feel safe. This is her safety bubble.

This is a good session in which to raise the issue of trust. Trauma is a boundary violation, and when there's interpersonal violence, trust is broken. Some focus questions can include'

- How important is trust in a relationship?
- How does it develop?
- How do you know when to trust someone?
- How do you know when not to trust someone?
- Did this group help you develop a sense of trust?
- How did that happen?
- How did you help increase the trust in the group?

The Mind and Body Connection

▦ Time

Two hours

▦ Goal of the Session

To understand the connection between the mind and the body

▦ Participant Objectives

At the end of this session, participants will be able to:

1. Give examples of emotional wellness
2. Recognize feelings in the body
3. Demonstrate how to express and contain feelings
4. Demonstrate how to communicate more effectively

▦ Materials Needed

- Relaxing music and equipment to play music
- Each participant's and the facilitator's workbook
- A pencil or pen for the facilitator and each woman
- A newsprint flip-chart pad, an easel, and felt-tip pens
- Crayons or colored pencils for the women
- Masking tape
- Facial tissues
- *Optional: Butcher paper for life-size body images*
- *Optional: Small boxes for the Creating a Container activity*

continued

THE MIND AND BODY CONNECTION

■ **Session Overview**

- Quiet Time
- Check-In
- Review of Between-Sessions Activity
- Goal of the Session
- Lecture: The Mind-Body Connection
- Lecture: Emotional Wellness
- Activity: Creating a Container
- Activity: Feelings and the Body
- Activity: Communication and Feelings
- Reflection
- Between-Sessions Activity
- Closing

continued

THE MIND AND BODY CONNECTION

Background Information for the Facilitator

Preparing for the Review of Between-Sessions Activity

Prior to the session, create a blank Self-Soothing Chart (found on page 318 in this guide) using a different sheet of flip-chart paper for each section.

As an Option to the Feelings and the Body Activity

Rather than using the drawings on page 123 in the workbook for this activity, you may have the women draw larger body shapes on flip-chart paper or trace their own life-size body shapes on butcher paper. To do this, you'll need extra sheets of flip-chart paper or large sheets of butcher paper that can be taped together. Be conscious, however, of drawing actual body shapes if you have women in the group who struggle with their body image, due to obesity or eating disorders. If that is an issue for members of your group, it may be best to use the workbooks for this activity.

Preparing for the Communication and Feelings Activity

The size of the group will determine whether everyone can do this together or whether you'll need to form subgroups of three or four members each. Each subgroup will need a timekeeper.

continued

The Session

TIME & TOPIC	FACILITATOR NOTES	DISCUSSION WITH WOMEN
2 min. **Quiet Time**	*Begin playing the soft music.* *After one and a half to two minutes, ask the women to take a deep breath and focus on the group.*	Welcome to session 9 of *Beyond Trauma: A Healing Journey for Women.* This session is about the mind-body connection. First, let's get settled for a few minutes. You may want to sit silently in order to let yourself unwind and relax. You may want to focus on your breathing. You may prefer to stand and slowly walk around the room. Some of you may want to do tapping on the top of your head, your forehead, your cheeks, and your shoulders. Or you may want to find a focal point in the room and just look at it for the next minute or so. Let's begin our quiet time.
5–10 min. **Check-In**	 *Allow participants to briefly share their answers.*	What have you been thinking about as a result of the last session? Have your attempts to do the grounding and self-soothing activities generated any particular feelings?
5–10 min. **Review of Between-Sessions Activity**	*Fill out the large Self-Soothing Chart you have created, based on comments from the group members about their experiences. They may learn things from the experiences of others.*	Would anyone like to share a grounding or self-soothing activity you did since our last group session and how it worked for you? What type of activity worked best for you?

TIME & TOPIC	FACILITATOR NOTES	DISCUSSION WITH WOMEN
	Allow participants to briefly share their answers.	Would anyone like to share with the group any reflections you've had on setting your personal boundaries? Did anyone think about their inner child's needs since our last session?
1 min. **Goal of the Session**		Today our goal is to understand the connection between the mind and the body.
10–15 min. **Lecture: The Mind-Body Connection**		We know traumatic events can affect us in a variety of ways. One way is that our brains become overwhelmed, and it becomes difficult to make sense of or process what's happening. The unprocessed, emotionally charged bits of trauma can be stored in our memories and in our bodies, and they make us vulnerable to being triggered. The emotions and reactions that many women struggle with in the present are like mental and emotional scars from past abuse or trauma that hasn't been dealt with. As we know, trauma can result in a disconnection between memory and feeling. Some women have memories without feeling, and some have feelings without memory. Some women may have emotional feelings but are numb in their bodies. One of the most important parts of healing is getting the memories and the feelings connected and expressed and getting the feelings and the body's reactions to them connected and acknowledged. This is what we'll focus on in this session on the mind-body connection.

TIME & TOPIC	FACILITATOR NOTES	DISCUSSION WITH WOMEN
		When the feelings and stress from a traumatic event aren't expressed, they often are stored and then later expressed through the body. For example, difficult menstrual periods, eating disorders, headaches, chronic fatigue, thyroid disorders, back pain, and suppression of the immune system are some of the ways in which the body can express painful experiences. Clearly, our bodies and our minds, including our emotions, are very connected. If you aren't aware of what your body needs, you can't take care of it properly. If you don't feel hungry, you don't nourish yourself. If you mistake anxiety for hunger, you eat. And if you don't feel full, you keep eating. This is why sensory awareness and body awareness is an important part of trauma recovery and healing. What kinds of experiences have left you feeling numb? What role have alcohol and other drugs played in disconnecting you from your feelings? What has helped you reconnect with your feelings?
	Allow participants to briefly share their answers.	
10 min. **Lecture: Emotional Wellness**	*As you present this material, the women may want to follow along on page 119 in their workbook.*	Trauma can greatly affect a woman's emotional development. Addiction also affects emotional development. A woman may have shut down emotionally after a traumatic experience. This is called *psychic numbing*. She may need help finding the words to express how she feels. She may also need to learn how to express her feelings appropriately and how to contain, or hold, them until she's in a safe or appropriate environment

TIME & TOPIC	FACILITATOR NOTES	DISCUSSION WITH WOMEN
		to share them. Other women may be overwhelmed and flooded by feelings, and they also need to learn expression and containment. When a woman learns how to appropriately express and contain her feelings, she's no longer controlled by them. In the last session, we talked about a zipper as a way of thinking about boundaries. The zipper is also useful when we think about containment. If you are flooded or overwhelmed by feelings, try to visualize having a zipper on a compartment that allows you to safely close up your feelings for the time being. You can unzip the zipper when you know it's a good time to express those feelings. Try to think of a time when your feelings "broke out" and you expressed them at what wasn't the best time. Or maybe it was the right time, but you couldn't express your feelings adequately. It's important to clarify what our feelings are before we express them. Then, we need to determine whether it will do us any good to express them in the current situation or with these particular people. This is what we mean by *appropriate*. Please turn to page 120 in your workbook. Here are some tips for when you're overwhelmed by a feeling or having trouble containing it. Who will volunteer to read the first one?
	Have a different woman read each of the items.	

TIME & TOPIC	FACILITATOR NOTES	DISCUSSION WITH WOMEN
	TIPS FOR WHEN YOU'RE OVERWHELMED BY A FEELING OR HAVING TROUBLE CONTAINING IT 1. Slow down or even stop what you're doing. 2. Ask yourself, "What am I feeling?" Try to name the feeling. 3. Ask yourself, "Does the intensity of this feeling match the situation?" Give yourself some time to sort this out. 4. Then ask, "As I have this feeling, how old am I?" It's possible your inner child may be having this feeling. 5. If the intensity doesn't match the current situation, or if you feel younger than your current age, the feeling is probably connected to the past. **FIVE STEPS TO EMOTIONAL WELLNESS** 1. Become aware of when you're having a feeling and how you're feeling. Tune in to yourself. 2. Name the feeling. Label it. 3. Try to locate the feeling in your body. Where are you experiencing the sensations? 4. Express the feeling in an appropriate way. 5. Learn to contain the feeling.	The mind-body connection also affects emotional wellness. In addition to expressing our feelings, we can learn to become aware of what's going on in our bodies. We can become aware of sensations in our bodies, including tension, and how our feelings affect our tone of voice, the volume of our voice, our sensations of temperature, and so on. Being aware of what's going on in our bodies is a foundation of emotional awareness. On page 120 of your workbook, you'll find a list of Five Steps to Emotional Wellness. Take a look at the five steps that can help us begin to create emotional wellness. Who will volunteer to read them?

TIME & TOPIC	FACILITATOR NOTES	DISCUSSION WITH WOMEN
10–15 min. **Activity: Creating a Container**	*Read the following slowly:*	Now we're going to do the Containment activity that we learned in the last session, but in a slightly different way. 1. In your head, create a list of all the thoughts and feelings that are bothering you right now. Include any strong negative emotions, thoughts, and memories. 2. Now close your eyes or lower your eyelids. 3. Take a deep breath and let it out. 4. Imagine a container of some kind that can hold thoughts and feelings. It can be a trash can, a box with a lock, or even a hole in the ground. Make sure it has a lid. 5. Now imagine depositing any of those negative or difficult thoughts and feelings into the container. Place all of them in the container, knowing that it's just for a brief period of time. Put the lid on. 6. You can retrieve these items anytime you want or need to deal with them. For now, however, you can focus on other things. 7. When you're ready, slowly open your eyes.
	Give the women crayons or colored pencils. Allow three to five minutes for the women to draw their containers.	Please turn to page 121 in your workbook and draw a picture of your container. When a feeling is overwhelming, it helps to be able to contain it or put it on hold. When we can get some distance from our feelings, we're more able to manage them and not be overwhelmed by them. The Creating a Container activity can be used to soothe or calm yourself when you're feeling anxious

TIME & TOPIC	FACILITATOR NOTES	DISCUSSION WITH WOMEN
	Optional: *If you have time in this session, you can distribute empty small boxes and have the women decorate them with crayons, colored felt-tip pens, decals, etc., and use them as containers for feelings that are overwhelming. Do this instead of drawing containers.*	or stressed. It can also help to control your feelings when they seem overwhelming and you need to focus on something else. Who would like to share her experience of doing this activity or perhaps describe her container?
15–20 min. **Activity: Feelings and the Body**	*Use the crayons or colored pencils again for this activity.* *Optional:* *The women may draw larger body shapes on flip-chart paper or trace their own life-size body shapes on butcher paper instead of using the drawings in the workbook (see the precaution, however, in the background information at the beginning of this session).*	Now let's turn our attention to page 123 in your workbooks. Under the heading Feelings and the Body, there are drawings of the front and back of a woman's body. We can use these to begin to work on the emotional wellness list.

TIME & TOPIC	FACILITATOR NOTES	DISCUSSION WITH WOMEN
	Give the following instructions slowly.	Begin by closing your eyes or lowering your eyelids. How are you feeling emotionally? Are you feeling anger, fear, calmness, relief, happiness, anticipation, or what? Try to get in touch with what you're feeling right now.
	Pause.	
		Our bodies often offer clues to our emotional states. Some indications of emotional responses in the body are headaches, feelings of being hot or cold, tightness or pain in the stomach, clenched fists, tension in the neck and jaw, pain in the back, hunched shoulders, shallow breathing, a rapid heartbeat, feeling calm and peaceful, and so on. For instance, if you feel angry, perhaps your heart is beating fast, your face feels hot, or you're perspiring. If you feel happy, perhaps you feel "bouncy" in your legs. Or you feel a calmness in your body when you feel everything is okay.
	Allow one or two minutes for the women to complete this.	Using one color *[of crayon or colored pencil]*, show on the diagram where one of your emotional feelings is reflected in your body.
		Use another color to draw your facial expression. If you have difficulty with this, be patient with yourself. It doesn't have to be a great work of art. It's more about being aware of how our face reflects our feelings.
	Allow about two minutes for the women to complete this.	Now focus on your body and begin to notice what you're feeling physically. Sense what you're feeling and where it is in your body. Notice your feet on the floor, your legs, your lower back, your stomach, your upper back, your neck, your arms, your hands, your face, your heartbeat, the warmth or coldness of your skin, and so on. Is there any numbness or tingling? Is your stomach growling?

TIME & TOPIC	FACILITATOR NOTES	DISCUSSION WITH WOMEN
	Pause. *Allow about five minutes for the women to complete this.* *Allow five to ten minutes for this round of sharing.*	Is anything twitching? Does your body feel heavy or light? Now use different colors *[pencils or crayons]* to indicate where all your other physical feelings are. Write down anything that you feel, such as "tense," "cold," "warm," "stiff," "pain," "sore," "tight," "smooth," "restless," and so on, on that part of the body drawing. Use a different color for each feeling. Let's stop here, even though you may not feel finished with this. Can you each share something you learned from this activity? Or share one or two feelings and where they're located in your body?
35 min. **Activity: Communication and Feelings**	*If there are three to five women in the group, everyone can do this together. If the group is larger, you'll need to divide the women into subgroups of three to four members each. You'll need a timekeeper for each subgroup. One woman in each subgroup can volunteer to serve as its timekeeper.* *Call time after one minute.*	Another aspect of emotional wellness is how we communicate our feelings. We're going to do an activity that will help us develop our communication skills. We need to be aware that there are some communication patterns that limit us or constrict us emotionally. These are often learned in our families, or this emotional constriction can happen as a result of abuse and other forms of trauma. So first we'll experience forms of communication that do not connect people. We'll start by looking at one other person in the group for one minute without speaking. You may have noticed that, when you don't speak, you start to assume things about other people. You rely on other cues to tell you about other people's moods, thoughts,

TIME & TOPIC	FACILITATOR NOTES	DISCUSSION WITH WOMEN
		and so on. In troubled or abusive families, this often is how people communicate. Kids learn to "read" or guess what's going on, because people don't communicate directly and openly. Relying on nonverbal communication without checking out assumptions creates miscommunication and disconnection between people.
		The second type of communication that doesn't connect people is communicating "nonrisky facts." Some families often talk only about safe or nonrisky facts. Here's an example.
	Give an example of a nonrisky fact from your own life. Some examples are "I have two cats" and "I took the bus here."	
		Now I want each of you to share two nonrisky facts—different from the ones I used—with the people in your group. You each will have about thirty seconds to do this. Timekeeper(s), please track the time for each person.
	Allow time for each person to share her nonrisky facts.	
		In many families, another form of communication is opinions. Here's an example.
	Discuss a personal opinion for approximately thirty seconds. An example is "Women who work can be good mothers."	
		In your group, have each person share one strong opinion. You'll have about one minute each. Timekeeper(s), please track the time.
	Allow time for each person to share her strong opinion.	
		Opinions are important, but they need to be communicated as opinions, rather than as facts, so they don't shut others out of the conversation. Sometimes strong, opinionated statements can hinder communication.

TIME & TOPIC	FACILITATOR NOTES	DISCUSSION WITH WOMEN
	Give a personal example, such as "Nothing goes right for me. My new boss is so unhelpful, no wonder no one likes me at work."	"Poor me, ain't it awful?" stories are another form of non-interpersonal communication. Here's an example.
		In your group, have each person share a "poor me" story. You'll have about one minute each. Timekeeper(s), please monitor the time.
	Allow time for each person to share her "poor me" story.	We have experienced several forms of communication: nonverbal, nonrisky facts, opinions, and "poor me" stories. We can see how these forms of communication can limit or constrict a person's ability to connect with others. Let's shift now to the language of feelings. Many noncommunicative, stressed families don't share feelings. It doesn't feel safe to do so. When children grow up in families that only communicate nonverbally, use nonrisky facts, give opinions as facts, and tell "poor me" stories, it's difficult to develop emotional wellness. So we're going to practice communicating feelings. Let's start with the feeling of sadness. Here's an example.
	Share a sad feeling you have had, such as sadness about the death of a pet or family member or friend. *Allow time for each person in the group to share a situation when she felt sad.*	In your group, please each share something that has been sad for you. You'll have about one minute each. Timekeeper(s), please keep time for each speaker.
	Share an angry feeling you've had, such as getting mad when your teenage son dropped out of school or when someone forgot to pick you up as planned.	Now let's talk about anger. Here's an example.

Duplicating this page is illegal. Do not copy this material without written permission from the publisher.

343

TIME & TOPIC	FACILITATOR NOTES	DISCUSSION WITH WOMEN
	Allow time for each group member to share a situation when she felt angry.	"Each of you, please share something that makes you angry. You'll have one minute each. Timekeeper(s), please keep time for each speaker.
	Share a feeling of joy, such as getting to see your first grandchild.	Now, let's talk about joy. Here's an example.
	Interrupt the group(s) after about thirty seconds by saying, "Stop." Ask the women how it feels to be interrupted. You'll find that they're irritated because they didn't have time to talk and share their feelings. Say that this is the point you're making. Ask the women to discuss how they felt when they were stopped from sharing feelings, especially now that they're more bonded with their group(s), having already shared some personal feelings. What's happening between them is now more important than what the facilitator is saying or doing. After this discussion, give the group members time to finish sharing their joyful feelings. Then, if there are subgroups, ask the women to rejoin the total group.	In your group, share something that gives you a joyful feeling.
	Allow participants a few minutes to answer the questions about their group sharing on page 124 in their workbook.	How did it feel to share feelings within your group? For those of us who don't do this often, it may feel strange or overwhelming. As you do this more and more, it'll feel more comfortable. The sharing of feelings is an important part of the healing journey. This is why it's so important to have safe, supportive people in your life.

TIME & TOPIC	FACILITATOR NOTES	DISCUSSION WITH WOMEN
2 min. **Reflection**	*Allow participants a few minutes to answer the question in the Reflection section on page 125 in their workbooks.*	Earlier, we talked about containment as a part of emotional wellness. Emotional wellness is when you have a feeling, you can name it, you can locate it in your body, and you know how to express it. But if you choose not to express it at a particular time, and you hold it or contain it until there is a better time, that's "containment." Remember, you can use a "zipper" or the personal container that you created to contain your feelings. This is different from "numbing" or "stuffing." For example, what if I came to work angry about something that happened before I got here? Being angry all day at work or being angry in the group would not be appropriate. I have to save or contain my feelings to process and deal with later.
5 min. **Between-Sessions Activity**		For the Between-Sessions Activity, as you go through the next week *[or between now and the next session]*, continue to use your body chart, indicating where you are sensing feelings in your body. Also, on page 126 in your workbook, write about one experience you have of containment.
1 min. **Closing**		Thank you for your participation and commitment during this session. I look forward to seeing you again at our next session on *[date and time]*.

ADAPTING THE SESSION FOR USE WITH GIRLS

As part of the Creating a Container activity, it's important that you do the part that is marked as optional for the women. Provide each girl with a small box with a lid. The girls can decorate their boxes with colored markers, construction and/or wrapping paper, decals, glitter, and so on. Once the girls have decorated their containers, ask if there are any volunteers who would like to discuss any things that are in their containers. When a girl feels overwhelmed by a feeling (any feeling she is experiencing now or from the past), she can write the name of the feeling on a piece of paper and place it in the box and put the lid on it. This is a good way to practice containment. In some settings, you may want to suggest they leave their containers with the staff, where they'll be safe.

You also may want to make some changes in the content of the lecture material. For example, The Mind-Body Connection can be discussed in terms of what they experienced when they first arrived at the program or what it feels like to speak up in the group. Then discuss what they're thinking, what they're feeling, what their bodies are doing, and so on. In the Emotional Wellness lecture, you might say, "When a girl your age suffers from a trauma or begins using alcohol and other drugs frequently, it can affect how her brain looks at the world. Sometimes this means she isn't able to understand her feelings, sometimes she doesn't have any feelings at all, and sometimes she tucks her feelings away in a place that's safe so she doesn't have to deal with them. Other times, she doesn't know what to do with the feelings, and they come out as anger or frustration or other feelings that she has a difficult time identifying."

Our Feelings

▣ Time

Two hours

▣ Goal of the Session

To allow women to experience their feelings

▣ Participant Objectives

At the end of this session, participants will be able to:

1. Identify their feelings
2. Demonstrate how to share feelings
3. Define what *empathy* and *compassion* mean

▣ Materials Needed

- Relaxing music and equipment to play music
- Each participant's and the facilitator's workbook
- A pencil or pen for the facilitator and each woman
- A newsprint flip-chart pad, an easel, and felt-tip pens
- Masking tape
- Facial tissues

continued

OUR FEELINGS

■ **Session Overview**

- Quiet Time
- Check-In
- Review of Between-Sessions Activity
- Goal of the Session
- Lecture: Feelings
- Activity: The Observer Self
- Discussion: Powerful Shared Feelings
- Activity: Losses
- Lecture: Empathy and Compassion
- Activity: Yoga Pose
- Activity: Meeting a Feeling
- Lecture: Happiness
- Reflection
- Between-Sessions Activity
- Activity: Affirmation
- Closing

continued

OUR FEELINGS

Background Information for the Facilitator

Working with Intense Feelings

Difficulty with intense feelings is one of the primary issues for women who've experienced trauma. This typically is called *emotional dysregulation*. Throughout this program, you've been assisting the women with emotional regulation. In this session, there's additional emphasis on feelings. If someone becomes emotionally overwhelmed, you have a variety of activities (breathing exercises, tapping, using her container, etc.) that you can remind her to use to help with her intense feelings.

For Women Who Have Anger Issues

For women who have difficulty containing their anger, there is a gender-responsive and trauma-informed curriculum: *Beyond Anger and Violence* (Covington 2014). It is designed for women in community settings. There also is a program for women in correctional settings: *Beyond Violence* (Covington 2013).

Using Guided Imagery (Visualization)

This technique of helping the women imagine scenarios that are different from their everyday realities offers them an opportunity to safely envision using different behaviors. It allows them to break through boundaries or barriers that may be hindering their healing processes. It opens up their world to possibilities.

For some trauma survivors, closing their eyes for an activity can be very difficult. This is why the instructions give the women the choice of closing their eyes or lowering their eyelids. Maintaining a soothing voice and relaxed style in explaining the visualization will help the women in the group feel relaxed.

continued

OUR FEELINGS

It's important in a visualization activity to slowly bring the women out of the experience and into the "here and now." Once you've finished the visualization and asked the women to open their eyes, remember to indicate that the visualization has ended.

The Session

TIME & TOPIC	FACILITATOR NOTES	DISCUSSION WITH WOMEN
2 min. **Quiet Time**	*Begin playing the soft music.* *After one and a half to two minutes, ask the women to take a deep breath and focus on the group.*	Welcome to session 10 of *Beyond Trauma*. Let's get settled for a few minutes. You may want to sit silently in order to let yourself unwind and relax. You may want to focus on your breathing. You may prefer to stand and slowly walk around the room. Some of you may want to do tapping on the top of your head, your forehead, your cheeks, and your shoulders. Or you may want to find a focal point in the room and just look at it for the next minute or so. Let's begin our quiet time.
5–10 min. **Check-In**	 *Allow participants to briefly share their answers.*	This session is about feelings. In our last session, we learned that we can hold feelings in our bodies. I'd like each of you to identify where you're holding a feeling in your body.
5–10 min. **Review of Between-Sessions Activity**	*Encourage as many of the women as possible to share.*	Who will volunteer to share an experience of containing a feeling?

TIME & TOPIC	FACILITATOR NOTES	DISCUSSION WITH WOMEN
1 min. **Goal of the Session**		The goal of today's session is to allow us to explore and feel our feelings.
3–5 min. **Lecture: Feelings**	*Present the following information or have participants take turns reading this information aloud together on page 127 of their workbooks.*	In our last session, we talked about how we can develop emotional wellness. We did a communication activity and also discussed containment. Expression and containment of feelings are both very important skills people can learn by practicing them over time. Expression and containment can be difficult when emotions arise immediately. It may feel strange, initially, to stop and work through the steps that help you contain and express your emotions appropriately, but, eventually, it will feel more comfortable. Some people believe there are six basic human emotions: anger, sadness, fear, happiness, disgust, and surprise. And there are many other feelings that are secondary, such as guilt, pride, jealousy, and excitement. At first, it might seem that expression and containment of our feelings should be easy, because there are so few basic emotions. But containing these emotions can actually be very difficult for many people—especially trauma survivors and recovering alcoholics and substance abusers. Women may experience many feelings they feel they can't share with others, especially with men. Or they may feel "flooded" by feelings that can't be contained. Many trauma survivors become overly reactive and respond quickly and abruptly to other people's words and actions.

TIME & TOPIC	FACILITATOR NOTES	DISCUSSION WITH WOMEN
15 min. **Activity:** **The Observer** **Self**	*Read the following instructions slowly and pause between the steps.*	One way to practice containment is by using the box you envisioned in an earlier session. Another way is a technique called the Observer Self. The observer part of our self is that part that's capable of seeing what's going on without judging it or reacting to it. The Observer Self is merely a witness. With practice, we can develop this part of ourselves. 1. Pick a situation you have been in recently when there was a problem and you experienced a lot of feelings. Now close your eyes or lower your eyelids and get totally involved in the scene of the problem. Keep focused on this situation. 2. Be aware of how you're feeling as you involve yourself in this situation. 3. Notice the look on your face. 4. Notice the faces of others around you. 5. Notice how you move your body. 6. Notice the energy around you. 7. Just feel this experience for a moment as though it's happening right now. 8. Now leave the situation and move to a spot above it. Look down on the scene you've just left behind and see it in its entirety. 9. Notice what you're doing. 10. Notice how others are reacting to you. 11. Look at the roles you and others are playing out. 12. Look at the place where it's happening: the city, the neighborhood, the culture. 13. Now, very slowly, go back into the scene again. Totally immerse yourself back into the center of it.

TIME & TOPIC	FACILITATOR NOTES	DISCUSSION WITH WOMEN
	Allow a few seconds of silence.	
		14. Be aware of how your body feels.
		15. Allow this scene to come to an end in whatever way you wish to resolve it for now.
	Allow a few seconds of silence.	
		16. Slowly open your eyes and come back into this room.
	Allow participants a few minutes to write about this experience on pages 128–129 in their workbooks.	How did it feel to be totally in the situation? How did it feel to be observing it?
		Did you notice the difference in your body between being in the situation and being out of it? What was the difference?
	Allow participants to briefly share their answers.	
		Most women feel better when using the Observer Self. In addition to helping us develop containment, practicing the Observer Self technique can teach us more about ourselves and our reactions and behaviors in different situations. This technique also allows us to practice detachment. Detachment allows us to be less reactive. This is different from dissociation. With dissociation, you're disconnected and lost or split off from what's happening—removed from reality. With the Observer Self—or detachment—you're very present, developing and using more awareness and consciousness, not less. The Observer Self is a part of mindful awareness. It allows us to make mindful judgments about how we react and respond to situations. This empowers us.

TIME & TOPIC	FACILITATOR NOTES	DISCUSSION WITH WOMEN
15 min. **Discussion: Powerful Shared Feelings**		There are many feelings that women who've been abused share. Some of them are anger, loss, grief, and shame. Let's talk about anger first. Sometimes women are angry at their abusers or at people who they feel didn't protect them. In some cases, these are their mothers. Sometimes, if they can't express their anger, they turn it inward and become depressed. Some anger may come out in self-harming behavior, such as cutting or burning. In some cases, anger is covering up another feeling, such as fear or sadness.
	Write "Anger" on the flip-chart pad and list the women's responses to the question. Common responses are yell, cry, hit their children, take time alone, exercise, and throw things. *Give participants a few minutes to write the ways they express anger on pages 130–131 in their workbooks.*	What are some of the ways in which women express anger?
	Write "Loss" on the flip-chart pad and list the women's experiences of loss.	Now let's talk about loss. It's a common feeling among women who've been abused and also among women who have problems with addiction. Some women have had multiple losses: of their children, their family members, their childhood innocence, and their health. Think back on your life and the losses you've experienced. What are some of them?

Duplicating this page is illegal. Do not copy this material without written permission from the publisher.

355

TIME & TOPIC	FACILITATOR NOTES	DISCUSSION WITH WOMEN
	Write "Grief" on the flip-chart pad and list the women's responses. Typical responses are cry, isolate themselves, pray, use rituals, make scrapbooks, write, and honor anniversaries of loss. You can suggest that the women make notes in their workbooks on page 132, if there is time.	What is grief? Grief is a response to loss, and it includes sadness. What are some ways in which people grieve for their losses?
	Write "Shame" on the flip-chart pad and list the women's responses to the question. Allow the women to spend a few minutes writing about how shame has affected their lives in the space provided on pages 133–134 in their workbooks.	Now let's talk about shame. Shame is the feeling that there's something wrong or bad about you. Many women experience shame. Especially when women are abused, either as children or as adults, they often feel ashamed and believe somehow the abuse was their fault. Sometimes these women have been taught by their abusers to believe that when someone really gets to know them, that person will find out how bad or stupid or disappointing they are and will then want to leave them or abuse them. This unresolved trauma can take a terrible toll on their future attempts at relationships. Substance-abusing women often feel shame because of the stigma society places on addicted women. Shame is learned. It can come from people who influence us as well as from cultural and social messages. Shame can become a very destructive issue in a woman's self-concept.

Shame is different from guilt, which is when a woman feels there is something wrong or bad about her behavior.

What kinds of things cause a woman to feel shame? In this list, what are some things that women are taught by society to feel shame about? |

TIME & TOPIC	FACILITATOR NOTES	DISCUSSION WITH WOMEN
10–15 min. **Activity: Losses**	*After two to three minutes, ask the women to stop writing.* *Give everyone an opportunity to briefly share. If people want to pass, let them.* *After the women have shared their losses, ask them how they felt listening to others describe their losses.*	Please turn to page 131 in the workbook. You will find a place to write about the losses in your life. Take a few moments to write some of your thoughts about losses in your life. If you feel comfortable doing so, please share one loss you've had in your life. Who will volunteer to start?
3–5 min. **Lecture: Empathy and Compassion**	*Have the women spend a few minutes answering the two questions about empathy and compassion in the space provided on pages 134–135 in their workbooks, if time allows.*	The ability to share in another person's feelings and emotions is called *empathy*. Some of us seem to have empathy naturally, and others do not. Yet it's an important feeling to have in our relationships with others and for our own well-being. If a woman falls down and is frightened, you will probably sense her emotional distress. Empathy, or feeling with another person, is different from sympathy, which is feeling sorry for another person. In this group, we've had the opportunity to share feelings and empathize with one another. This has occurred through a process of sharing personal or intimate experiences, being nonjudgmental listeners for one another, and recognizing the same feelings in ourselves that other group members feel. Developing the feeling of empathy enables us to be more compassionate. This is when we sense the suffering or trouble of another person and we care about it. We often may want to help. It's important for our relationships to learn to feel empathy and compassion. It's also important for us to feel compassion for ourselves and the pain we've suffered.

TIME & TOPIC	FACILITATOR NOTES	DISCUSSION WITH WOMEN
5–8 min. **Activity:** **Yoga Pose**	*The third yoga pose in this curriculum is the Modified Triangle pose. (Appendix 2 contains instructions and illustrations for all the yoga poses.)*	Now let's do another yoga pose. Yoga poses can help you be more consciously aware of your body and your breathing. This is particularly important if you have a history of abuse or other forms of trauma. The Modified Triangle pose targets tissues in the inner legs, lower back, and hips. It offers a nice stretch to the side of the body and the ribs. The spinal twist massages and supports the spinal column and soothes the nerves that branch out from each of the vertebrae and connect with every other part of the body. Symbolically, the triangle, or pyramid shape, represents the balance and unity between the three interconnected aspects of being: mind, body, and spirit.

MODIFIED TRIANGLE YOGA POSE

1. Please stand and face your chair.

2. Hold your arms out to your sides in a "T" position.

3. Open your legs wide until your ankles align under your wrists. This wide stance offers a solid and steady foundation for the pose.

4. Place both hands on the seat of your chair, with your hands apart—about the width of your shoulders. Keep your arms straight.

5. Bend forward from the hips. This may yield a nice hamstring stretch. Hold this for several breaths.

6. With your legs straight, keep your left foot facing forward, but pivot the right foot out so its toes point to the side. This will create a tug to the inner right leg.

7. Next, reach toward the ceiling or sky with your left arm and hand. Your left hip will follow, so your chest and gaze will be toward the left. Hold this pose while taking five to ten breaths.

This exercise stretches the inner leg while rotating the spine in a gentle twist, stimulating the tissues of the lower back.

8. If you have difficulty reaching upward with a straight arm, you can place your reaching hand on your hip instead.

9. Now bring both hands back to your seat, with your hands apart—about the width of your shoulders. Keep your arms straight.

10. We will repeat the Modified Triangle exercise on the other side.

11. Hold your arms out to your sides in a "T" position.

12. Open your legs wide until your ankles align under your wrists.

13. Place both hands on the seat of your chair.

TIME & TOPIC	FACILITATOR NOTES	DISCUSSION WITH WOMEN

14. Bend forward from the hips. Hold this for several breaths.

15. With your legs straight, keep your right foot facing forward, but pivot the left foot out so its toes point to the side.

16. Next, reach toward the ceiling or sky with your right arm and hand. Your right hip will follow, so your chest and gaze will be toward the right. Hold this pose for five to ten breaths.

17. If you have difficulty reaching upward with a straight arm, you can place your reaching hand on your hip instead.

Now please have a seat and get comfortable in your chairs.

Anyone want to share their experience with this pose?

15–20 min.

Activity: Meeting a Feeling

If the group members have a great deal of difficulty with anger, you may want to have all the women choose anger as the feeling to understand better.

As you read these instructions, pause between each numbered item, to allow the women time to breathe, envision what is suggested, and so on.

Please pick a feeling you have often, one you've had very recently, or one you'd like to understand better.

1. Close your eyes and begin to relax, noticing your breath as you breathe in and out.

2. Begin to balance your breath by breathing in to a count of four and breathing out to a count of four.

3. Notice any tension or pain anywhere in your body and visualize sending fresh air to these tense areas.

4. Let the tension or pain go as you breathe out. Feel yourself letting go.

5. Imagine yourself walking on a lovely country path.

6. The sun is shining. The leaves are rustling in the trees. And birds are singing.

TIME & TOPIC	FACILITATOR NOTES	DISCUSSION WITH WOMEN
		7. You are walking on this path toward a place . . . a small house . . . where a wise friend has been many times and has encouraged you to explore.
		8. As you walk along, you see a beautiful, small building in front of you.
		9. On the front door of the house, there's a note to you from your friend, welcoming you. Knowing that you've found the right place, you enter the building and begin to look for the staircase your friend described to you.
		10. In your imagination, see yourself standing at the top of a staircase that is brightly lit from a lantern light above it.
		11. Another lantern light is sitting at the top of the stairs, and you pick it up.
		12. You're looking down at seven steps. You're going to walk down them to the bottom, knowing that you'll be completely relaxed when you get there and that you can stop at any step.
	When counting the steps, keep your voice even, allowing the same amount of time between each count.	13. You are going down the steps: seven . . . six . . . five . . . four . . . three . . . two . . . one.
		14. Now you're at the bottom, and you are standing there holding the lantern light. This is the light of consciousness.
		15. You realize you've come here to explore your inner self. With your free hand, you pick up a strong, silken cord that you can pull anytime you wish to be lifted up out of your inner self. You know you're safe, and you feel ready to start your exploration.

TIME & TOPIC	FACILITATOR NOTES	DISCUSSION WITH WOMEN
		16. Now you begin to explore your inner self.
		17. Walk around inside yourself and look for the feeling that you picked.
		18. When you find the feeling, shine your light on it.
		19. See what it looks like.
		20. Walk around it and look at its shape.
	Pause.	
		21. Notice its size.
	Pause.	
		22. Notice what color it is.
	Pause.	
		23. Now ask your feeling what it's doing for you.
	Pause.	
		24. Then ask what it needs from you.
	Pause.	
		25. Ask the feeling if it has any more information for you.
		26. Then thank the feeling for making itself known to you.
		27. Shine your light on it, say good-bye, and explain that you may visit again.
		28. Surround the feeling with love and appreciation.
	When counting the steps, keep your voice even, allowing the same amount of time between each count.	29. Now it's time to go back to the bottom of the stairs, using your lantern to light the way. When you reach the stairs, begin to walk up the seven stairs to the top. One . . . two . . . three . . . four . . . five . . . six . . . seven.

TIME & TOPIC	FACILITATOR NOTES	DISCUSSION WITH WOMEN
		30. Return the lantern to its place at the top of the stairs. Then walk outside.
		31. As you leave the beautiful small house, silently thank your friend for telling you about this opportunity.
		32. Begin to feel the sunshine. Hear the birds chirping. And the wind rustling.
		Now please take a few deep breaths and bring yourself back into this room and the group.
	Allow three to five minutes for the women to draw their feelings and answer the questions about the feeling.	Please turn to page 138 in your workbook. There's space for you to draw a picture of the feeling you met. It may be a specific shape, design, or symbol. Please answer the questions on page 139 of your workbook too.
	Allow participants to briefly share their answers.	Let's go around the group so you can share your drawings and tell us what you learned from the feeling—what it does for you, what it needs, and so on.
5–8 min. **Lecture: Happiness**		One of the feelings that people want in their lives is happiness. So often we think that happiness is something we'll feel when we have the right job, the right partner, or the right amount of money. Or maybe we think happiness will come after we do all of our healing work. However, people who study happiness have found that happiness doesn't come from things. What's going on in your life—health, money, relationships, prestige, and so on—predicts only about 10 percent of your happiness. A man named Shawn Achor (2013) studied happiness, and his findings may be surprising to you. You don't achieve happiness by achieving success or making more money or anything that's external.

TIME & TOPIC	FACILITATOR NOTES	DISCUSSION WITH WOMEN
	Present the following information or have participants take turns reading this information aloud together on page 140 of their workbooks. *List the things on the flip-chart pad as you describe them.*	You feel happy when the chemical dopamine is released in your brain. That's it. So, how can you increase the dopamine in your brain? Well, one way is to take two minutes every day to do one of these things. 1. Write down three things you're grateful for. 2. Write in your diary or journal or workbook about one positive experience you've had in the last twenty-four hours. 3. Learn to meditate, to teach your brain to focus. 4. Use the first text or email you write every day to praise or thank someone you know. Or say something nice to the first person you see each day. Spread the happy. It's important to spend two minutes each day doing one of these four things for the next twenty-one days. Research shows that this will increase your happiness. Do one of these things in the next day or so and then write about it on pages 140–141 in your workbook.
5 min. **Reflection**	*If there is time, allow participants to spend some time writing or drawing about their experience in this session. Then have participants briefly share their answers. If people want to pass, let them.*	Now let's do our reflection. What was an important part of today's session for you?

TIME & TOPIC	FACILITATOR NOTES	DISCUSSION WITH WOMEN
5 min. **Between-Sessions Activity**		For your Between-Sessions Activity, practice your Observer Self in two situations. Do this before our next session. Please also notice when you feel empathy for another person or compassion for yourself. And please pick one of the four ways to increase your happiness and use this technique each day before our next session.
5 min. **Activity: Affirmation**		Now let's do a simple activity that can let a positive belief soak in or reinforce a calming self-statement or affirmation. 1. Begin to breathe slowly and deeply. Do slow breathing, just as you did when you were blowing bubbles. 2. Hold the nail bed of your thumb between the thumb and pointing finger of the other hand. 3. Create an image or phrase in your mind. This can be an affirmation or statement that's comforting or soothing to you. Examples are "I am feeling peaceful," "I am safe," and "I am relaxed." Or you can verbalize a soothing image, such as "I am floating on a cloud." 4. Say the phrase aloud. As you say it, squeeze the sides of your thumb's nail bed and hold it for each breath, exhaling and then inhaling.
	Allow time for the women to repeat the phrasing and breathing ten times.	5. Repeat this using a different finger each time. Try to use slow breathing (count to seven or more as you inhale and then count to seven or more as you exhale).
	Allow participants to briefly share their answers.	How do you feel now?

TIME & TOPIC	FACILITATOR NOTES	DISCUSSION WITH WOMEN
1 min. **Closing**		Today we've had another powerful session, and you've made that happen. I want to thank you all for sharing. It's very special to see how connected you've become as a group. I look forward to seeing you at our next session on *[date and time]*.

Session Notes

ADAPTING THE SESSION FOR USE WITH GIRLS

When discussing feelings of anger, loss and grief, and shame, you can ask the girls some additional questions. For example:

- Are there other words you use for this feeling?
- What might trigger this emotion?
- How does your body feel?
- Do you ever express this feeling with your behavior?
- How do the people around you respond to you when you are communicating this feeling?

In discussing anger with the girls, you may want to use the Anger Funnel as a way for the girls to understand that sometimes there are feelings that are buried or unexpressed (such as hurt, sadness, fear, insecurity, or frustration) that then come out as anger. (A copy can be found in appendix 4.)

Hurt, Sadness, Fear, Insecurity, Frustration

Anger, Rage, and Violence

Adapted from *Helping Men Recover: A Program for Treating Addiction.* Copyright 2011 by S. Covington, D. Griffin & R. Dauer. This material is used by permission of John Wiley & Sons, Inc.

continued

ADAPTING THE SESSION FOR USE WITH GIRLS

Some focused questions on anger are "What are some ways in which girls your age show their anger?" "How do you express your anger?" "How have you seen others express their anger?"

In discussing shame, you may want to substitute the word *embarrassment.*

Be sure you spend some time on the steps to achieve happiness. Girls receive many messages about what should make them happy. They're particularly sensitive to these messages because they're uniquely targeted. Girls usually believe their happiness is based on things external to themselves, such as friends, clothes, grades, popularity, and dates. An option would be to do a collage on the media messages about happiness versus true happiness. Also, you can encourage them to do their selected steps every day for twenty-one days.

Healthy Relationships

▦ Time

Two hours

▦ Goals of the Session

1. To learn the elements of a healthy relationship
2. To realize the healing power of healthy relationships

▦ Participant Objectives

By the end of this session, participants will be able to:

1. Define a healthy relationship
2. Explain how respect, mutuality, and compassion are at the core of a loving relationship

▦ Materials Needed

- Relaxing music and equipment to play music
- Each participant's and the facilitator's workbook
- A pencil or pen for the facilitator and each woman
- A newsprint flip-chart pad, an easel, and felt-tip pens
- Magazines for the collage activity
- A piece of poster board for each participant
- Colored felt-tip pens or crayons, glue sticks, and scissors for the participants (a set for every woman or every two women is preferable)
- Masking tape
- *Optional: A DVD player and monitor and Segment 10: Characteristics of a Healthy Relationship from the* Beyond Trauma *Participant Video*
- Facial tissues

continued

Duplicating this page is illegal. Do not copy this material without written permission from the publisher.

369

HEALTHY RELATIONSHIPS

■ **Session Overview**

- Quiet Time
- Check-In
- Review of Between-Sessions Activity
- Goals of the Session
- Discussion: What Is a Healthy Relationship?
- Lecture: Defining a Healthy Relationship
- Lecture: The Brain and Relationships
- Lecture: The Relationship Wheel
- *Optional:* Beyond Trauma *Participant Video (Segment 10: Characteristics of a Healthy Relationship)*
- Lecture: Characteristics of a Healthy Relationship
- Activity: Yoga Pose
- Discussion: Contrasting the Relationship Wheel and the Power and Control Wheel
- Activity: The Relationship Wheel
- Lecture: The Wheel of Love
- Activity: Love Collage
- Reflection
- Between-Sessions Activity
- Activity: Palms Down, Palms Up
- Closing

continued

HEALTHY RELATIONSHIPS

Background Information for the Facilitator

Preparing for the Love Collage Activity

You'll need more magazines for the women to use in creating their collages—enough for all of them to be able to find pictures and words to use. You'll also need to leave time at the end of this activity for each woman to briefly share her collage with the group. This will take approximately one minute per person.

Preparing for the Between-Sessions Activity

You'll want to remind participants to choose an object to bring to the next session. You should plan to bring an object as well.

The Session

TIME & TOPIC	FACILITATOR NOTES	DISCUSSION WITH WOMEN
2 min. **Quiet Time**	*Begin playing the soft music.* *After one and a half to two minutes, ask the women to take a deep breath and focus on the group.*	Welcome to session 11 of *Beyond Trauma: A Healing Journey for Women*. This session is about healthy relationships. First, let's get settled. You may want to sit silently in order to let yourself unwind and relax, or you may want to focus on your breathing. You may prefer to stand and slowly walk around the room. Some of you may want to do tapping on the top of your head, your forehead, your cheeks, and your shoulders. Or you may want to find a focal point in the room and just look at it for the next minute or so. Let's begin our quiet time now.
5–10 min. **Check-In**	*Allow participants to check in. If people want to pass, let them, but be sure to follow up with anyone who passes after this session.*	Welcome to one of our most upbeat sessions. We'll be exploring the subjects of healthy relationships and love. These are actually some of the best healing tools for trauma survivors. First, let's check in. How about a quick weather report from each of you: one or two sentences about how you are feeling, as in "sunny," "gray and cloudy," and so on.

TIME & TOPIC	FACILITATOR NOTES	DISCUSSION WITH WOMEN
5–10 min. **Review of Between-Sessions Activity**	*Allow participants to respond.*	Let's talk about when and how you used the Observer Self technique we practiced in the last session. Please share when you used it and what the result was. Now please share a situation in which you felt empathy or compassion. Please also let us know which of the happiness exercises you're doing each day.
1 min. **Goals of the Session**		The goals of today's session are to learn the elements of a healthy relationship and to realize the healing power of healthy relationships.
5–10 min. **Discussion: What Is a Healthy Relationship?**	*Write the women's responses on the flip-chart pad.* *Write the women's responses on the flip-chart pad.*	What is a healthy relationship? Please tell us in your own words what you think a healthy relationship is. Have you had one or seen one? What did it look like and sound like?
3–5 min. **Lecture: Defining a Healthy Relationship**	*As you name the following elements of a healthy, growth-fostering relationship, write each one on the flip-chart pad. Instead of writing them on the flip chart, you can also review them together on page 145 in the workbook.*	Here's how psychologists define a healthy, growth-fostering relationship (Miller 1986, 1990). It's one in which each person: 1. *Feels a greater sense of zest, vitality, and energy.* This happens because you're both putting energy into the relationship, and the energy is moving between you. In contrast, several days later, you may meet a different friend and, afterward, you may feel sapped and exhausted. This can happen when you're the one giving the energy to the relationship, and your friend is just taking.

TIME & TOPIC	FACILITATOR NOTES	DISCUSSION WITH WOMEN
		2. The second element of a healthy relationship is that each person *feels more able to act and does act*. A healthy relationship empowers you to act, and you feel free to take action in your life.
		3. The third element is that each person *has a more accurate perception of herself and the other person*. "Because I'm in this relationship with you, I see parts of myself that I wouldn't see or know if I were alone."
		4. The fourth element is that each person *feels a greater sense of self-worth*. "I feel good about myself in this relationship with you."
		5. The fifth element is that each person *feels more connected to the other person and feels a greater motivation for connection with other people* beyond those in this specific relationship. "As time goes on, I feel more and more connected to you, and I also feel a desire to have friends and be connected to others."
3–5 min. **Lecture: The Brain and Relationships**		In some of our earlier sessions, we talked about the effects of trauma on the brain. Researchers have learned that there are parts of the brain that are very connected to relationships and the ability to have healthy relationships. Today we also know that healthy relationships are an important part of healing from trauma. This new area of study is called *relational neuroscience* (Banks 2015). We discussed this earlier in session 4 when we talked about SEEDS (Arden 2014). If you remember, the first S is for social connectivity. There is hardwiring throughout our brains and bodies that's

Duplicating this page is illegal. Do not copy this material without written permission from the publisher.

375

TIME & TOPIC	FACILITATOR NOTES	DISCUSSION WITH WOMEN
		designed to help us engage in satisfying, emotional connection with others. Different parts of our brains determine how we connect with others, such as how calm we feel around others, how accepted we feel by others, how we resonate with the feelings of others, and how we're energized by our relationships with others. Amy Banks, a psychiatrist, has developed the C.A.R.E. system that can help us retrain or rewire our brains. Her book is titled *Four Ways to Click: Rewire Your Brain for Stronger, More Rewarding Relationships.* This is a resource some of you may want to investigate.

Relational neuroscience has also discovered that when we're cut off from others, our brains suffer. This can result in chronic irritability and anger, depression, addiction, and chronic physical illness. This is similar to the information we learned in an earlier session about the Adverse Childhood Experiences Study. From that, we learned about the effects of negative childhood experiences. Now we know that we're just not as healthy when we try to stand on our own and be totally independent. This is what many of us were told was the goal of adult development; however, it isn't true. The goal of adult development is to be connected with others. The human brain is built to operate within a network of caring human relationships. We reach our human potential through safe and caring relationships. Even if we don't have these now, it's possible to heal and strengthen our brains in order to create them. |

TIME & TOPIC	FACILITATOR NOTES	DISCUSSION WITH WOMEN
		One of the themes in our sessions has been the power of relationships. They have the power to create tremendous harm and pain. Relationships also have the power to create deep healing.
5 min. **Lecture: The Relationship Wheel**		Let's take a look at page 146 in your workbook. This is the Relationship Wheel. The core of healthy relationships is respect, mutuality, and compassion. **Relationship Wheel** Relationship Wheel reprinted with permission from Institute for Relational Development. Copyright © 2000 by Stephanie Covington and Anne Dosher. "The Discipline of Compassion." Unpublished manuscript.
	Present the following information or read it aloud together as a group from the workbook.	*Respect* is the appreciation of someone's values. It begins to grow when we become aware of the person's integrity. We learn to respect others when we see the good decisions they make when the choices are difficult. We often earn respect when we're willing to do the right thing or take the "right action," particularly when the choice is difficult.

TIME & TOPIC	FACILITATOR NOTES	DISCUSSION WITH WOMEN
		Mutuality means there is an equal investment in the relationship. Each person has a willingness and desire to really see the other as well as to be seen, to really hear the other as well as to be heard, and to respect the other's vulnerability as well as to be vulnerable. Mutuality also means there's an awareness of the "we," not a sole focus on the self or the other. As we noted in the last session, compassion is similar to empathy, but it occurs on a deeper level. *Empathy* is understanding others' feelings and being able to feel with them. *Compassion* means we go a step further and join with the other person in her struggle or pain. When we're compassionate, we give of ourselves to be with the other person emotionally. When we're compassionate, we want to help the person who is suffering.
8 min. Optional: ***Beyond Trauma* Participant Video** Segment 10	**Segment 10: Characteristics of a Healthy Relationship** *Rather than deliver this next lecture yourself, you may choose to show segment 10 of the video instead. You could also have the group read this information aloud together on pages 147–149 in their workbooks. Or they can follow your lecture in their workbooks.*	Let's watch a video segment that talks about the characteristics of a healthy relationship.
5–10 min. **Lecture: Characteristics of a Healthy Relationship**	*As you name the following characteristics, write each one on the flip-chart pad. You may also want to write important aspects of each one.*	Now we'll look at characteristics that go a long way toward creating a healthy relationship. I want to emphasize the importance of supportive relationships in our lives. Supportive relationships help sustain recovery and healing.

1. The first one is *similarities*. Of course, similarities of temperament and shared interests between partners are certainly desirable, important, and contribute to fun. However, some of the more important similarities are the role of the relationship in each person's life and a shared vision of the future. Support for sobriety is also a crucial similarity if one or both of the partners are committed to recovery.

2. The second characteristic is *the ability to deal with change*. Life is always changing, requiring us to change and adapt along with it. Because people do change, their needs and perspectives on life are also bound to change over time. In love relationships, the changing needs of one of the partners can cause a major relationship conflict. Therefore, the ability to deal effectively with change is a crucial skill in relationships.

3. The third characteristic is *compatible values*. Some couples never discussed or paid attention to each other's values when they met. When a relationship moves into any kind of depth, values inevitably come into play. However, discussing values isn't enough. People's *real* values are reflected in how they live and what they do, rather than just what they say. Learning about people's values by observation takes time.

4. The fourth is *effective, open communication*. Good communication is fundamental to all human relationships. The clearness of the intent behind the message is one key to being understood.

TIME & TOPIC	FACILITATOR NOTES	DISCUSSION WITH WOMEN
		When a speaker isn't aware of her or his motives or isn't clear about her or his intent when speaking, and when the person's words or body language don't fit the context, the result is a mixed message. Mixed messages are confusing to the other person and can indicate that the speaker is insincere or not sure of what she or he really wants to say. Open and clear communication can reduce conflict by eliminating needless misunderstandings and resentments. 5. The fifth characteristic is *effective conflict resolution and anger resolution*. The closer the love relationship, the more individual differences become apparent—and the greater the possibility of conflict. Not only are differences to be expected, they can be wonderful assets in a relationship. However, differences can create challenges, particularly if there isn't open communication or if the two people don't have negotiation skills. When anger arises, it needs to be expressed clearly by using an "I" statement. An "I" statement is one that expresses the speaker's feelings or situation rather than blaming the other person. An "I" statement tells the other person how the situation affects you but doesn't attempt to describe the other person. Of course, effective anger resolution and conflict resolution don't include any threat of harm or violence. 6. The sixth characteristic is *effective negotiation*. Negotiation is a way of resolving conflict through problem solving. One way to think about negotiation is in terms of needs and wants. Needs are essential things a person

TIME & TOPIC	FACILITATOR NOTES	DISCUSSION WITH WOMEN
		has to have; wants are preferences. In a relationship, one person's needs should have preference over the other person's wants. Another way to negotiate is to think about what the relationship needs versus what each individual may need or want. In negotiation, the two parties discuss what each is willing to give or give up to move closer to a mutually satisfying settlement. 7. The seventh characteristic is *firm personal boundaries*. People have physical, emotional, and intellectual boundaries that can be violated in different ways. In order to create a strong love relationship, it's important for each person not only to know when and how to set clear limits but also to accept and honor the boundaries and limits set by the partner. Ideally, personal boundaries are based on your own internal cues, not on reactions to external triggers. 8. The eighth characteristic is *healthy sexual expression*. Healthy sexuality is a source of sensual and physical pleasure. It can be an expression of trust, love, tenderness, fondness, creativity, and playfulness. Sexuality is a powerful form of communication. It's important for partners to identify what they communicate or—more commonly—what they don't communicate to each other about sex. Building a climate of intimacy in which they feel free to express their sensuality and sexuality with each other is crucial. 9. The ninth characteristic is *shared quality time*. In our complicated world, there can be vast differences between the time needs and the time availability of

TIME & TOPIC	FACILITATOR NOTES	DISCUSSION WITH WOMEN
		two partners. At its best, quality time is leisure time, open-ended, without built-in schedules or endings. It's time in which events, communication, and activities are allowed to unfold at their own pace, without a specific agenda. It requires nothing except a couple's willingness to be with each other openly, accepting and allowing whatever comes. Although it may be difficult to arrange time for just the two persons, without friends, children, and other family members, it's an important element of a relationship. 10. The tenth characteristic is *friendship*. It's the cornerstone of intimate relationships. Friendship certainly isn't a precondition for starting an intimate love relationship, but it's hard to imagine that, over time, a relationship could evolve into a healthy, successful, loving partnership without developing a strong element of friendship (Covington and Beckett 1988). These characteristics of healthy relationships are by no means limited to romantic-love partnerships. They are important for any relationship that holds the promise of openness and intimacy and healing, including friendship. Those of you who are interested in learning more about relationships may want to read *Leaving the Enchanted Forest: The Path from Relationship Addiction to Intimacy* (Covington and Beckett 1988). This was the first book written by Stephanie Covington, the author of this program, and many people have found it very helpful.

TIME & TOPIC	FACILITATOR NOTES	DISCUSSION WITH WOMEN
5 min. **Activity:** **Yoga Pose**	*The fourth yoga pose in this curriculum is the Twisted Branches to Open Wings set of poses. (Appendix 2 contains instructions and illustrations for all the yoga poses.)*	Now let's do another yoga pose. This one is called Twisted Branches to Open Wings. The two poses in it complement one another and offer muscular release to the upper back, shoulders, and chest. They work in harmony to stimulate the lungs and heart. In yoga, lungs symbolically represent the ability to let go of stagnant energy (by exhaling) and invite in new life and possibility (by inhaling). Combining breath and movement aids the transformation of grief into a desire to explore the fullness of life and to feel safe doing so. Stimulating the heart helps a person move out of anxiety and into the ability to trust one's intuition and insight, create healthy boundaries, and experience joy.

TWISTED BRANCHES TO OPEN WINGS YOGA POSE

1. Please stand.

2. Because each person's bone structure is different, Twisted Branches can be done in a number of ways, so you can find the one that feels best for your body. The gentlest pose is simply to cross your arms in front of your chest, resting your crossed hands on your shoulders in what looks like a self-hug. Do this while taking five to ten breaths.

3. The second option is to cross your upper arms by resting the elbow of one arm in the soft elbow crease of the opposite arm. Your hands may be back to back, or you may be able to bring the palms together. Crossing your arms in front causes your shoulder blades to stretch, which facilitates the release of tension in the upper back. Take five to ten breaths while doing this pose.

TIME & TOPIC	FACILITATOR NOTES	DISCUSSION WITH WOMEN

4. Then release your arms and clasp your hands together behind your back to create the Open Wings pose. Depending on your bone structure and level of comfort, your arms can be straight or your elbows can be bent. This compresses and relaxes the tissues of the upper back and the shoulder blades, while simultaneously offering a stretch across the chest.

5. Drop your chin toward your chest to provide a new level of release in the back of the head, neck, and upper back. Hold this pose while taking five to ten breaths.

6. Repeat the Twisted Branches pose with the other arm on top. Take five to ten breaths.

7. Then complete another Open Wings pose. Take five to ten breaths.

Now please relax and take your seats.

5–10 min.

Discussion: Contrasting the Relationship Wheel and the Power and Control Wheel

Now let's look at the differences between the Relationship Wheel and the Power and Control Wheel. You'll find them both on page 151 in your workbook.

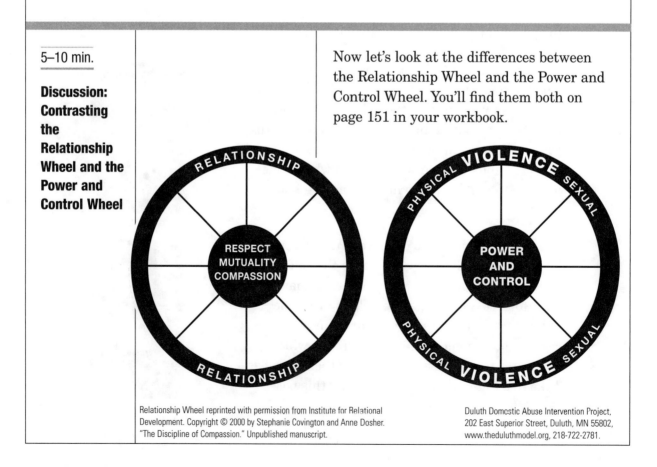

Relationship Wheel reprinted with permission from Institute for Relational Development. Copyright © 2000 by Stephanie Covington and Anne Dosher. "The Discipline of Compassion." Unpublished manuscript.

Duluth Domestic Abuse Intervention Project, 202 East Superior Street, Duluth, MN 55802, www.theduluthmodel.org, 218-722-2781.

	Allow participants to briefly share their answers.	In the center of the Relationship Wheel are respect, mutuality, and compassion. The Power and Control Wheel shows power and control at the center of violence and abuse. Do you remember when we discussed power and control? What roles do power and control play in your current relationships? In the session on power and abuse, we looked at various examples of abuse on the Power and Control Wheel. When you look at the Power and Control Wheel and the Relationship Wheel, what comes up for you? What are you thinking and feeling?
10 min. **Activity: The Relationship Wheel**	*Give each participant a pencil or pen. After about seven minutes, call time. Tell the women they can work more on their Relationship Wheels between the sessions [if this is possible].*	Now look at the Relationship Wheel on page 153 in your workbook. What would you want on your Relationship Wheel? You can use some of the things we just discussed or add anything else that's important to you. Some women add things like "a partner with good mental health" and "economic equality." Take six or seven minutes and begin to fill in the spokes on your Relationship Wheel.
5 min. **Lecture: The Wheel of Love**	*Draw the Wheel of Love on the flip-chart pad.* Wheel of Love reprinted with permission from Institute for Relational Development. Copyright © 2000 by Stephanie Covington and Anne Dosher. "The Discipline of Compassion." Unpublished manuscript.	

TIME & TOPIC	FACILITATOR NOTES	DISCUSSION WITH WOMEN
		The core of the Relationship Wheel creates the Wheel of Love. Love is created by respect, mutuality, and compassion. Love is both a feeling and a behavior. Most of us spend our time focusing on or searching for the feeling of love. The reality is that we know when someone truly loves us by his or her behavior. Feeling love can be easy; we even talk about "falling in love" as though it's an accident. And people often mistake physical attraction, or lust, for love. Real love is created by respect, mutuality, and compassion. Remember, love is both a feeling and a behavior. Falling in love is often easy. Acting in a loving way often is more difficult. The challenge we all have in our lives is to become more loving human beings.

Love is also a key way in which relationships have the power to heal trauma, both by experiencing someone else's loving behavior and by acting in loving ways toward others.

What has stood out for you in this session so far? What is the most important thing you have learned? |
| | *Allow participants to briefly share their answers.* | I'd like to close this discussion of love with a quotation from a famous German writer, Rainer Maria Rilke:

"For one human being to love another; that is perhaps the most difficult of all our tasks, the ultimate, the last test and proof, the work for which all other work is but preparation."

—Rainer Maria Rilke |

TIME & TOPIC	FACILITATOR NOTES	DISCUSSION WITH WOMEN
25–30 min. **Activity:** **Love Collage**	*You'll need to allot about twenty minutes for the women to work on their collages and about one minute per person at the end of this activity for each woman to briefly share her collage with the group.* *Distribute the collage materials to the group members: poster boards (one per person), magazines, colored felt-tip pens or crayons, glue sticks, and scissors.* *If the women need to share any of the materials, such as glue sticks and scissors, make that clear.* *After fifteen to twenty minutes, tell the women they have five minutes left. After five minutes, call time and ask the women to share their collages with the group.*	Now we're going to create collages about love. We have many magazines you can take pictures and words from. You may want to draw or write on your collages. Each person will have her own poster board for her collage. This time, I'd like you to select and arrange images and words into three sections in your collage: those that depict for you love in the past, love in the present, and what you hope for love in the future. When we use the word *love*, it can mean more than romantic love. You'll have about twenty minutes to work on your collages.
5 min. **Reflection**	*Give participants about a minute to write their answer to this question in the Reflection section of their workbook on page 156. Then have participants briefly share their answers. If people want to pass, let them.*	What did you learn about yourself or your relationships from this session?

TIME & TOPIC	FACILITATOR NOTES	DISCUSSION WITH WOMEN
5 min. **Between-Sessions Activity**		Please turn to page 157 in your workbook. You'll see a Relationship Scale.

THE RELATIONSHIP SCALE

1. Similarities	1	2	3	4	5	6	7	8	9	10
2. Ability to Deal with Change	1	2	3	4	5	6	7	8	9	10
3. Compatible Values	1	2	3	4	5	6	7	8	9	10
4. Effective, Open Communication	1	2	3	4	5	6	7	8	9	10
5. Effective Conflict/ Anger Resolution	1	2	3	4	5	6	7	8	9	10
6. Effective Negotiation	1	2	3	4	5	6	7	8	9	10
7. Firm Personal Boundaries	1	2	3	4	5	6	7	8	9	10
8. Healthy Sexual Expression	1	2	3	4	5	6	7	8	9	10
9. Shared Quality Time	1	2	3	4	5	6	7	8	9	10
10. Friendship	1	2	3	4	5	6	7	8	9	10

Relationship Scale Chart [pp. 115-16] from *Leaving the Enchanted Forest* by Stephanie Covington and Liana Beckett. Copyright © 1988 by Stephanie Covington and Liana Beckett. Reprinted by permission of HarperCollins Publishers.

TIME & TOPIC	FACILITATOR NOTES	DISCUSSION WITH WOMEN
		For your Between-Sessions Activity, think about one of your current relationships. It doesn't have to be a sexual relationship. Then circle the number on the scale that shows where you rate your relationship *now*. Your rating should be based on specific behaviors or situations. The number 1 represents the low end of the scale, and 10 represents the high end. Then mark with an arrow the place on the scale where you *want* your relationship to be. Finally, choose one item from the list that is a top priority for you. Think about what you can do to change this in your relationship, and consider discussing your wish with this other person. Second, continue to think about the love in your life. You can make some notes about your collage in your workbook on page 155. Keep working on your collage if you like. You may want to create a poem, picture, or song, or use some other creative means, but do something to express your feelings about the love you have and want in your life. Third, you may also want to continue filling in the spaces on your Relationship Wheel with the things that are important to you in a relationship. Finally, please bring something important to you to the next session. It may be an actual object (such as a special stone or a ring or a necklace or knickknack) or something that represents or symbolizes what is important to you (such as a photograph or drawing). Also, please bring your love collage back to the next session.

TIME & TOPIC	FACILITATOR NOTES	DISCUSSION WITH WOMEN
1–2 min. **Activity: Palms Down, Palms Up**	*Read the following slowly:*	Now let's do Palms Down, Palms Up again. 1. Sit comfortably with your back straight. Close your eyes or lower your eyelids and focus on your breathing. Take a slow, deep breath while counting to four. Then exhale slowly, counting to four. 2. Do this four more times until your breathing is slow and relaxed. 3. Keep breathing slowly and evenly. Hold your hands gently in front of you with your palms up and imagine them holding all the negative or upsetting thoughts and feelings you have had today. 4. Now turn your palms down. Imagine yourself emptying your hands of all the negative or upsetting things you've been carrying today. Let go of them. 5. Keep breathing slowly. Now, turn your palms up. Your palms are up and open to receive positive energy, thoughts, and feelings. Your palms are open to receive support and help. 6. Now slowly open your eyes. Remember, anytime you need to let go of something negative and receive the positive, you can take a few minutes to do this activity.
1 min. **Closing**		Congratulations on completing session 11 of this program. I hope this session has been inspiring for you, and you'll have a vision for the types of relationships you want in your life. Our next session is on *[date and time],* and we'll take time in that session to celebrate this group.

ADAPTING THE SESSION FOR USE WITH GIRLS

In the opening discussion about relationships, ask the girls about the relationships they see in the media. What do magazine ads, television shows, and films portray as important characteristics or qualities in relationships? Are these images based on people's real lives or on fantasy? Is reality TV real or not?

You may want to have the girls relook at the two teen wheels presented at the end of session 3 (the Teen Power and Control Wheel and the Equality Wheel for Teens are located in appendix 4) before they create their Relationship Wheels.

You also can adapt the Relationship Wheel and ask the girls to create a wheel of friendships between girls. They would fill in the spokes with the qualities they think are important in girls' friendships. What are the qualities they want in these relationships?

Depending on your group, the girls can do the Love Collage as it's described, or you can modify it. There could be two parts to the collage: one on love portrayed in the media and the other on love based on respect, mutuality, and compassion. Be sure when you're introducing these concepts that you have some discussion to ensure that the girls understand the meaning of each of these words.

MODULE C: SESSION 12

Endings and Beginnings

▨ Time

Two hours

▨ Goal of the Session

To understand the importance of connection in women's lives

▨ Participant Objectives

By the end of this session, participants will be able to:

1. Explain how to end relationships respectfully
2. Identify the important women in their lives
3. Describe the importance of connection and spirituality

▨ Materials Needed

- Relaxing music and equipment to play music

- Each participant's and the facilitator's workbook

- A pencil or pen for the facilitator and each woman

- A newsprint flip-chart pad, an easel, and felt-tip pens

- Masking tape

- A pretty piece of fabric, a scarf, or a tablecloth

- *Optional: A meaningful object (as described in session 11)*

- *Optional: A DVD player and monitor and Segment 11: Closing of
  the* Beyond Trauma *Participant Video*

- Facial tissues

continued

ENDINGS AND BEGINNINGS

■ **Session Overview**

- Quiet Time
- Check-In
- Review of Between-Sessions Activity
- Goal of the Session
- Activity: Building an Altar
- *Optional: Activity*
- Lecture and Discussion: Endings
- Activity: Appreciation
- Lecture and Discussion: The Meaning and Importance of Spirituality
- Lecture: Twelve Step Programs and Spirituality
- Activity: Loving Kindness Meditation
- *Optional: Meditation: Simple Guidelines to Practice Mindfulness*
- Activity: Mea1ningful Women in Our Lives
- *Optional: Readings*
- *Optional:* Beyond Trauma *Participant Video (Segment 11: Closing)*
- Closing

continued

ENDINGS AND BEGINNINGS

Background Information for the Facilitator

Preparing for the Building an Altar Activity

Bring a pretty piece of cloth, a scarf, or a tablecloth to the session. This will serve as the base for building an "altar" on which the women will place the objects they have brought. You may want to bring an object of your own and talk about it in the group.

Optional Activities and Readings

This session contains several options: an activity, a meditation, three readings, and the video. Knowing your group as you do, please pick the options you believe will resonate with the women.

The Session

TIME & TOPIC	FACILITATOR NOTES	DISCUSSION WITH WOMEN
2 min. **Quiet Time**	*Begin playing the soft music.* *After one and a half to two minutes, ask the women to take a deep breath and focus on the group.*	Welcome to session 12 of *Beyond Trauma: A Healing Journey for Women.* This session is about endings and beginnings. First, let's get settled. You may want to sit silently in order to let yourself unwind and relax, or you may want to focus on your breathing. You may prefer to stand and slowly walk around the room. Some of you may want to do tapping on the top of your head, your forehead, your cheeks, and your shoulders. Or you may want to find a focal point in the room and just look at it for the next minute or so. Let's begin our quiet time now.
5–10 min. **Check-In**	*Allow participants to briefly share their answers. If people want to pass, let them. If anyone expresses significant distress, plan to follow up with her after the session.*	What are you thinking and/or feeling after our session on healthy relationships? How are you feeling about this being our last session?
10 min. **Review of Between-Sessions Activity**		For your Between-Sessions Activity, you completed the Relationship Scale in your workbooks. You rated your relationship now and where you want your relationship to be, and you chose one item from the list that is a top priority. You thought about what you can do

TIME & TOPIC	FACILITATOR NOTES	DISCUSSION WITH WOMEN
	Encourage as many women as possible to share.	to improve your relationship, and maybe you discussed your wish with that person. Who will share her top priority and what she thinks she might do about it?
	Encourage as many women as possible to share.	Now who will share how it went when she discussed it with the other person in the relationship?
		It often takes two people to change a relationship, and often one person needs to start the process, so I congratulate those of you who had the courage to do this.
		Did anyone add to her collage? Who would like to share about that?
	Allow participants to briefly share their answers.	You also may have continued to fill in the spaces on your Relationship Wheel with the things that are important to you in a relationship. Does anyone want to share any additions she made to her wheel?
1 min. **Goal of the Session**		The goal of this session is to understand the importance of connection in women's lives. This is our time to say good-bye. Today we'll talk about the connections we've formed in this group and in our lives outside this group. We'll discuss the importance and meaning of these connections in our past, present, and future lives.
10 min. **Activity: Building an Altar**	*Put a pretty piece of cloth, a scarf, or a tablecloth in the center of the group on the floor to hold the objects the women have brought. (If you sit around a table, place it in the center.) The women*	

TIME & TOPIC	FACILITATOR NOTES	DISCUSSION WITH WOMEN
	have about a minute each to share. *When the women have finished sharing, place your object and tell what it represents for you.*	At the end of our last session, I asked you to bring something important to you to this session—something that represents what's meaningful and important to you. For those of you who brought things, would you please share a little about what your item means to you and why you chose to share it with us today? When you finish sharing, please place your object in the center of the circle. You can also place posters, your love collages, poems, songs, and anything else you brought in the center. In a way, we've created an "altar"—a place where we've put things that are special to us in our lives. These things symbolize what's important to us. Who will start?
Optional: Activity	*You may also want to have the group members do something together that is meaningful, such as making a clay sculpture, singing a song, writing a poem, or creating a drawing that represents the group (with each woman adding something to the drawing).* *Also encourage the women to write about the item they brought after the session is over. There is space provided to do this on pages 159 and 160 in their workbooks.*	

TIME & TOPIC	FACILITATOR NOTES	DISCUSSION WITH WOMEN
10–15 min. **Lecture and Discussion: Endings**		As I said before, this last session is about endings and beginnings. We're at the end of our work together. Over our past sessions, we've looked at trauma and abuse in women's lives, we've talked about how common it is in our lives, we've examined how it has affected us, and we've learned some skills to help us heal. Now it's time to close our group.
	As you discuss the following, write the important points on the flip-chart pad.	When you think about ending a relationship, what things come to mind? How have you ended relationships in the past? Have you ended a relationship well? If so, how did you do it? How do you end a relationship in a healthy, respectful way?
	Allow participants to briefly share their answers. If the women don't suggest any of the following, add them to the list.	Here are some additional guidelines that may be helpful when ending a relationship. These are on page 160 in the workbook.

GUIDELINES FOR ENDING A RELATIONSHIP

1. Be direct and honest.

2. Speak with "I" statements rather than "you" statements.

3. Express feelings being experienced in the present.

4. Assume personal responsibility for change.

5. Decide the level of physical and emotional intimacy you want with the person in the future.

6. Act in a timely fashion. Establish and adhere to agreed-on timelines by which changes should occur.

7. Let the other person know what you appreciate about her or him.

8. Let the other person know what you appreciated about the relationship.

9. Tell her or him what you wish you'd been able to do differently.

TIME & TOPIC	FACILITATOR NOTES	DISCUSSION WITH WOMEN
		I think there are a few points in this list that can be helpful to us in ending our group today. One is to be direct and honest. Throughout our group sessions, we've been learning how to be direct and honest with one another as well as with ourselves. We've also learned that honesty without sensitivity can feel brutal. In addition, we are being direct, honest, and sensitive about our ending.
	Depending on the circumstances, the group, or some members of it, may have the option of continuing to meet.	Another is to decide the level of intimacy or contact you want with one another. Even though our group is ending, some of you may decide to continue seeing and supporting one another.

Another point is to act in a timely fashion. We were clear about the timeline of the group when we began. The starting and ending times of each session, as well as when the group would end, were discussed. Of course, this part of ending a relationship is easier when it's a group relationship, not a love relationship. But in ending any relationship, being clear about the timeline is important. |
| 15–20 min.

Activity: Appreciation | *Allow each woman about a minute to express, in a few words, something she appreciates about each woman in the group. As the women are sharing, encourage each person to write down in her workbook on page 161 the things people appreciate about her.* | An important step is to express appreciation for each other. We're going to take some time now for each of you to express something you appreciate about each woman in the group. Each of you will have about one minute overall to do this. |

TIME & TOPIC	FACILITATOR NOTES	DISCUSSION WITH WOMEN
	Give the women a few minutes to think about and write down what they appreciate about the group in their workbooks on page 162. Then allow each woman about a minute to express what she has written about the group.	The next step is to express appreciation for this group as a whole. You also have an opportunity now to share something you've appreciated about the group.
		Over the past eleven sessions, we've learned that one of the essential parts of healing from trauma is moving out of isolation and learning to create connection. We've learned that sharing about ourselves and sharing our feelings with others helps create connection. The amazing thing about deep connection is that it never really ends. When you have a deep connection with another, it stays with you—even if you don't still have contact with the person, you often still carry her or him with you.
10–15 min. **Lecture and Discussion: The Meaning and Importance of Spirituality**	*On the flip-chart pad, write the word* religion *and make a list of what the word means for the group members. Possible definitions could include structure, dogma, faith, church.* *Then write the word* spirituality *on the flip-chart pad and list the group's responses to what spirituality means. If no one mentions connection, add this to the spirituality list. Possible responses could include wholeness, personal, serenity, nature.*	There are many ways to heal from trauma. Spirituality is one way to gain serenity and a sense of connection. Often, there's confusion about the terms *spirituality* and *religion*. Let's consider what religion means and what spirituality means.

TIME & TOPIC	FACILITATOR NOTES	DISCUSSION WITH WOMEN
	Read the following definition slowly, allowing the women to think about what it means to them. They can also read along in their workbook on page 163. *Write the women's ideas on the flip-chart pad. If the following aren't included, you may choose to add them:* • *scheduling quiet time* • *praying* • *meditating* • *singing and listening to music or other centering activities* • *being out in nature* • *writing in a journal* • *attending a church, synagogue, mosque, or temple* • *helping others in need* • *creating a personal altar*	Some define spirituality as oneness, wholeness, connection to the universe, belief in something greater than yourself, and trust in a higher or deeper part of yourself. We often hear the word *connection* associated with the word *spirituality*. Spirituality often means connection on multiple levels: • connection with self • connection with others • connection with nature and the earth • connection with a Higher Power One of the ways people develop their spirituality is through practice. Women in Twelve Step programs practice steps that are based on spiritual principles. With practice comes a deeper spiritual connection and healing. We know trauma disconnects women from themselves, others, and the world around them. It also disconnects women from their spirituality. Can you think of some examples of how a woman can practice to get more in touch with her spiritual side?

TIME & TOPIC	FACILITATOR NOTES	DISCUSSION WITH WOMEN
		A personal altar might be a grouping of personal items that are meaningful to you, such as a seashell from a memorable walk on the beach after a month of sobriety, a collar from a beloved pet, a photo of a significant person or event, a pinecone from a hike, a family photo, a prize from a fair, or a candle. It can be a special location where you can stop, pause, reflect, pray, meditate, and feel connected to a sense of time and place, history, accomplishment, and hope.
	• *learning from others*	Holding a quiet, safe, respectful meeting where you and other women can come together to share your hopes, dreams, and what is meaningful can be empowering. Sharing intimate stories can be inspiring and freeing.
	• *celebrating*	Integrate celebrations, rituals, and traditions into your daily routine. As women, we need to learn to celebrate ourselves, even when we're alone. One example is celebrating milestones, such as a birthday, receiving a high school diploma or GED, staying sober, sticking with an exercise program, or facing a tough problem. It's important to celebrate internal and external accomplishments. Such celebrations can offer stability, direction, and connection to your cultural roots, and reinforce positive conceptions of womanhood. Spiritual activities and rituals offer relationship and connection with family members, peers, and the community; with beliefs and values; with healing and protection; with support from others who are committed to helping you reach your goals; and with joy and hope.

TIME & TOPIC	FACILITATOR NOTES	DISCUSSION WITH WOMEN
	Discuss this and encourage the women to pursue activities that feed them spiritually. *Allow women a minute or so to write their answers to these questions in their workbooks on pages 164 and 165. If there is time, have participants share what they wrote, if they'd like to.*	How much time do you give yourself each week for personal reflection, meditation, cultural traditions, or discussions about life, meaning, and values? If you want to develop the spiritual side of yourself, what can you do to make that happen?
1 min. **Lecture: Twelve Step Programs and Spirituality**		In a Twelve Step program, Step Eleven recommends prayer and meditation as the means of cultivating "conscious contact" with a Higher Power. This nurtures a spiritual awakening that opens a connection and helps the healing journey from trauma, as well as from addiction. Spiritual practices such as prayer and meditation are important to your spiritual life and help form a relationship with yourself, others, your surroundings, and a Higher Power. Spirituality helps build a strong bridge of connection to many parts of a woman's life (Covington 2000b).

TIME & TOPIC	FACILITATOR NOTES	DISCUSSION WITH WOMEN
10 min. **Activity: Loving Kindness Meditation**		Meditation can help us find serenity in our world. It can help us feel calm and at peace deep inside. The practice of Metta or Loving Kindness meditation is a beautiful support to other mindfulness practices. One recites specific words and phrases that call up a "boundless warm-hearted feeling." The strength of this feeling isn't limited. You begin with yourself and gradually extend the wish for well-being and happiness to all. Let's take a few minutes to practice this. You can do this with your eyes open or closed.

	Give the following instructions in a calm voice, allowing time for the women to do each thing. They are reprinted/adapted with permission from The Issue at Hand *by Gil Fronsdal (2001, 2008):*	1. First, sit in a comfortable and relaxed manner.
		
		2. Take two or three deep breaths with slow, long, and complete exhalations.
		
		3. Let go of any concerns or preoccupations.
		
		4. Imagine or feel your breath moving through the center of your chest, in the area of your heart.
		
		5. Loving kindness is first practiced toward oneself, since we often have difficulty loving others without first loving ourselves. Mentally repeat, slowly and steadily, the following phrases:
		   • May I be happy.
		   • May I be well.
		   • May I be safe.
		   • May I be peaceful and at ease.

TIME & TOPIC	FACILITATOR NOTES	DISCUSSION WITH WOMEN
		6. While you say these phrases, allow yourself to sink into the intentions they express. Loving Kindness meditation consists primarily of connecting to the intention of wishing ourselves or others happiness. However, if feelings of warmth, friendliness, or love arise in your body or mind, connect to them, allowing them to grow as you repeat the phrases. As an aid to this, you might keep an image of yourself in your mind's eye. This helps reinforce the intentions expressed in the phrases. 7. After a period of directing loving kindness toward yourself, bring to mind a friend or someone in your life who has cared deeply for you. This may be a parent, teacher, partner, sponsor, mentor, or special friend. Then slowly repeat phrases of loving kindness toward that person: • May you be happy. • May you be well. • May you be safe. • May you be peaceful and at ease. 8. As you say these phrases, again sink into their intention and heartfelt meaning. If any feelings of loving kindness arise, connect the feelings with the phrases so the feelings can become stronger as you repeat the words. 9. As you continue the meditation, you can bring to mind other friends, neighbors, acquaintances, strangers, animals, and even people with whom you have difficulty. You can place them all in one group for today's meditation. You can use the same phrases, repeating them again and again:

TIME & TOPIC	FACILITATOR NOTES	DISCUSSION WITH WOMEN
		• May you be happy.
		• May you be well.
		• May you be safe.
		• May you be peaceful and at ease.
		10. Sometimes, during Loving Kindness meditation, seemingly opposite feelings such as anger, grief, and sadness arise. Take these to be signs that your heart is softening, revealing what is held there. You can—with whatever patience, acceptance, and kindness you can muster—direct loving kindness toward those feelings. Above all, remember that there is no need to judge yourself for feeling this way.
		11. Now, envision our beautiful planet. See it from above, as though you were looking down on it from very far away. As you exhale, send blessings to all the people on Earth, all the plants and animals. Slowly repeat these phrases to all beings and to the planet itself:
		• May you be happy.
		• May you be well.
		• May you be safe.
		• May you be peaceful and at ease.
		• May all beings and this planet be free from suffering.
	Be silent for about thirty seconds.	
		Now please bring your attention back to this room. Feel your feet on the ground. When you're ready, open your eyes.
		How did that meditation feel? Do any of you want to share your experience with this meditation?

TIME & TOPIC	FACILITATOR NOTES	DISCUSSION WITH WOMEN
		This and other forms of meditation are ways to create connection with ourselves and our Higher Power. This is another skill you can use on your healing journey.
5 min. **Optional: Meditation: Simple Guidelines to Practice Mindfulness**	*You may prefer this Mindfulness activity.*	1. Gently smile to yourself as you mindfully observe and rest within the flow of every changing, moment-to-moment experience. 2. Be mindful of the waves of the breath as they come. 3. And flow. 4. Let this be your resting place and anchor of awareness. 5. From this foundation, mindfully notice how external perceptions arise and pass in the environment around you. 6. Mindfully attend to how sensations come and flow through your body. 7. As thoughts or mental images arise, be mindful of how they arise, abide, and pass. 8. As emotions come to your awareness, be mindful of the arising and passing of those feelings. 9. As desires, intentions, or other mind states arise, simply be mindful of how they come and flow. 10. Simply experience all things as they arise and pass, not holding on to any experience and not pushing any experience away.

TIME & TOPIC	FACILITATOR NOTES	DISCUSSION WITH WOMEN
		11. Mindfully rest in this flow with clear presence. Reprinted with permission from *Mindfulness, Meditation, and Mind Fitness* by Joel and Michelle Levey (Newburyport, MA: Red Wheel Weiser, 2015), www.WisdomAtWork.com.
10–15 min. **Activity: Meaningful Women in Our Lives**	*Have the women stand and hold hands in a circle around the objects in the center.*	Now it's time to begin our closing. We're going to do an activity that will help us recognize and experience ongoing connection. Please close your eyes or lower your eyelids for a minute and think about the women who've been important to you—who've been meaningful in your life. They may be your mother, your grandmother, another family member, a teacher, a therapist, a good friend, or others. There may be one woman or there may be several. Think about what you've received from each woman, what you learned, or what qualities you respected. When you are ready to share, please open your eyes. Let's go around the circle, with each of us saying the name of one of the women who've touched our lives and made a difference. Also, say one or two words about what you received from her, what you learned, or what qualities you respected.
	Allow time for each woman to share. When the women have shared, close with the following words.	

TIME & TOPIC	FACILITATOR NOTES	DISCUSSION WITH WOMEN
		What each of you have been given is always there for you. These lasting connections and their gifts are always there for you to receive. You just have to reach out and remember. And as we stand here, we've created a protective circle of women—of us and the special women in our lives—surrounding the things that are important to us, and a protective circle of love. Having a protective circle of women is an important part of healing.
	Encourage the women to take some time after the session to write more about the women who are important to them. There is space provided on page 167 in their workbooks.	
1 min. **Optional: Readings**	*You may choose to read either or both of the passages that follow.*	"The Way is long; let us go together. The Way is difficult; let us help each other. The Way is joyful; let us share it. The Way is ours alone; let us go in love. The Way grows before us; let us begin." — Zen Invocation "There is a goodness, a Wisdom that arises, sometimes gracefully, sometimes gently, sometimes awkwardly, sometimes fiercely, but it will arise to save us if we let it, and it arises from within us, like the force that drives green shoots to break the winter ground, it will arise and drive us into a great blossoming like a pear tree,

TIME & TOPIC	FACILITATOR NOTES	DISCUSSION WITH WOMEN
		into flowering, into fragrance, fruit, and song, into the wild wind dancing, sun shimmering, into the aliveness of it all, into that part of ourselves that can never be defiled, defeated, or destroyed, but that comes back to life, time and time again, that lives always, that does not die. Into the Divine." — China Galland, *The Bond Between Women: A Journey to Fierce Compassion*
5 min. Optional: ***Beyond Trauma*** **Participant Video** Segment 11	**Segment 11: Closing** *Before you close the session, you may choose to show segment 11 of the video that includes a closing statement from Stephanie Covington.*	Let's watch one last video segment with a message from the author, Stephanie Covington.
1 min. **Closing**		As our group comes to an end, let's remember the power of relationship and its ability to heal trauma. You each have contributed to the caring and safe relationships in our group. Yes, our group has come to an end, but you can always carry this experience with you as you make new beginnings and decisions about the next steps in your life. With each ending, space is created for new beginnings. I wish each of you a great new beginning on your healing journey!

ADAPTING THE SESSION FOR USE WITH GIRLS

Some of the focus questions for the check-in with girls can be changed to "Has anyone seen a difference in her relationships with her peers or family members since the last session?" "What has made the difference?"

In residential settings, the girls often like to do a craft project to create the item they bring to this final session.

It's particularly important for the girls to spend time expressing their appreciation to one another. So often, girls experience competition and meanness from one another. This circle of girls may be the first time they've had safe, close relationships within a group of girls. It may be the first time they've experienced safe relationships with other girls over a period of time. You can have each girl write her name on a piece of paper and then put all the names into a bowl. Then each group member can pull out a name, in turn, and say something positive and appreciative about that specific girl. They also can discuss the qualities of the group and what they've learned about themselves and other girls.

APPENDICES

APPENDIX 1

The Five Senses

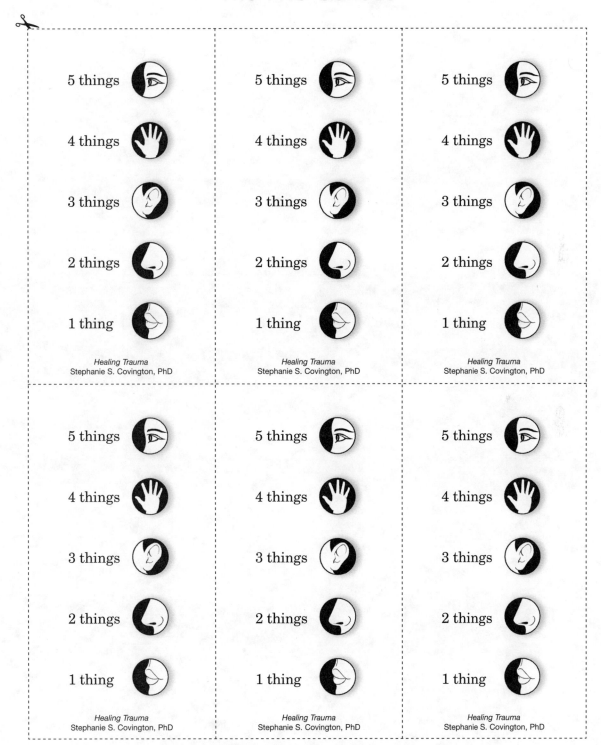

5 things

4 things

3 things

2 things

1 thing

Healing Trauma
Stephanie S. Covington, PhD

From *Healing Trauma: Strategies for Abused Women* by Stephanie Covington
(Center City, MN: Hazelden, 2011; rev. 2016 as *Healing Trauma: A Brief Intervention for Women*).

Yoga Poses

In addition to the many activities and exercises provided in this program, there are certain yoga poses that can help with the release of emotions stored in the body. *Yoga* is the Sanskrit word for *connection*. These poses help people become more consciously aware of their bodies and their breathing. This is particularly important for women with histories of trauma, particularly abuse. The four poses suggested for use in this setting are Breath of Joy, Seated Pigeon, Modified Triangle, and Twisted Branches to Open Wings. These poses are simple to teach, and the women can learn to do them by themselves in their living spaces. The poses are highly recommended as optional activities in various sessions. The following instructions and photographs are provided by Machelle Lee.

Machelle Lee is a certified and registered yoga instructor and massage therapist. She has a master's degree in mythology and depth psychology. Since 1991, she has led therapeutic-movement and yoga classes in various parts of the United States. Machelle weaves together modern psychology and different styles of yoga in a creative and grounded approach to self-development. She can be reached at www.machellelee.com.

Breath of Joy

The Breath of Joy yoga pose connects the use of breath with body movements to aid a physical and emotional release of tension. This is beneficial for letting go (or at least loosening the grip) of long-held anger or grief that's been stored in the body or in habitual thought patterns that aren't supportive of growth. The Breath of Joy consists of three quick inhalations through the nose and one audible exhalation through the mouth. The breaths are synchronized with arm movements to engage the whole body.

1. Begin in a standing position with your feet about hip-width apart. Take a short breath in through the nose while bringing your arms straight out in front of your chest.

2. Take another quick breath in through the nose while opening your arms wide in a "T" shape.

3. Take one last breath in while reaching your arms straight overhead.

420

4. With an audible "ahh" sound, exhale through your mouth while bringing your arms in a sweeping motion down to the side of your body.

5. Repeat the sequence of movements

6. Once the pattern of synchronizing your breath with movement is comfortable, you can do this pose a little quicker with one breath in three parts. You can also create a fuller body expression by bending your knees when dropping your chest into a forward bend during the exhalation and letting your arms swing down and past the hips.

7. Repeat the movements. Then rise to a standing position.

8. Inhale through the nose with your arms forward.

9. Inhale a bit more while spreading your arms out into the "T" position.

10. Inhale to your fullest lung capacity while bringing your arms overhead.

11. Finally, bend forward with your knees bent, exhaling through the mouth as your arms swing down and past your hips.

Usually, you'll repeat this five to ten times in a rhythmic flow.

For those who have limited mobility, a modification is to come down only halfway on the exhale.

Seated Pigeon

The Seated Pigeon pose provides a deep stretch through the side of the hip and the tissues that connect the outer hip and the outer side of the knee. This band of tissues often is tight, which can cause lower-back pain, knee problems, and aggravation of the sciatic nerve—sometimes felt as shooting pain through the outer hip, leg, or groin. Giving these tissues a modest stretch with this pose can bring relief from aches and also increase physical comfort when sitting or walking. Practicing this pose can also provide an emotional release of stress or trauma around the hips. It can aid in the release of anger or depression. Some people experience a physical feeling of release or relief, and others exhibit an emotional response, such as tears.

1. Sit straight in your chair, with both feet on the ground. Place your left foot on your right knee, so your legs resemble a number four when you're looking down at the shape.

2. Some people feel a tug immediately on the side of the left hip or buttock. It may radiate down the side of the leg toward the knee. If it isn't felt in these areas, simply lean forward. As the torso moves forward toward the legs, the tension to the outer hip is increased. You can hold on to the seat of your chair for support or lean your forearms on your knees. Hold this pose for one to three minutes for best results.

3. Now repeat the pose with your leg positions reversed. Remember to breathe while you're doing these movements.

Modified Triangle

The Modified Triangle pose targets tissues in the inner legs, lower back, and hips. It offers a nice stretch to the side of the body and the ribs. The spinal twist massages and supports the spinal column and soothes the nerves that branch out from each of the vertebrae and connect with every other part of the body. Symbolically, the triangle, or pyramid shape, represents the balance and unity between the three interconnected aspects of being: mind, body, and spirit.

1. Stand and face your chair.

2. Hold your arms out to your sides in a "T" position.

3. Open your legs wide until your ankles align under your wrists. This wide stance offers a solid and steady foundation for the pose.

4. Place both hands on the seat of your chair, with your hands apart—about the width of your shoulders. Keep your arms straight.

5. Bend forward from the hips. This may yield a nice hamstring stretch. Hold this for several breaths.

6. With your legs straight, keep your left foot facing forward, but pivot the right foot out so its toes point to the side. This will create a tug to the inner right leg.

7. Next, reach toward the ceiling or sky with your left arm and hand. Your left hip will follow, so your chest and gaze will be toward the left. Hold this pose while taking five to ten breaths.

8. If you have difficulty reaching upward with a straight arm, you can place your reaching hand on your hip instead.

9. Now bring both hands back to your seat, with your hands apart—about the width of your shoulders. Keep your arms straight.

10. Repeat the Modified Triangle exercise on the other side. Hold your arms out to your sides in a "T" position. Open your legs wide until your ankles align under your wrists. Place both hands on the seat of your chair. Bend forward from the hips. Hold this for several breaths.

11. With your legs straight, keep your right foot facing forward, but pivot the left foot out so its toes point to the side.

12. Next, reach toward the ceiling or sky with your right arm and hand. Your right hip will follow, so your chest and gaze will be toward the right. Hold this pose for five to ten breaths. If you have difficulty reaching upward with a straight arm, you can place your reaching hand on your hip instead.

Twisted Branches to Open Wings

In Twisted Branches to Open Wings, two poses complement one another and offer muscular release to the upper back, shoulders, and chest. They work in harmony to stimulate the lungs and heart. In yoga, lungs symbolically represent the ability to let go of stagnant energy (by exhaling) and invite in new life and possibility (by inhaling). Combining breath and movement aids the transformation of grief into a desire to explore the fullness of life and to feel safe doing so. Stimulating the heart helps a person move out of anxiety and into the ability to trust one's intuition and insight, create healthy boundaries, and experience joy.

1. Stand up.

2. Because each person's bone structure is different, Twisted Branches can be done in a number of ways, so you can find the one that feels best for your body. The gentlest pose is simply to cross your arms in front of your chest, resting your crossed hands on your shoulders in what looks like a self-hug. Do this while taking five to ten breaths.

3. The second option is to cross your upper arms by resting the elbow of one arm in the soft elbow crease of the opposite arm. Your hands may be back to back, or you may be able to bring the palms together. Crossing your arms in front causes your shoulder blades to stretch, which facilitates the release of tension in the upper back. Take five to ten breaths while doing this pose.

4. Then release your arms and clasp your hands together behind your back to create the Open Wings pose. Depending on your bone structure and level of comfort, your arms can be straight or your elbows can be bent. This compresses and relaxes the tissues of the upper back and the shoulder blades, while simultaneously offering a stretch across the chest.

5. Drop your chin toward your chest to provide a new level of release in the back of the head, neck, and upper back. Hold this pose while taking five to ten breaths.

6. Repeat the Twisted Branches pose with the other arm on top. Take five to ten breaths.

7. Then complete another Open Wings pose. Take five to ten breaths.

The yoga photos/instructions were provided by Machelle Lee and are reproduced from *Beyond Violence*. Copyright 2013 by S. Covington. This material is reproduced with permission of John Wiley & Sons, Inc., and Machelle Lee.

Local Resources

Please research the local services available in your community for women who have experienced abuse in the past or who are currently in an abusive relationship. Please provide this completed handout to each woman in session 3. She can then transfer this information to her workbook.

Local Resources for Women in Abusive Relationships

NAME OF PROGRAM	TYPE OF SERVICE	PHONE NUMBER

Local Resources for Women Who Have Experienced Abuse

NAME OF PROGRAM	TYPE OF SERVICE	PHONE NUMBER

Handouts for the Girls' Adaptation

- Teen Power and Control Wheel (session 3, page 172, and session 11, page 391)

- Equality Wheel for Teens (session 3, page 173, and session 11, page 391)

- Ten Warning Signs of Abuse (session 3, page 174, and session 4, page 211)

- Local Resources for Girls (session 3, page 175)

- History of Trauma Chart (session 4, page 209)

- Teenagers and Sleep (session 5, page 240)

- Family Map (session 6, page 272)

- Simple Rules for Stopping Rape (session 7, page 296)

- Anger Funnel (session 10, page 367)

Teen Power and Control Wheel

Developed from the Duluth Domestic Abuse Intervention Project, 202 East Superior Street, Duluth, MN 55802, www.theduluthmodel.org, 218-722-2781.
Produced and distributed by National Center on Domestic and Sexual Violence, www.ncdsv.org, Austin, Texas.

Duplicating this page for personal or group use is permissible.

Equality Wheel for Teens

Developed from the Duluth Domestic Abuse Intervention Project, 202 East Superior Street, Duluth, MN 55802, www.theduluthmodel.org, 218-722-2781.
Produced and distributed by National Center on Domestic and Sexual Violence, www.ncdsv.org, Austin, Texas.

Ten Warning Signs of Abuse

1. Checking your cell phone or email without permission
2. Continually putting you down
3. Extreme jealousy or insecurity
4. Explosive temper
5. Isolating you from family or friends
6. Making false accusations
7. Mood swings
8. Physically hurting you in any way
9. Possessiveness
10. Telling you what to do

If you need help with dating abuse, contact the National Teen Dating Abuse Helpline: **www.loveisrespect.org.**

Chat: 24/7/365 | **Call:** 1-866-331-9474
Text: love is to 22522

"The Signs" presented by Center for Nonprofit Leadership at Adelphia University, School of Social Work and produced by Digital Bodega. Reprinted with permission. Available online at https://vimeo.com/85676862.

Ten Warning Signs of Abuse

1. Checking your cell phone or email without permission
2. Continually putting you down
3. Extreme jealousy or insecurity
4. Explosive temper
5. Isolating you from family or friends
6. Making false accusations
7. Mood swings
8. Physically hurting you in any way
9. Possessiveness
10. Telling you what to do

If you need help with dating abuse, contact the National Teen Dating Abuse Helpline: **www.loveisrespect.org.**

Chat: 24/7/365 | **Call:** 1-866-331-9474
Text: love is to 22522

"The Signs" presented by Center for Nonprofit Leadership at Adelphia University, School of Social Work and produced by Digital Bodega. Reprinted with permission. Available online at https://vimeo.com/85676862.

Ten Warning Signs of Abuse

1. Checking your cell phone or email without permission
2. Continually putting you down
3. Extreme jealousy or insecurity
4. Explosive temper
5. Isolating you from family or friends
6. Making false accusations
7. Mood swings
8. Physically hurting you in any way
9. Possessiveness
10. Telling you what to do

If you need help with dating abuse, contact the National Teen Dating Abuse Helpline: **www.loveisrespect.org.**

Chat: 24/7/365 | **Call:** 1-866-331-9474
Text: love is to 22522

"The Signs" presented by Center for Nonprofit Leadership at Adelphia University, School of Social Work and produced by Digital Bodega. Reprinted with permission. Available online at https://vimeo.com/85676862.

Ten Warning Signs of Abuse

1. Checking your cell phone or email without permission
2. Continually putting you down
3. Extreme jealousy or insecurity
4. Explosive temper
5. Isolating you from family or friends
6. Making false accusations
7. Mood swings
8. Physically hurting you in any way
9. Possessiveness
10. Telling you what to do

If you need help with dating abuse, contact the National Teen Dating Abuse Helpline: **www.loveisrespect.org.**

Chat: 24/7/365 | **Call:** 1-866-331-9474
Text: love is to 22522

"The Signs" presented by Center for Nonprofit Leadership at Adelphia University, School of Social Work and produced by Digital Bodega. Reprinted with permission. Available online at https://vimeo.com/85676862.

Local Resources for Girls

Please research the local services available in your community for girls who have experienced abuse in the past or who are currently in an abusive relationship. Please provide this completed handout to each girl in session 3. She can then transfer the information to her workbook.

Local Resources for Girls in Abusive Relationships

NAME OF PROGRAM	TYPE OF SERVICE	PHONE NUMBER

Local Resources for Girls Who Have Experienced Abuse

NAME OF PROGRAM	TYPE OF SERVICE	PHONE NUMBER

History of Trauma Chart

	CHILD	ADOLESCENT
A. Event(s)		
B. Life before the event(s)		
C. Life after the event(s)		
D. Overall impact of the event(s)		

Teenagers and Sleep

Most adolescents are very sleep deprived, and sleep deprivation will affect many aspects of adolescents' functioning, as follows:

- *Mood.* Sleep deprivation will cause a teenager to be moody and irritable. In addition, she'll have a difficult time regulating her mood. For example, she'll become frustrated or upset more easily.

- *Behavior.* Teenagers who are sleep deprived are more likely to engage in risk-taking behaviors, such as drinking alcohol, driving fast, and engaging in other dangerous activities.

- *Cognitive ability.* Inadequate sleep will result in problems with attention, memory, decision making, reaction time, and creativity—all of which are important in school.

- *Academic performance.* Studies show that teenagers who get less sleep are more apt to get poor grades in school, fall asleep in school, and have tardiness and/or absences.

- *Drowsy driving.* Teenagers are at the highest risk for falling asleep at the wheel. Drowsy driving is most likely to occur in the middle of the night (2:00 to 4:00 a.m.) and in midafternoon (3:00 to 4:00 p.m.).

- *Complexion.* Lack of sleep increases a teenager's chances of having pimples and acne.

Family Map

Instructions: Refer to the sample Family Map below. On your blank map, draw circles to represent all the members of your family. Draw lines between your family members and yourself that describe your current relationship with each person.

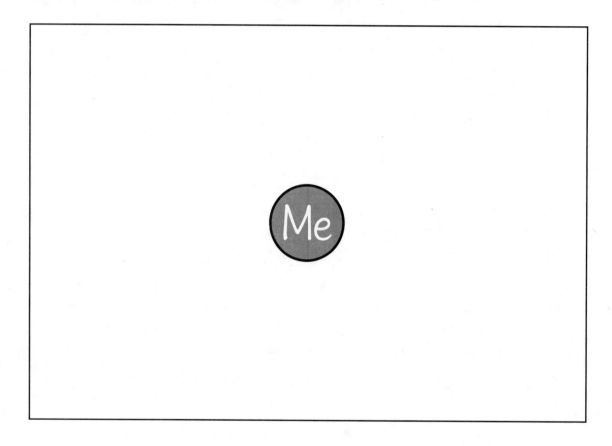

Key

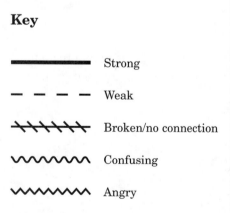

_____ Strong

— — — — — Weak

++++++++ Broken/no connection

∿∿∿∿∿ Confusing

⋀⋁⋀⋁⋀ Angry

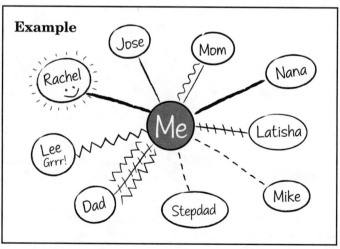

Example

Adapted from Covington, S. 2004. *Voices: A Program of Self-Discovery and Empowerment for Girls.* Carson City, NV: The Change Companies.

Simple Rules for Stopping Rape

No sex if . . .

- She has not given clear, verbal, affirmative consent.
- She has not given consent this time, even if she has on previous occasions. Continue to ask for consent.
- She's drunk or high.
- She seems unsure if she wants to (you should never pressure anyone into it).
- She's passed out.
- It seems like there's any other reason she might regret it in the morning. (Even if it's not rape, do you really want to be someone's morning-after regret, when she can remember you as a total gentleman instead?)

Simple Rules for Stopping Rape

No sex if . . .

- She has not given clear, verbal, affirmative consent.
- She has not given consent this time, even if she has on previous occasions. Continue to ask for consent.
- She's drunk or high.
- She seems unsure if she wants to (you should never pressure anyone into it).
- She's passed out.
- It seems like there's any other reason she might regret it in the morning. (Even if it's not rape, do you really want to be someone's morning-after regret, when she can remember you as a total gentleman instead?)

Simple Rules for Stopping Rape

No sex if . . .

- She has not given clear, verbal, affirmative consent.
- She has not given consent this time, even if she has on previous occasions. Continue to ask for consent.
- She's drunk or high.
- She seems unsure if she wants to (you should never pressure anyone into it).
- She's passed out.
- It seems like there's any other reason she might regret it in the morning. (Even if it's not rape, do you really want to be someone's morning-after regret, when she can remember you as a total gentleman instead?)

Simple Rules for Stopping Rape

No sex if . . .

- She has not given clear, verbal, affirmative consent.
- She has not given consent this time, even if she has on previous occasions. Continue to ask for consent.
- She's drunk or high.
- She seems unsure if she wants to (you should never pressure anyone into it).
- She's passed out.
- It seems like there's any other reason she might regret it in the morning. (Even if it's not rape, do you really want to be someone's morning-after regret, when she can remember you as a total gentleman instead?)

Anger Funnel

Hurt, Sadness, Fear, Insecurity, Frustration

Anger, Rage, and Violence

Facilitator Feedback Form

Dear Group Facilitator:

I would appreciate hearing about your experience with the *Beyond Trauma* program. Any information you would like to share with me will be greatly appreciated.

Please describe your role in addressing trauma. _____

_____

_____

_____

Describe where you facilitated this program. _____

_____

_____

Describe your experience with the *Beyond Trauma* program. _____

_____

_____

_____

What did you find most useful? _____

_____

_____

_____

What did you find least useful? _____

_____

_____

_____

Why? How? _____

_____

_____

_____

Other suggestions/comments: _____

_____

_____

_____

_____

_____

_____

Thank you for your input.

Please return this form to:
Stephanie S. Covington, PhD, LCSW
Center for Gender & Justice
Institute for Relational Development
7946 Ivanhoe Avenue, Suite 201B
La Jolla, CA 92037
Fax: (858) 454-8598
Email: sc@stephaniecovington.com

Participant Feedback Form

Dear Recovering Woman:

I would appreciate hearing about your experience with the *Beyond Trauma* program. Any information you would like to share with me will be greatly appreciated.

Please describe yourself (age, ethnicity, etc.). _____

_____

_____

_____

Describe where you participated in this program. _____

_____

_____

Describe your experience with the *Beyond Trauma* program. _____

_____

_____

_____

What did you find most useful? _____

_____

_____

_____

What did you find least useful? _____

_____

_____

_____

Why? How? _____

_____

_____

_____

Other suggestions/comments: _____

_____

_____

_____

_____

_____

_____

_____

Thank you for your input.

Please return this form to:
Stephanie S. Covington, PhD, LCSW
Center for Gender & Justice
Institute for Relational Development
7946 Ivanhoe Avenue, Suite 201B
La Jolla, CA 92037
Fax: (858) 454-8598
Email: sc@stephaniecovington.com

Resources

Adult Survivors of Child Abuse (ASCA)
ASCA Program, The Morris Center
P.O. Box 281535
San Francisco, CA 94128
www.ascasupport.org

Adverse Childhood Experiences
www.acestoohigh.com
www.cdc.gov/ace

American Psychological Association
Resource Guide for Traumatized People:
www.apa.org/topics/trauma
750 First Street NE
Washington, DC 20002-4242
(800) 374-2721
www.apa.org

Anxiety and Depression Association of America
8701 Georgia Avenue, Suite 412
Silver Spring, MD 20910
(240) 485-1001
www.adaa.org/netforum/findatherapist

European Society for Traumatic Stress Studies
www.estss.org

Eye Movement Desensitization and Reprocessing (EMDR) Institute
P.O. Box 750
Watsonville, CA 95077
(831) 761-1040
www.emdr.com

Eye Movement Desensitization and Reprocessing International Association (EMDRIA)
5806 Mesa Drive, Suite 360
Austin, TX 78731
(866) 451-5200
www.emdria.org

Duplicating this page is illegal. Do not copy this material without written permission from the publisher.

443

Give Back Yoga Foundation
900 Baseline Road, Cottage 13B
Boulder, CO 80302-7547
(301) 792-5352
www.givebackyoga.org

International Society for the Study of Trauma and Dissociation
8400 Westpark Drive, Second Floor
McLean, VA 22102
(703) 610-9037
www.isst-d.org

International Society for Traumatic Stress Studies (ISTSS)
One Parkview Plaza, Suite 800
Oakbrook Terrace, IL 60181
(847) 686-2234
www.istss.org

Kripalu Center for Yoga and Health
P.O. Box 309
Stockbridge, MA 01262
(413) 448-3152
www.kripalu.org

The Mind & Life Institute
4 Bay Road, Suite 101
Hadley, MA 01035
(413) 387-0710
www.mindandlife.org

National Child Traumatic Stress Network (NCTSN)
www.nctsnet.org

- **The National Center for Child Traumatic Stress (NCCTS)—
  University of California, Los Angeles**
  11150 W. Olympic Boulevard, Suite 650
  Los Angeles, CA 90064
  (310) 235-2633

- **The National Center for Child Traumatic Stress (NCCTS)—
  Duke University**
  411 West Chapel Hill Street, Suite 200
  Durham, NC 27701
  (919) 682-1552

National Institute of Mental Health
6001 Executive Boulevard, Room 6200, MSC 9663
Bethesda, MD 20892-9663
(866) 615-6464
www.nimh.nih.gov

Psychology Self-Help Resources on the Internet
www.psywww.com/resource/selfhelp.htm

Recovery from Sexual Abuse: Blog Carnival
www.recoveryfromsexualabuse.blogspot.com

Sensorimotor Psychotherapy Institute
805 Burbank Street
Broomfield, CO 80020
(303) 447-3290
www.sensorimotorpsychotherapy.org

Sidran Institute
P.O. Box 436
Brooklandville, MD 21022-0436
(410) 825-8888
www.sidran.org/resources

Somatic Experiencing Trauma Institute
6685 Gunpark Drive, Suite 210
Boulder, CO 80301
(303) 652-4035
www.traumahealing.com

The Trauma Center at Justice Resource Institute
1269 Beacon Street
Brookline, MA 02446
(617) 232-1303
www.traumacenter.org

Trauma Matters Newsletter
Connecticut Trauma Initiative
c/o The Connecticut Women's Consortium
2321 Whitney Avenue, Suite 401
Hamden, CT 06518
(203) 909-6888
www.womensconsortium.org/newsletter.cfm

SELF-HELP GROUPS

Adult Children of Alcoholics (ACA)
World Service Organization, Inc.
P.O. Box 3216
Torrance, CA 90510
(310) 534-1815
www.adultchildren.org

Alcoholics Anonymous (AA)
World Services, Inc.
P.O. Box 459
New York, NY 10163
(212) 870-3400
www.aa.org

Clutterers Anonymous (CLA)
World Service Organization
P.O. Box 91413
Los Angeles, CA 90009-1413
(866) 402-6685
www.clutterersanonymous.org

Cocaine Anonymous (CA)
World Service Office
P.O. Box 492000
Los Angeles, CA 90049-8000
(310) 559-5833
www.ca.org

Crystal Meth Anonymous (CMA)
General Services
4470 W. Sunset Boulevard, Suite 107, PMB 555
Los Angeles CA 90027-6302
(855) 638-4373
www.crystalmeth.org

Debtors Anonymous
General Service Office
P.O. Box 920888
Needham, MA 02492-0009
(800) 421-2383
www.debtorsanonymous.org

Emotional Health Anonymous (EHA)
San Gabriel Valley Intergroup
P.O. Box 2081
San Gabriel, CA 91778
(626) 722-5779
www.emotionalhealthanonymous.org

Emotions Anonymous International (EA)
P.O. Box 4245
St. Paul, MN 55104-0245
(651) 647-9712
www.emotionsanonymous.org

Food Addicts Anonymous (FAA)
529 NW Prima Vista Boulevard, #301 A
Port St. Lucie, FL 34983
(772) 878-9657
www.foodaddictsanonymous.org

Food Addicts in Recovery Anonymous (FA)
World Service, Inc.
400 W. Cummings Park, Suite 1700
Woburn, MA 01801
(781) 932-6300
www.foodaddicts.org

Gamblers Anonymous (GA)
International Service Office
P.O. Box 17173
Los Angeles, CA 90017
(626) 960-3500
www.gamblersanonymous.org

Heroin Anonymous (HA)
World Services
24 W. Camelback Road #A
Phoenix, AZ 85013
www.heroinanonymous.org

Marijuana Anonymous (MA)
World Services
340 S. Lemon Avenue, #9420
Walnut, CA 91789-2706
(800) 766-6779
www.marijuana-anonymous.org

Narcotics Anonymous (NA)
World Services, Inc.
P.O. Box 9999
Van Nuys, CA 91409
(818) 773-9999
www.na.org

Nicotine Anonymous
World Services
6333 E. Mockingbird Lane, Suite 147-817
Dallas, TX 75214
(877) 879-6422
www.nicotine-anonymous.org

On-Line Gamers Anonymous (OLGA)
World Services
P.O. Box 67
Osceola, WI 54020
(612) 245-1115
www.olganon.org

Overeaters Anonymous, Inc. (OA)
P.O. Box 44020
Rio Rancho, NM 87174-4020
(505) 891-2664
www.oa.org

Pills Anonymous (PA)
www.pillsanonymous.org

Recoveries Anonymous (RA)
Universal Services
P.O. Box 1212
East Northport, NY 11731
www.r-a.org

Sex Addicts Anonymous (SAA)
P.O. Box 70949
Houston, TX 77270
(800) 477-8191
www.sexaa.org

Sex and Love Addicts Anonymous (SLAA)
www.slaafws.org

Sexaholics Anonymous (SA)
International Central Office
P.O. Box 3565
Brentwood, TN 37024
(866) 424-8777
www.sa.org

Sexual Compulsives Anonymous (SCA)
P.O. Box 1585, Old Chelsea Station
New York, NY 10011
(800) 977-4325
www.sca-recovery.org

Spenders Anonymous
www.spenders.org

Survivors of Incest Anonymous (SIA)
World Service Office
P.O. Box 190
Benson, MD 21018-9998
(410) 893-3322
www.siawso.org

Underearners Anonymous (UA)
P.O. Box 1839
New York, NY 10163-1839
www.underearnersanonymous.org

Workaholics Anonymous (WA)
World Service Organization
P.O. Box 289
Menlo Park, CA 94026-0289
(510) 273-9253
www.workaholics-anonymous.org

FEDERAL PUBLICATIONS

Available from the National Clearinghouse on Alcohol and Drug Information (NCADI):

Addressing the Needs of Women and Girls: Core Competencies for Mental Health and Substance Abuse Service Professionals. 2011. Publication No. (SMA) 11-4657. Rockville, MD: Center for Substance Abuse Treatment, U.S. Department of Health and Human Services, Substance Abuse and Mental Health Services Administration (www.samhsa.gov).

Helping Yourself Heal: A Recovering Woman's Guide to Coping with Childhood Abuse Issues. 2003. Publication No. (SMA) 03-3789. Rockville, MD: Center for Substance Abuse Treatment, U.S. Department of Health and Human Services, Substance Abuse and Mental Health Services Administration (www.samhsa.gov).

Substance Abuse Treatment: Addressing the Specific Needs of Women. 2009. TIP 51, Treatment Improvement Protocol (TIP) Series. Publication No. (SMA) 14-4426. Rockville, MD: Center for Substance Abuse Treatment, U.S. Department of Health and Human Services. Available online at: http://store.samhsa .gov/product/TIP-51-Substance-Abuse-Treatment-Addressing-the-Specific -Needs-of-Women/SMA14-4426

Substance Abuse Treatment and Domestic Violence. 2002. TIP 25, Treatment Improvement Protocol (TIP) Series. Publication No. (SMA) 02-3627. Rockville, MD: Center for Substance Abuse Treatment, U.S. Department of Health and Human Services. Available online at: http://store.samhsa.gov/product/TIP-25 -Substance-Abuse-Treatment-and-Domestic-Violence/SMA12-4076.

Substance Abuse Treatment for Persons with Child Abuse and Neglect Issues. 2002. TIP 36, Treatment Improvement Protocol (TIP) Series. Publication No. (SMA) 02-3694. Rockville, MD: Center for Substance Abuse Treatment, U.S. Department of Health and Human Services. Available online at: http://store .samhsa.gov/product/TIP-36-Substance-Abuse-Treatment-for-Persons-with -Child-Abuse-and-Neglect-Issues/SMA12-3923.

Trauma-Informed Care in Behavioral Health Services. 2014. TIP 57, Treatment Improvement Protocol (TIP) Series. Publication No. (SMA) 14-4816. Rockville, MD: Center for Substance Abuse Treatment, U.S. Department of Health and Human Services. Available online at: http://store.samhsa.gov/product/TIP -57-Trauma-Informed-Care-in-Behavioral-Health-Services/SMA14-4816.

References

Achor, S. 2013. *Before Happiness: The 5 Hidden Keys to Achieving Success, Spreading Happiness, and Sustaining Positive Change.* New York: Crown, Random House.

Aday, R. H., M. H. Dye, and A. K. Kaiser. 2014. "Examining the Traumatic Effects of Sexual Victimization on the Health of Incarcerated Women." *Women & Criminal Justice* 24 (4): 341–61.

Alderman, T. 1997. *The Scarred Soul: Understanding and Ending Self-Inflicted Violence.* Oakland, CA: New Harbinger Publications.

Alderman, T., and K. Marshall. 1998. *Amongst Ourselves: A Self-Help Guide to Living with Dissociative Identity Disorder.* Oakland, CA: New Harbinger Publications.

American Psychiatric Association. 2013. *Diagnostic and Statistical Manual of Mental Disorders.* 5th ed. Washington, DC: American Psychiatric Association.

Arden, J. B. 2014. *The Brain Bible: How to Stay Vital, Productive, and Happy for a Lifetime.* New York: McGraw-Hill.

Avdimiretz, N., L. Phillips, and I. Bratu. 2012. "Focus on Pediatric Intentional Trauma." *Journal of Trauma and Acute Care Surgery* 72 (4): 1031–34.

Banks, A. 2015. *Four Ways to Click: Rewire Your Brain for Stronger, More Rewarding Relationships.* New York: Jeremy Tarcher/Penguin.

Bedi, S., E. C. Nelson, M. T. Lynskey, V. V. McCutcheon, A. C. Heath, P. A. Madden, and N. G. Martin. 2011. "Risk for Suicidal Thoughts and Behavior after Childhood Sexual Abuse in Women and Men." *Suicide and Life-Threatening Behavior* 41 (4): 406–15.

Bepko, C. 1991. *Feminism and Addiction.* New York: Haworth Press.

Berenson, D. 1991. "Powerlessness: Liberation or Enslaving? Responding to the Feminist Critique of the Twelve Steps." In *Feminism and Addiction,* edited by C. Bepko. New York: Haworth Press.

Berry, C. 2003. *When Helping You Is Hurting Me.* New York: Crossroads.

Berzofsky, M., C. Krebs, L. Langton, M. Planty, and H. Smiley-McDonald. 2013. *Female Victims of Sexual Violence, 1994–2010.* Washington, DC: Bureau of Justice Statistics.

Black, M. C., K. C. Basile, M. J. Breiding, S. G. Smith, M. L. Walters, M. T. Merrick, J. Chen, and M. R. Stevens. 2011. *The National Intimate Partner and Sexual Violence Survey: 2010 Summary Report.* Atlanta, GA: National Center for Injury Prevention and Control, Centers for Disease Control and Prevention.

Bloom, B., B. Owen, and S. Covington. 2003. *Gender Responsive Strategies: Research, Practice, and Guiding Principles for Women Offenders.* Washington, DC: National Institute of Corrections.

Bloom, S. L. 2000. "Creating Sanctuary: Healing from Systematic Abuses of Power." *Therapeutic Communities* 21 (2): 67–91.

Bloom, S. L., S. Yanosy, and L. C. Harrison. 2013. "A Reciprocal Supervisory Network: The Sanctuary Model." In *Trauma and the Therapeutic Relationship: Approaches to Process and Practice,* edited by D. Murphy and S. Joseph. London: Palgrave MacMillan.

Bond, K., N. Messina, and S. Calhoun. 2010. *Enhancing Substance Abuse Treatment and HIV Prevention for Women Offenders: Final Report.* Report to the National Institute on Drug Abuse, Grant No. 1 R01 DA022149-01. Unpublished manuscript.

Bonomi, A. E., M. L. Anderson, J. Nemeth, F. P. Rivara, and C. Buettner. 2013. "History of Dating Violence and the Association with Late Adolescent Health." *BMC Public Health* 13 (1): 821–33.

Breiding, M. J., S. G. Smith, K. C. Basile, M. L. Walters, J. Chen, and M. T. Merrick. 2014. *Prevalence and Characteristics of Sexual Violence, Stalking, and Intimate Partner Violence Victimization—National Intimate Partner and Sexual Violence Survey, United States, 2011.* Washington, DC: Centers for Disease Control and Prevention.

Brown, L. 2014. "Cultural Competence." In *Treating Complex Traumatic Stress Disorders,* edited by C. Courtois and J. Ford. New York: Guilford Press.

Brown, P., and J. Wolfe. 1994. "Substance Abuse and Posttraumatic Stress Disorder Comorbidity." *Drug and Alcohol Dependence* 35: 51–59.

Calhoun, L. G., and R. G. Tedeschi. 1999. *Facilitating Posttraumatic Growth: A Clinician's Guide.* New York: Routledge.

Calhoun, L. G., and R. G. Tedeschi. 2013. *Posttraumatic Growth in Clinical Practice.* New York: Brunner Routledge

Calhoun, S., N. Messina, J. Cartier, and S. Torres. 2010. "Gender-Responsive Treatment for Women in a Prison Setting: Client and Staff Perspectives." *Federal Probation* 74 (3): 27–33.

Catalano, S. 2007. *Intimate Partner Violence in the United States.* Washington, DC: Bureau of Justice Statistics.

———. 2012. *Intimate Partner Violence, 1993–2010.* Washington, DC: Bureau of Justice Statistics.

Centers for Disease Control and Prevention. 2008. "Adverse Health Conditions and Health Risk Behaviors Associated with Intimate Partner Violence— United States, 2005." *Morbidity and Mortality Weekly Report* 57 (5): 113–17. Available online at http://www.cdc.gov/mmwr/preview/mmwrhtml /mm5705a1.htm.

Center for Nonprofit Leadership. n.d. "The Signs" presented at Adelphia University, School of Social Work and produced by Digital Bodega. Available online at https://vimeo.com/85676862.

Center on Addiction and Substance Abuse. 2010. *Behind Bars II: Substance Abuse and America's Prison Population.* New York: CASA Columbia

Chen, L. P., M. H. Murad, M. L. Paras, K. M. Colbenson, A. L. Sattler, E. N. Goranson, and A. Zirakzadeh. 2010. "Sexual Abuse and Lifetime Diagnosis of Psychiatric Disorders: Systematic Review and Meta-Analysis." *Mayo Clinic Proceedings* 85 (7): 618–29.

Courtois, C. 2014. *It's Not You: It's What Happened to You.* Dublin, OH: Telemachus Press.

Courtois, C., and J. Ford. 2013. *Treatment of Complex Trauma: A Sequenced, Relationship-Based Approach.* New York: Guilford Press.

———, eds. 2014. *Treating Complex Traumatic Stress Disorders: Scientific Foundations and Therapeutic Models.* New York: Guilford Press.

Covington, S. 1994. *A Woman's Way through the Twelve Steps.* Center City, MN: Hazelden.

———. 1998a. "The Relational Theory of Women's Psychological Development: Implications for the Criminal Justice System." In *Female Offenders: Critical Perspectives and Effective Intervention,* edited by R. Zaplin. Gaithersburg, MD: Aspen Press.

———. 1998b. "Women in Prison: Approaches in the Treatment of Our Most Invisible Population." *Women & Therapy* 21 (1): 141–55.

———. 2000a. *Awakening Your Sexuality: A Guide for Recovering Women.* Center City, MN: Hazelden.

———. 2000b. *A Woman's Way through the Twelve Steps Workbook.* Center City, MN: Hazelden.

———. 2002. "Helping Women Recover: Creating Gender-Responsive Treatment." In *Handbook of Women's Addiction Treatment: Theory and Practice,* edited by S. L. A. Straussner and S. Brown. San Francisco: Jossey-Bass.

———. 2003. *Beyond Trauma: A Healing Journey for Women.* Center City, MN: Hazelden.

———. 2004. *Voices: A Program of Self-Discovery and Empowerment for Girls.* Carson City, NV: The Change Companies.

———. 2007. "Women and the Criminal Justice System." *Women's Health Issues* 17 (4): 1–6.

———. 2008. *Helping Women Recover: A Program for Treating Addiction* (with a special edition for the criminal justice system). Rev. ed. San Francisco: Jossey-Bass.

———. 2009. *A Woman's Way through the Twelve Steps Facilitator Guide* and *Program DVD.* Center City, MN: Hazelden.

———. 2013. *Beyond Violence: A Prevention Program for Criminal Justice-Involved Women.* Hoboken, NJ: John Wiley.

———. 2014. *Beyond Anger and Violence: A Program for Women.* Hoboken, NJ: John Wiley.

Covington, S., and L. Beckett. 1988. *Leaving the Enchanted Forest: The Path from Relationship Addiction to Intimacy.* San Francisco: HarperCollins Publishers.

Covington, S., and B. Bloom. 2003. "Gendered Justice: Women in the Criminal Justice System." In *Gendered Justice: Addressing Female Offenders,* edited by B. Bloom. Durham: NC: Carolina Academic Press.

Covington, S., C. Burke, S. Keaton, and C. Norcott. 2008. "Evaluation of a Trauma-Informed and Gender-Responsive Intervention for Women in Drug Treatment." *Journal of Psychoactive Drugs* 5:387–98.

Covington, S., and A. Dosher. 2000. "The Discipline of Compassion." Unpublished manuscript.

Covington, S., D. Griffin, and R. Dauer. 2011. *Helping Men Recover: A Program for Treating Addiction* (with a special edition for the criminal justice system). San Francisco: Jossey-Bass, A Wiley Imprint.

Covington, S., and J. Kohen. 1984. "Women, Alcohol, and Sexuality." *Advances in Alcohol and Substance Abuse* 4 (1): 41–56.

Covington, S., and J. Surrey. 1997. "The Relational Model of Women's Psychological Development: Implications for Substance Abuse." In *Gender and Alcohol: Individual and Social Perspectives,* edited by S. Wilsnack and R. Wilsnack. New Brunswick, NJ: Rutgers University Press.

Dass-Brailsford, P., and A. C. Myrick. 2010. "Psychological Trauma and Substance Abuse: The Need for an Integrated Approach." *Trauma, Violence, and Abuse* 11 (4): 202–13.

Davidov, D. M., H. Larrabee, and S. M. Davis. 2015. "United States Emergency Department Visits Coded for Intimate Partner Violence." *The Journal of Emergency Medicine* 48 (1): 94–100.

Devries, K. M., J. M. Mak, L. J. Bacchus, J. C. Child, G. Falder, M. Petzold, J. Astbury, and C. H. Watts. 2013. "Intimate Partner Violence and Incident Depressive Symptoms and Suicide Attempts: A Systematic Review of Longitudinal Studies." *PLOS Medicine* 10 (5): e1001439.

Donziger, S. R., ed. 1996. *The Real War on Crime: The Report of the National Criminal Justice Commission.* New York: HarperPerennial.

Duerk, J. 1993. *Circle of Stones.* Philadelphia, PA: Innisfree Press.

Duluth Domestic Abuse Intervention Project. 1999. *Power and Control Wheel.* Duluth, MN: Minnesota Program Development.

Evans, E., D. Levin, L. Li, and Y. Hser. 2013. "Explaining Long-Term Outcomes among Drug Dependent Mothers Treated in Women-Only versus Mixed-Gender Programs." *Journal of Substance Abuse Treatment* 45 (3): 293–301.

Fallot, R., and M. Harris. 2008. "Trauma-Informed Services." In *The Encyclopedia of Psychological Trauma,* edited by G. Reyes, J. D. Elhai, and J. D. Ford, 660–62. Hoboken, NJ: John Wiley.

Federal Bureau of Investigation. 2011. *Crime in the United States, 2010.* Washington, DC: U.S. Department of Justice

Felitti, V. J. 2000. *"One Page" ACE Questionnaire Handout.* Self-published. Personal communication with S. Covington on December 7, 2015.

Felitti, V., and R. Anda. 2010. "The Relationship of Adverse Childhood Experiences to Adult Medical Disease, Psychiatric Disorders and Sexual Behavior: Implications for Healthcare." In *The Impact of Early Life Trauma on Health and Disease: The Hidden Epidemic,* edited by R. A. Lanius, E. Vermetten, and C. Pain. Cambridge, England: Cambridge University Press.

Felitti, V. J., R. F. Anda, D. Nordenberg, D. F. Williamson, A. M. Spitz, V. Edwards, M. P. Koss, et al. 1998. "The Relationship of Adult Health Status to Childhood Abuse and Household Dysfunction." *American Journal of Preventive Medicine* 14:245–58.

Figley, C. 2002. "Compassion Fatigue: Psychotherapists' Chronic Lack of Self-Care." *Journal of Clinical Psychology* 58 (11): 1433–41.

Figley, C., R. Giel, S. Borgo, S. Briggs, and M. Harotis-Fatouros. 1995. "Prevention and Treatment of Community Stress: How to Be a Mental Health Expert at the Time of Disaster." In *Extreme Stress and Communities: Impact and Intervention,* edited by S. E. Hobfoll and M. W. de Vries. London: Kluwer Academic Publishers.

Finkelstein, N. 1996. "Using the Relational Model as a Context for Treating Pregnant and Parenting Chemically Dependent Women." In *Chemical Dependency: Women at Risk,* edited by B. Underhill and D. Finnegan. New York: Harrington Park Press / Haworth Press.

Forbes, D., S. Fletcher, A. Phelps, D. Wade, M. Creamer, and M. O'Donnell. 2013. Impact of Combat and Non-military Trauma Exposure on Symptom Reduction Following Treatment for Veterans with Posttraumatic Stress Disorder." *Psychiatry Research* 206 (1): 33–36.

Ford, J., and C. Courtois, eds. 2013. *Treating Complex Traumatic Stress Disorders in Children and Adolescents.* New York: Guilford Press.

Forneris, C. A., G. Gartlehner, K. A. Brownley, B. N. Gaynes, J. Sonis, E. Coker-Schwimmer, and K. N. Lohr. 2013. "Interventions to Prevent Post-Traumatic Stress Disorder: A Systematic Review." *American Journal of Preventive Medicine* 44 (6): 635–50.

Fronsdal, G. 2001, 2008. *The Issue at Hand: Essays on Buddhist Mindfulness Practice.* Redwood City, CA: Insight Meditation Center.

Galland, China. 1999. *The Bond Between Women: A Journey to Fierce Compassion.* New York: Riverhead / Penguin.

Gatt, J. M., L. M. Williams, P. R. Schofield, C. Dobson Stone, R. H. Paul, S. M. Grieve, and C. B. Nemeroff. 2010. "Impact of the HTR3A Gene with Early Life Trauma on Emotional Brain Networks and Depressed Mood." *Depression and Anxiety* 27 (8): 752–59.

Gladstone, G. L., G. B. Parker, P. B. Mitchell, G. S. Malhi, K. Wilhelm, and M. P. Austin. 2004. "Implications of Childhood Trauma for Depressed Women: An Analysis of Pathways from Childhood Sexual Abuse to Deliberate Self-Harm and Revictimization." *American Journal of Psychiatry* 161:1417–25.

Greenfield, S. F., E. M. Trucco, R. K. McHugh, M. Lincoln, and R. J. Gallop. 2007. "The Women's Recovery Group Study: A Stage 1 Trial of Women-Focused Group Therapy for Substance Use Disorders versus Mixed-Gender Group Drug Counseling." *Drug and Alcohol Dependency* 90 (1): 39–47.

Grella, C. E., K. Lovinger, and U. S. Warda. 2013. "Relationships among Trauma Exposure, Familial Characteristics, and PTSD: A Case-Control Study of Women in Prison and in the General Population." *Women & Criminal Justice* 23 (1): 63–79.

Hamby, S. L., D. Finkelhor, H. A. Turner, and R. Ormrod. 2011. *Children's Exposure to Intimate Partner Violence and Other Family Violence.* Washington, DC: U.S. Department of Justice, Office of Justice Programs, Office of Juvenile Justice and Delinquency Prevention.

Harris, M. 1998. *Trauma Recovery and Empowerment: A Clinician's Guide to Working with Women in Groups.* New York: Simon & Schuster.

Harris, M., and R. Fallot, eds. 2001. *Using Trauma Theory to Design Service Systems.* San Francisco: Jossey-Bass.

Harvey, M. R. 1996. "An Ecological View of Psychological Trauma and Trauma Recovery. *Journal of Traumatic Stress* 9 (1): 3–23.

———. 2007. "Towards an Ecological Understanding of Resilience in Trauma Survivors: Implications for Theory, Research, and Practice. *Journal of Aggression, Maltreatment, & Trauma* 14 (1–2): 9–32.

Hays, P. A. 2007. *Addressing Cultural Complexities in Practice: Assessment, Diagnosis and Therapy.* Washington, DC: American Psychological Association.

Herman, J. 1997. *Trauma and Recovery: The Aftermath of Violence—from Domestic Abuse to Political Terror.* New York: Basic Books.

———. 2014. "Foreword." In *Treating Complex Traumatic Stress Disorders: Scientific Foundations and Therapeutic Models,* edited by C. Courtois and J. Ford, xiii–xvii. New York: Guilford Press.

Howell, K. H., S. A. Graham-Bermann, E. Czyz, and M. Lilly. 2010. "Assessing Resilience in Preschool-Age Children Exposed to Intimate Partner Violence." *Violence and Victims* 25 (2): 150–64.

Institute for Health and Recovery. 2012. *Developing Trauma-Informed Organizations: A Tool Kit.* Cambridge, MA: Institute for Health and Recovery.

Iverson, K. M., A. Dick, K. A. McLaughlin, B. N. Smith, M. E. Bell, M. R. Gerber, and K. S. Mitchell. 2013. "Exposure to Interpersonal Violence and Its Associations with Psychiatric Morbidity in a U.S. National Sample: A Gender Comparison." *Psychology of Violence* 3 (3): 273–87.

Jordan, J., A. Kaplan, J. Miller, I. Stiver, and J. Surrey. 1991. *Women's Growth in Connection: Writings from the Stone Center.* New York: Guilford Press.

Jordan, J. V., and L. M. Hartling. 2002. "New Developments in Relational-Cultural Theory." In *Rethinking Mental Health and Disorder: Feminist Perspectives,* edited by M. Ballou and L. S. Brown, 48–70. New York: Guilford Press.

Kabat-Zinn, J. 2012. *Mindfulness for Beginners.* Boulder, CO: Sounds True.

Kasl, C. 1992. *Many Roads, One Journey.* New York: HarperCollins.

Kelly, J., and W. White, eds. 2010. *Addiction Recovery Management: Theory, Research and Practice.* New York: Humana Press.

Kendall-Tackett, K. 2005. "Introduction: Women's Experiences of Stress and Trauma." In *Handbook of Women, Stress and Trauma*, edited by K. Kendall-Tackett. New York: Brunner-Routledge.

Kessler, R. C. 2000. "Posttraumatic Stress Disorder: The Burden to the Individual and to Society." *Journal of Clinical Psychiatry* 61 (Supplement 5): 4–12.

Kessler, R. C., K. A. McLaughlin, K. C. Koenen, M. Petukhova, and E. D. Hill. 2012. "The Importance of Secondary Trauma Exposure for Post-Disaster Mental Disorder." *Epidemiology and Psychiatric Sciences* 21 (1): 35–45.

Kilpatrick, D. G., B. E. Saunders, and D. W. Smith. 2003. *Youth Victimization: Prevalence and Implications.* Washington, DC: National Institute of Justice.

Krebs, C., C. Lindquist, T. Warner, B. Fisher, and S. Martin. 2009. "College Women's Experiences with Physically Forced, Alcohol- or Other Drug-Enabled, and Drug-Facilitated Sexual Assault Before and Since Entering College." *Journal of American College Health* 57 (6): 639–49.

Langton, L., M. Berzofsky, C. P. Krebs, and H. Smiley-McDonald. 2012. *Victimizations Not Reported to the Police, 2006–2010.* Washington, DC: U.S. Department of Justice, Bureau of Justice Statistics.

Levey, J., and M. Levey. 2015. *Mindfulness, Meditation, and Mind Fitness.* Newburyport, MA: Red Wheel Weiser.

Levine, P. 1997. *Waking the Tiger: Healing Trauma.* Berkeley, CA: North Atlantic Books.

———. 2010. *In an Unspoken Voice: How the Body Releases Trauma and Restores Goodness.* Berkeley, CA: North Atlantic Books.

Lhamon, C. E., and J. W. Runcie. 2015. Letter from the U.S. Department of Education to Senator Barbara Boxer, April 28. Washington, DC: U.S. Department of Education.

Lorde, A. 1984. *Sister Outsider.* Freedom, CA: Crossing Press.

Margolin, G., and K. A. Vickerman. 2007. "Post-traumatic Stress in Children and Adolescents Exposed to Family Violence: Overview and Issues." *Professional Psychological Research: Research and Practice* 38 (6): 613–19.

Mason, S. M., A. J. Flint, A. L. Roberts, J. Agnew-Blais, K. C. Koenen, and J. W. Rich-Edwards. 2014. "Posttraumatic Stress Disorder Symptoms and Food Addiction in Women by Timing and Type of Trauma Exposure." *JAMA Psychiatry* 71 (11): 1271–78.

McLean, C. P., A. Asnaani, B. T. Litz, and S. G. Hofmann. 2011. "Gender Differences in Anxiety Disorders: Prevalence, Course of Illness, Comorbidity and Burden of Illness." *Journal of Psychiatric Research* 45 (8): 1027–35.

Messina, N., S. Calhoun, and J. Braithwaite. 2014. "Trauma-Informed Treatment Decreases Posttraumtic Stress Disorder among Women Offenders." *Journal of Trauma and Dissociation* 15 (1): 6–23.

Messina, N., S. Calhoun, and U. Warda. 2012. "Gender-Responsive Drug Court Treatment: A Randomized Control Trial." *Criminal Justice and Behavior,* published online, doi: 10.1177/0093854812453913.

Messina, N., and C. Grella. 2006. "Childhood Trauma and Women's Health Outcomes in a California Prison Population." *American Journal of Public Health* 96 (10): 1842–49.

———. 2008. *Final Report of the Gender Responsive Treatment for Women in Prison Project.* Submitted to the National Institute on Drug Abuse, Rockville, MD.

Messina, N., C. E. Grella, J. Cartier, and S. Torres. 2010. "A Randomized Experimental Study of Gender-Responsive Substance Abuse Treatment for Women in Prison." *Journal of Substance Abuse Treatment* 38 (2): 97–107.

Miller, D., and L. Guidry. 2001. *Addictions and Trauma Recovery: Healing the Body, Mind & Spirit.* New York: W. W. Norton & Company.

Miller, E., J. Breslau, W. J. Chung, J. G. Green, K. A. McLaughlin, and R. C. Kessler. 2011. "Adverse Childhood Experiences and Risk of Physical Violence in Adolescent Dating Relationships." *Journal of Epidemiology and Community Health* 65 (11): 1006–13.

Miller, J. 1982. *Women and Power.* Work in Progress Working Paper Series, no. 82-01. Wellesley, MA: Stone Center, Wellesley College.

———. 1986. *What Do We Mean by Relationships?* Work in Progress Working Paper Series, no. 22. Wellesley, MA: Stone Center, Wellesley College.

———. 1990. *Connections, Disconnections, and Violations.* Work in Progress Working Paper Series, no. 33. Wellesley, MA: Stone Center, Wellesley College.

Minkoff, K. 1989. "An Integrated Treatment Model for Dual Diagnosis of Psychosis and Addiction." *Hospital and Community Psychiatry* 40 (10): 1031–36.

Mitchell, K. S., S. E. Mazzeo, M. R. Schlesinger, T. D. Brewerton, and B. N. Smith. 2012. "Comorbidity of Partial and Subthreshold PTSD among Men and Women with Eating Disorders in the National Comorbidity Survey Replication Study." *International Journal of Eating Disorders* 45 (3): 307–15.

Najavits, L. 2002. *Seeking Safety: A Treatment Manual for PTSD and Substance Abuse.* New York: Guilford Press.

Najavits, L., R. Weiss, S. Reif, D. Gastfriend, L. Siqueland, J. Barber, S. Butler, M. Thase, and J. Blaine. 1998. "The Addiction Severity Index as a Screen for Trauma and Post-Traumatic Stress Disorder." *Journal of the Study of Alcohol* 59 (1): 56–62.

Najavits, L., R. Weiss, and S. Shaw. 1997. "The Link between Substance Abuse and Post-Traumatic Stress Disorder in Women: A Research Review." *American Journal on Addictions* 6 (4): 273–83.

Najt, P., P. Fusar-Poli, and P. Brambilla. 2011. "Co-occurring Mental and Substance Abuse Disorders: A Review on the Potential Predictors and Clinical Outcomes." *Psychiatry Research* 186 (2): 159–64.

National Association of State Mental Health Program Directors. 2008. *Training Curriculum for the Reduction of Seclusion and Restraint.* Alexandria, VA: National Technical Assistance Center, National Association of State Mental Health Program Directors.

National Scientific Council on the Developing Child. 2007. *The Science of Early Childhood Development: Closing the Gap between What We Know and What We Do.* Cambridge, MA: Harvard University Center on the Developing Child.

Nelson-Zlupko, L., M. M. Dore, E. Kauffman, and K. Kaltenbach. 1996. "Women in Recovery: Their Perceptions of Treatment Effectiveness." *Journal of Substance Abuse Treatment* 13 (1): 51–59.

Nickerson, A., I. M. Aderka, R. A. Bryant, B. T. Litz, and S. G. Hofmann. 2011. "Accidental and Intentional Perpetration of Serious Injury or Death: Correlates and Relationship to Trauma Exposure." *Journal of Trauma and Acute Care Surgery* 71 (6): 1821–28.

Noll, J. G., L. A. Horowitz, G. A. Bonanno, P. K. Trickett, and F. W. Putnam. 2003. "Revictimization and Self-Harm in Females Who Experienced Childhood Sexual Abuse: Results from a Prospective Study." *Journal of Interpersonal Violence* 18:1452–71.

Ogden, P., and J. Fisher. 2013. *The Body as a Resource: A Therapist's Manual for Sensorimotor Psychotherapy.* New York: W. W. Norton.

Ortner, N. 2013. *The Tapping Solution: A Revolutionary System for Stress-Free Living.* Carlsbad, CA: Hay House, Inc.

Pacella, M. L., B. Hruska, and D. L. Delahanty. 2013. "The Physical Health Consequences of PTSD and PTSD Symptoms: A Meta-analytic Review." *Journal of Anxiety Disorders* 27 (1): 33–46.

Pearlman, L., and J. Caringi. 2014. "Living and Working Self-Reflectively to Address Vicarious Trauma." In *Treating Complex Traumatic Stress Disorders: Scientific Foundations and Therapeutic Models,* edited by C. A. Courtois and J. D. Ford, 202–24. New York: Guilford Press.

Pennebaker, J. W. 2012. *Opening Up: The Healing Power of Expressing Emotions.* New York: Guilford Press.

Pérez-Fuentes, G., M. Olfson, L. Villegas, C. Morcillo, S. Wang, and C. Blanco. 2013. "Prevalence and Correlates of Child Sexual Abuse: A National Study." *Comprehensive Psychiatry* 54 (1): 16–27.

Prendergast, M. L., N. P. Messina, E. A. Hall, and U. S. Warda. 2011. "The Relative Effectiveness of Women-Only and Mixed-Gender Treatment for Substance-Abusing Women." *Journal of Substance Abuse Treatment* 40 (4): 336–48.

Quiros, L., and R. Berger. 2015. "Responding to the Sociopolitical Complexity of Trauma: An Integration of Theory and Practice." *Journal of Loss and Trauma* 20 (2): 149–59.

Rapping, E. 1996. *The Culture of Recovery.* Boston: Beacon Press.

Rees, S., D. Silove, T. Chey, L. Ivancic, Z. Steel, M. Creamer, and D. Forbes. 2011. "Lifetime Prevalence of Gender-Based Violence in Women and the Relationship with Mental Disorders and Psychosocial Function." *JAMA* 306 (5): 513–21.

Riegger-Krause, W. 2014. *Health Is in Your Hands: Jin Shin Jyutsu—Practicing the Art of Self-Healing.* New York: Upper West Side Publishing.

Roberts, E., and E. Amidon, eds. 1996. *Life Prayers from Around the World.* San Francisco: HarperSanFrancisco.

Root, M. 1992. "Within, Between and Beyond Race." In *Racially Mixed People in America,* edited by M. Root. Thousand Oaks, CA: Sage Publications.

———. 1997. "Women of Color and Traumatic Stress in 'Domestic Captivity': Gender and Race as Disempowering Statues." In *Ethnocultural Aspects of Posttraumatic Stress Disorder: Issues, Research, and Clinical Applications,* edited by A. J. Marsella et al. Washington, DC: American Psychological Association.

Roth, S., E. Newman, D. Pelcovitz, B. A. van der Kolk, and F. S. Mandel. 1997. "Complex PTSD in Victims Exposed to Sexual and Physical Abuse: Results from the DSM-IV Field Trial for Posttraumatic Stress Disorder." *Journal of Traumatic Stress* 10:539–55.

San Diego Association of Governments (SANDAG). 2007. "Beyond Trauma: Providing Trauma-Informed Services to Women in Drug Treatment." *Criminal Justice Bulletin* 1–11.

Scaer, R. 2014. *The Body Bears the Burden: Trauma, Dissociation, and Disease.* New York: Routledge.

Sedlak, A. J., J. Mettenburg, M. Basena, I. Petta, K. McPherson, A. Greene, and S. Li. 2010. *Fourth National Incidence Study of Child Abuse and Neglect: Report to Congress.* Washington, DC: U.S. Department of Health and Human Services, Administration for Children and Families.

Staton-Tindall, M., J. L. Duvall, C. Leukefeld, and C. B. Oser. 2007. "Health, Mental Health, Substance Use, and Service Utilization among Rural and Urban Incarcerated Women." *Women's Health Issues* 17:183–92.

Steele, C. 2000. "Providing Clinical Treatment to Substance Abusing Trauma Survivors." *Alcohol Treatment Quarterly* 18 (3): 72.

Stern, D. 1985. *The Interpersonal World of the Infant.* New York: Basic Books.

Stoltenborgh, M., M. H. van Ijzendoorn, E. M. Euser, and M. J. Bakermans-Kranenburg. 2011. "A Global Perspective on Child Sexual Abuse: Meta-analysis of Prevalence around the World." *Child Maltreatment* 16 (2): 79–101.

Trickett, P. K., J. G. Noll, and F. W. Putnam. 2011. "The Impact of Sexual Abuse on Female Development: Lessons from a Multigenerational, Longitudinal Research Study." *Development and Psychopathology* 23:453–76.

Ullman, S. E., M. Relyea, L. Peter-Hagene, and A. L. Vasquez. 2013. "Trauma Histories, Substance Use Coping, PTSD, and Problem Substance Use among Sexual Assault Victims." *Addictive Behaviors* 38 (6): 2219–23.

United Nations General Assembly. 1993. *Declaration on the Elimination of Violence against Women (A/RES/48/104).* New York: United Nations. http://www.un.org/documents/ga/res/48/a48r104.htm (accessed November 5, 2002).

U.S. Department of Health and Human Services. 2007. *Child Maltreatment 2005.* Washington, DC: U.S. Government Printing Office.

———. 2011. *Child Abuse and Neglect Statistics.* Washington, DC: U.S. Government Printing Office.

van der Kolk, B. 2014. *The Body Keeps the Score: Brain, Mind and Body in the Healing of Trauma.* New York: Viking Penguin.

Violence Policy Center. 2013. *When Men Murder Women: An Analysis of 2011 Homicide Data.* Washington, DC: Violence Policy Center.

Wells, T. 1970, 1972. *Woman—Which Includes Man, of Course: An Experience in Awareness.* Self-published.

White, W. L., M. Boyle, and D. Loveland. 2002. "Alcoholism/Addiction as a Chronic Disease: From Rhetoric to Clinical Reality." *Alcoholism Treatment Quarterly* 20 (3–4): 107–29.

Whitfield, C. L., R. F. Anda, S. R. Dube, and V. J. Felitti. 2003. "Violent Childhood Experiences and the Risk of Intimate Partner Violence in Adults: Assessment in a Large Health Maintenance Organization." *Journal of Interpersonal Violence* 18 (2): 166–85.

Williams, M. B, and J. F. Sommer. 2013. *Simple and Complex Post-Traumatic Stress Disorder: Strategies for Comprehensive Treatment in Clinical Practice.* New York: Routledge.

Winnecott, D. W. 1965. *The Maturational Process and the Facilitation Environment: Studies in the Theory of Emotional Development.* New York: International University Press.

Wolff, N., B. C. Frueh, J. Shi, D. Gerardi, N. Fabrikant, and B. E. Schumann. 2011. "Trauma Exposure and Mental Health Characteristics of Incarcerated Females Self-Referred to Specialty PTSD Treatment." *Psychiatric Services* 62 (8): 954–58.

Woon, F. L., S. S. Sood, and D. W. Hedges. 2010. "Hippocampal Volume Deficits Associated with Exposure to Psychological Trauma and Posttraumatic Stress Disorder in Adults: A Meta-analysis." *Progress in Neuro-Psychopharmacology* 34 (7): 1181–88.

World Health Organization. 2013. *Global and Regional Estimates of Violence against Women: Prevalence and Health Effects of Intimate Partner Violence and Non-partner Sexual Violence.* Geneva, Switzerland: Media Centre.

Duplicating this page is illegal. Do not copy this material without written permission from the publisher.

463

About the Author

Stephanie S. Covington, PhD, LCSW, is an internationally recognized clinician, organizational consultant, and lecturer. For more than thirty years her work has focused on the creation of gender-responsive and trauma-informed services. Her extensive experience includes designing women's services at the Betty Ford Center, developing programs for women in criminal justice settings, and being the featured therapist on the Oprah Winfrey Network TV show *Breaking Down the Bars.*

She has also served as a consultant to the United Nations Office on Drugs and Crime (UNODC) in Vienna and was selected for the federal Advisory Committee for Women's Services (ACWS). Educated at Columbia University and the Union Institute, Dr. Covington has conducted seminars for behavioral health professionals, community organizations, criminal justice professionals, and recovery groups in the United States, Canada, Mexico, Europe, Africa, Iceland, and New Zealand. She has served on the faculties of the University of Southern California, San Diego State University, and the California School of Professional Psychology. She has published extensively, including ten gender-responsive, trauma-informed treatment curricula. Dr. Covington is based in La Jolla, California, where she is co-director of both the Institute for Relational Development and the Center for Gender and Justice.

Other Publications by
Stephanie S. Covington, PhD

Awakening Your Sexuality: A Guide for Recovering Women

Beyond Anger and Violence: A Program for Women (facilitator guide, participant workbook, and DVD)

Beyond Violence: A Prevention Program for Criminal Justice–Involved Women (facilitator guide, participant workbook, and DVD)

Exploring Trauma: A Brief Intervention for Men with Roberto A. Rodriguez (CD-ROM with facilitator guide and workbooks

Healing Trauma: A Brief Intervention for Women with Eileen Russo (CD-ROM with facilitator guide and workbooks)

Helping Men Recover: A Program for Treating Addiction with Dan Griffin and Rick Dauer (facilitator guide and *A Man's Workbook*)

Helping Men Recover: A Program for Treating Addiction, special edition for use in the criminal justice system, with Dan Griffin and Rick Dauer (facilitator guide and *A Man's Workbook*)

Helping Women Recover: A Program for Treating Addiction (facilitator guide and *A Woman's Journal*)

Helping Women Recover: A Program for Treating Substance Abuse, special edition for use in the criminal justice system (facilitator guide and *A Woman's Journal*)

Leaving the Enchanted Forest: The Path from Relationship Addiction to Intimacy with Liana Beckett

Voices: A Program of Self-Discovery and Empowerment for Girls (facilitator guide and Interactive Journal)

A Woman's Way through the Twelve Steps (published in Spanish as *La mujer y su practica de los Doce Pasos*)

A Woman's Way through the Twelve Steps: Program DVD

A Woman's Way through the Twelve Steps Facilitator Guide

A Woman's Way through the Twelve Steps Workbook (published in Spanish as *La mujer y su práctica de los Doce Pasos: Libro de ejercicios*)

Women and Addiction: A Gender-Responsive Approach (manual, DVD, and CE test)

Women in Recovery: Understanding Addiction (published in Spanish as *Mujeres en recuperación: Entendiendo la adicción*)

About Hazelden Publishing

As part of the Hazelden Betty Ford Foundation, Hazelden Publishing offers both cutting-edge educational resources and inspirational books. Our print and digital works help guide individuals in treatment and recovery, and their loved ones. Professionals who work to prevent and treat addiction also turn to Hazelden Publishing for evidence-based curricula, digital content solutions, and videos for use in schools, treatment programs, correctional programs, and electronic health records systems. We also offer training for implementation of our curricula.

Through published and digital works, Hazelden Publishing extends the reach of healing and hope to individuals, families, and communities affected by addiction and related issues.

For more information about Hazelden publications,
please call **800-328-9000**
or visit us online at **hazelden.org/bookstore**.